INTRODUCING SYSTEMS AND CONTROL

iNTRODUCING SYSTEMS AND CONTROL

David M. Auslander
Professor of Mechanical Engineering
University of California, Berkeley

Yasundo Takahashi
Professor of Mechanical Engineering
University of California, Berkeley

Michael J. Rabins
Professor of System Engineering
Polytechnic Institute of New York

McGraw-Hill Book Company

New York   St. Louis   San Francisco   Düsseldorf   Johannesburg   Kuala Lumpur   London
Mexico   Montreal   New Delhi   Panama   Rio de Janeiro   Singapore   Sydney   Toronto

Library of Congress Cataloging in Publication Data

Auslander, David M
  Introducing systems and control.

  Includes bibliographical references.
    1. System analysis. 2. Control theory.
3. Feedback control systems. I. Takahashi, Yasundo,
date, joint author. II. Rabins, Michael Jerome,
date, joint author. III. Title.
QA402.A95   620'.72   73-17231
ISBN 0-07-002491-X

Introducing Systems and Control

4 5 6 7 8 9 10   KPKP   7832109

CONTENTS

PREFACE

This book is intended for undergraduate courses in any discipline dealing with dynamic systems and feedback control. The authors have attempted throughout to use examples which provide physical insights into problem-solving as well as the theoretical background necessary for the reader's further study and professional work. While including the traditional material of current control course syllabii in the text, we have chosen to emphasize how the most up-to-date theoretical and computational tools can be applied to real problems.

We fervently believe that engineers and scientists have both the opportunity and the obligation to seek useful applications of these techniques to a wide variety of human needs. In keeping with this belief, we discuss applications in industrial control as well as in such areas of emerging interest as ecology, health, conservation and resource utilization.

Throughout the text, we have tried to reflect recent natural developments in technology and education. For example, in light of the widespread availability of computer facilities, we introduce digital and analog computation and simulation early in the book, often preceding the equivalent analytical development. By so doing, we feel it becomes possible to deal with realistic nonlinear problems from the outset and then proceed to analytical treatments for linearized versions of these problems. We believe this approach will permit students to gain a broader perspective on the role that linear system theory plays in dynamic system problem-solving.

We have also departed from the traditional approach in control education by introducing in the first part of the book the state philosophy in the context of the development of system models. Then we cover the important traditional approaches to system analysis, including transfer functions and frequency response. Subsequently, we decide which will be the "best" mathematical formulation or solution technique for each topic depending on its particular characteristics. Whichever formulation we use to explore a given class of problems — classical or state space — we attempt to stress the continuity and equivalence of the approaches rather than their distinctions.

The purpose of the first three chapters is to orient the reader to a system model formulation in state space that can serve as a basis for computer simulation as well as for theoretical treatment. Computer simulation, the most generally applicable technique for dynamic system analysis, is the subject of Chapter 4. Both digital and analog simulation are presented for nonlinear and linear systems.

Since computer solutions are specific in that they apply only to a single point in the parameter space, we introduce linear system theory in Chapter 5 to provide the generality necessary for analyzing system behavior. We approach the solution to the n-th order, free, diagonalized case and then develop it to the forced, n-th order matrix differential equation by using eigenvalues and eigenvectors. The analytical development is continued in Chapter 6 with the Laplace transform and transfer functions.

Feedback control is the main theme of Chapter 7. Because the transfer function viewpoint is so well suited to single variable feedback systems, it is presented as the core material of the chapter. Systems which do not lend themselves to the transfer function approach are analyzed by using computer simulation. The transfer function approach to linear systems is continued in Chapter 8 with the introduction of the frequency response concept and frequency domain design techniques for feedback systems.

The material presented in the last two chapters, discrete-time systems, and noise and probabilistic systems, is not normally offered at the undergraduate level. We have chosen to include it here because we feel that undergraduates can understand it and benefit from this early exposure.

It should be possible to cover the entire book in a one semester course (40 to 50 class hours) for advanced junior or senior students in engineering or science. For a one quarter course of about 30 class hours, the most probable coverage is through Chapter 8. In either case, the instructor may expand upon individual chapters or omit some at his or her discretion without fear of compromising the thrust of the book.

The contributions to the development of this text are many and varied: several of our colleagues commented on the manuscript or offered their advice, notably Professor O. Elgerd at the University of Florida and Professors P. Mendelson and N. Hauser at the Polytechnic Institute of New York. Numerous student users of the original course notes brought errors to our attention. We are particularly thankful to Fred Burg at the Polytechnic Institute of New York and Jacques Leibovitz at the University of California, Berkeley, for their careful review of the manuscript. This final printed version was entirely the work of Saragraphics of Berkeley, who did the art work and designed the cover, and the aforementioned Fred Burg, who did the composition and design of the text and whose heroic efforts we gratefully acknowledge. We freely acknowledge our incalculable debt to our wives and, in addition, would like to take this opportunity to note the considerable editorial assistance of Joan Rabins and Vivian Auslander and the artistic assistance of Ponchan Takahashi.

David M. Auslander

Yasundo Takahashi

Michael J. Rabins

CHAPTER 1
INTRODUCTION

Four themes thread through all of dynamic systems and control theory: the search for cause and effect relationships; the view that the current output of a system is a result of its past inputs; the use of a system's own output to regulate it; and the definition of relevant interactions among a system's component parts. The watchwords used to describe these modus operandi are *causality, dynamics, feedback* and *system decomposition*, which are discussed in the four sections of this chapter.

These four concepts not only form the basis of a technical discipline traditionally applied to the design and analysis of engineering systems, they also play a strong role in our personal decision-making activities. Take an electric kitchen stove, for instance. In its everyday use we take account of its dynamic behavior when we make provision for the fact that the water will continue to boil after the burner has been turned off. We rely on a feedback controller when we set the oven temperature and let it regulate itself. Causality and system decomposition come into play in case of a malfunction as we isolate component parts of the system for easier troubleshooting and identify the input and output signals from each of the components.

In recent years, dynamic systems and control theory has come to be respected not only as a finely honed technical tool but also as a realistic means of perceiving varieties of events and experiences outside the usual realm of engineering. As its reputation for flexibility and usefulness has grown, it has come to be used more widely in other areas such as ecology, biology and physiology, economics and management. Our philosophy that this is a healthy and meaningful development is reflected by our choice of both

1

engineering and nonengineering example problems throughout this book. We believe that applying engineering techniques to these familiar, yet difficult areas outside engineering leads to keener insights into underlying principles. Concomitantly, we hope that application of the theory in this text to unusual or particularly demanding problems will spur researchers to greater efforts in development of new theory and techniques.

1.1 CAUSALITY: INPUT AND OUTPUT

Events (outputs) are consequences of causes (inputs). Whether a particular signal is viewed as an input or output depends on the process we are studying. For example, in examining the thermometer of household thermostats, the room temperature is an input and the temperature reading is the output. On the other hand, looking at the furnace and radiator system, the oil input is an input and the room temperature is an output. This case is typical in that although the same signal can be viewed as either input or output under different circumstances, its causal relationship is fixed in a specific process. Neither the causality of the thermometer nor the causality of the furnace-radiator system can be reversed. Changing the reading on the thermometer will not have any direct effect on the room temperature, nor will changing the room temperature have any direct effect on the oil flow. By connecting the thermostat to the furnace controller, we are using feedback to regulate the room temperature. Then, a change in any one of the system's variables will affect all of the others. The most effective way to analyze such a system, however, is to decompose it into its component parts and identify the causal relationships for each component.

The birth rate in the United States serves as another example of causality. Considering the birth rate as an output, can we say that the large amount of publicity about overpopulation and zero-population-growth is an input to the process, and, as such, is the cause of the birth rate declining in 1972 to just below the population maintainence level? The overall number we call birth rate is really a combination of millions of individual decisions made in the course of the year. Although we can hypothesize that social pressure via mass communication is the mechanism for population control of humans, only experts in demography, working with dynamic systems experts, can devise procedures to further test the validity of the hypothesis. In a complex system such as this one, hypotheses concerning causality can never be proved,

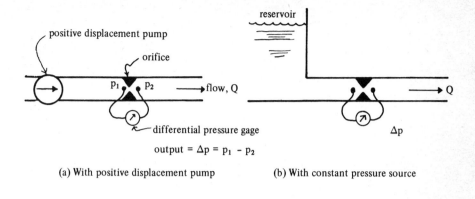

Fig. 1-1 An Orifice System

but if enough evidence is amassed they can become useful decision-making tools. As a further note, in this case the causality is irreversible.

The orifice in a pipe with liquid flowing, Fig. 1-1, is an example of an element with reversible causality. If the pump is a *positive displacement* type (such as a piston or gear pump), the flowrate through the orifice will be the input and the pressure drop across it the output. Written in mathematical form, this would be $\Delta p = f(Q)$, where p is pressure and Q is volume flowrate. If, instead of the pump, the upstream end of the pipe was connected to a reservoir, or other constant pressure source, Fig. 1-1(b), then pressure drop would be the input and flow the output, or $Q = f(\Delta p)$.

1.2 SYSTEMS WITH DYNAMICS

A dynamic system is one whose present output depends on *past* inputs. A system whose current output depends only on current inputs is called *static*. Note that the more popular notion of *dynamic* as "active," "changing with time" can apply to either dynamic or static systems; a static system's output will be changing in time if its input is changing. A dynamic system will be changing in time if it is not in an equilibrium state.

To see some examples of static and dynamic systems, let's consider an automobile. The angular position of the front wheels is statically dependent on the position of the driver's steering wheel. That is, a measurement of the position of the steering wheel at any instant gives a very good indication of the position of the front wheels at that same instant. On the other hand, measuring the angular position of the front wheels at any instant gives one very little information about the current angular velocity of the whole car and even less information about its current heading. The whole past history of inputs must be known to deduce this information solely from knowledge of the inputs (i.e., without direct measurement). Likewise, because of the car's momentum, its forward velocity is dynamically dependent on the accelerator position. If the car in question has an engine that responds very quickly, its forward acceleration might be statically dependent on the accelerator position, but in most cars the dynamics of the engine response are obvious to the driver.

The above discussion points to a singularly important concept: whether a process is considered to be static or dynamic *depends on the time scale* involved. Since, in nature, nothing ever happens instantaneously, it would be theoretically correct to consider all systems dynamic. This would, however, put an impossible burden on our analytic and computational capabilities. Thus, if the engine responds to changes in the accelerator position much faster than the car responds to changes in the engine power output, considering the engine to be static will make analysis of the car's performance much simpler without serious loss of accuracy. Since the time span of interest depends on the purpose of the investigation, the designations static and dynamic are inseparable from the context of the goals of the study.

An extreme example of a dynamic system is one that appears to have no input at all, the so-called *autonomous* system. Such a system is responding to an input that was present at some time in the past and is now no longer present. Consider an isolated population of some species, for example. Letting N equal the total number of individuals, which is the system output, and b and m equal the birth and mortality rates per unit of population per unit of time, we have

        b N dt = number of individuals born in dt time interval
and   m N dt = number of individuals dying in dt time interval

where t is running time (the independent variable). A population balance gives the following equation:

$$\frac{dN}{dt} = (b - m)N \qquad (1\text{-}1)$$

Since bN and mN are the rates of population *supply* and *loss*, respectively, we expect the population to decrease with time if mN is greater than bN; N will increase when mN is less than bN; and N will stay constant (an *equilibrium state*) when mN equals bN.

A simple analysis applies if the parameters b and m are constant. Letting $r = b - m =$ constant, we rewrite Eq. (1-1) in the following form:

$$\frac{dN}{dt} = rN \qquad (1\text{-}2)$$

If the *initial* value N_0 of the population $N(t)$ at a specified time origin ($t = 0$) is known (for instance, total human population at the turn of the century), then the solution of the first order differential equation (1-2) will be

$$N(t) = e^{rt}N_0 \qquad (1\text{-}3)$$

The population will grow exponentially (the Malthusian population explosion) when m is less than b (that is, for r positive), as in Fig. 1-2.

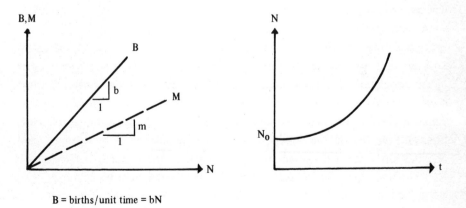

B = births/unit time = bN
M = deaths/unit time = mN

Fig. 1-2 Population Explosion

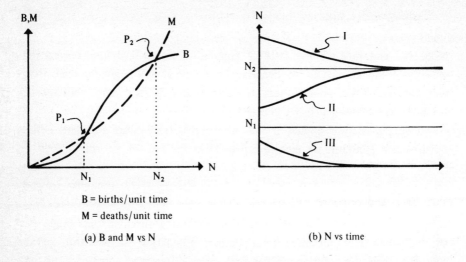

B = births/unit time
M = deaths/unit time

(a) B and M vs N   (b) N vs time

Fig. 1-3   Equilibrium Populations, N_1 and N_2

In a real ecosystem, even if a species is completely isolated from others, the system parameters b and m will vary with time (evolution, for instance), and as a function of N itself and other environmental factors (like weather conditions, etc.). If b and m (hence B and M, which are the birth and death rates per unit time, respectively) depend on N as shown in Fig. 1-3, there will be two equilibrium states P_1 and P_2. Four different types of responses are possible in this case. If the initial population is equal to either N_1 or N_2, the population will remain constant with time because the birth and death rates are exactly balanced at these two points (the *equilibrium* points). If the initial population is greater than N_2, we can see from Fig. 1-3(a) that the death rate will exceed the birth rate until the population is reduced to N_2, perhaps because of lack of food due to crowding. This is the response labelled I in (b) of the figure. If the initial population is between N_1 and N_2, the birth rate will exceed the death rate until the population increases to N_2, response curve II. Finally, if the initial population is below N_1 the species (or this local population of that species) is headed for extinction as in response curve III, because the death rate is greater than the birth rate right to the point of zero population. At these very low populations, extinction might be caused by insufficient protection for the young, inability to find mates or other consequences of a too sparse population.

Equilibrium points are generally classified according to their stability properties. In simple terms, an equilibrium point is considered stable if for values of the system variables near the equilibrium point the response tends towards that point. P_2 in Fig. 1-3(a) is a stable equilibrium point. For values of N near N_2, the response will return to N_2 as shown by responses I and II in Fig. 1-3(b). Point P_1 is an example of an unstable equilibrium. For values of N near N_1, the responses tend to move away from the equilibrium point, as shown by responses II and III. Regardless of whether the equilibrium is stable or unstable, it is defined as an equilibrium point because any time the system variables are exactly equal to an equilibrium value they stay at that value. Thus the response will be unchanging with time anytime $N = N_1$ or $N = N_2$ or $N = 0$ (which is also an equilibrium value for this system). The system of Eq. (1-2), Fig. 1-2, has only one equilibrium point, at $N = 0$, and that is an unstable equilibrium because for any positive value of N_0 the response increases exponentially.

1.3 FEEDBACK CONTROL

Feedback control systems are ubiquitous in nature. The nonchalance of a robin, perched on a telephone wire which is swaying in the breeze, attests to its possession of an exquisitely tuned balance control system. A person riding a bicycle, skiing, or surfing demonstrates how well that balance control is developed in humans. Eye-hand coordination in human motor control is another example: the muscle inputs that provide the motive force for hand motion are constantly adjusted on the basis of information that is fed back to the brain from visual stimuli. These examples are but one branch in a forest of possibilities. There are feedback control systems for all facets of physiology, from body temperature control to salt concentration control to blood flow rate control. The key to all of these systems is that, in some way, a measurement of the system output is used to regulate the system's input in such a manner that the output stays close to some desired value. Use of this structure performs a vital function for the organism: it makes the system relatively insensitive to external disturbances and thus able to function in a changing environment.

Engineers use the same principles in the design of technological systems. The best known feedback control system is almost certainly the room temperature control system. Using a temperature measuring element, the thermostat turns heating and cooling equipment on and off in a way that assures that the room temperature will remain at a comfortable level regardless of outside conditions. The price for this freedom from external disturbance is extra cost for designing, purchasing and powering the necessary control equipment. The alternative to a house that can regulate its own temperature through the year with hardly any attention except maintainence of the equipment is an *open loop* system. The term open loop refers to a system with no feedback control. In such a case, it would not be very difficult to adjust the furnace output to a level that keeps the house warm and toasty. But as soon as the outside temperature changed, so would the house temperature. Since the daily temperature cycle can have highs and lows that differ by $20°F$ $(10°C)$ or more, the furnace (or air conditioner) would require almost constant readjustment to keep the inside temperature steady. Note that by this act of constant readjustment we have replaced the mechanical controller by a human one! In the absence of any feedback control the room temperature would vary widely.

The difficult − and interesting − part of control system design comes as a consequence of the dynamics in the behavior of systems we want to control. Recalling from our previous discussion of static versus dynamic that this designation can only be made in relation to the purpose of the study, we can gain some insight into where difficulties are likely to appear in controller design. At one extreme, if we are not very demanding of speed in a system's response under feedback control, the control task is not very difficult. For very slow changes in the input, we can consider the system being controlled to be static and achieve satisfactory control by making small changes in the input and then waiting to observe the effects of the initial change before making more. Using the information thus gained, we can devise a strategy for the next move, and so on. If all situations were this easy, there would not be much reason to study dynamic system and control theory. But at 65 mph (100 km/h) in an automobile, we cannot afford the luxury of treating the control object as static. We must be willing to make decisions and take action before the consequences of that action are fully known. To do this we must be able to predict accurately the system's response to our inputs.

Control system design increases in difficulty as we increase our demands on speed of performance relative to the characteristic speed of response of the uncontrolled system. As we push to higher performance goals for a control system, we must make use of more sophisticated theory in the design of the controller itself and we must have much greater knowledge of the dynamic characteristics of the object being controlled.

Careful design of control systems can be crucial to reliable system operation because failures in the controller can leave the primary system subject to possibly disasterous external influences. A dramatic example of this occurred on the Apollo 13 mission in April, 1970, when an oxygen tank exploded in outer space because of a failure in its thermostatic temperature control system.† Thorough knowledge of the operating characteristics enabled the astronauts and Mission Control personnel to land the Apollo capsule safely, thus averting a tragic accident.

It is therefore important to realize that in system design the overall system reliability, which is a function of the reliability of the individual components, must be a high priority design criterion. Dynamic system theory can also be very useful in investigating the possible consequences of a component malfunction.

1.4 SYSTEM DECOMPOSITION: A CASE STUDY OF A LEAKING TANK

Making measurements on dynamic systems, especially those with feedback control, is difficult because interactions among the elements of the system make it hard to isolate causality. Moreover, the dynamic characteristics spread the effect of a particular input over a long time interval and mix it with the effects of other inputs. A major operation in the dynamic system and control technique is the decomposition of a system into component parts in such a way that these problems are bypassed. This is achieved by 1) identifying elements whose characteristics can be measured with static experiments and 2) separating the characteristics of dynamic elements into those parts that can be measured with static experiments and those that can be described by a simple dynamic relation, usually integration for the systems we will be dealing with. To see how this is accomplished, we suggest an experiment that can be done in any kitchen with a graduated measuring cup, an empty tin can, a ruler and a watch with a sweep second hand.

The leaking tank system, pictured in Fig. 1-4, although simple enough for us to analyze here, has all the same fundamental problems that appear in

---

† H. S. F. Cooper, Jr., "An Accident in Space," *New Yorker*, Nov. 11, p. 48; Nov. 18, p. 75, 1972.

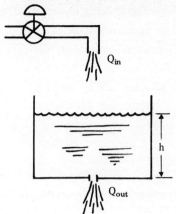

Fig. 1-4 A Leaking Tank System

more complex systems. Our goal is to be able to predict the height of liquid in the tank as a function of time for any arbitrary input, $Q_{in}(t)$. Our *tank* is a can with a hole punched in its bottom. The standard water faucet does well for the input. The primary decomposition of this system is into three components: the input element, the tank and the hole which functions as an orifice.

The tank is the dynamic element in this system because it is the only one that can store energy. We can decompose its characteristic into two parts: first a relation expressed by a simple integration

$$V = \int_0^t (Q_{in} - Q_{out})\, dt \qquad (1\text{-}4)$$

where V is the total volume of water in the tank. Note that this relation is a direct consequence of the law of conservation of mass and that Eq. (1-4) contains no unknown constants. The second step is to find the relationship between the volume of water in the tank and its height, h. This is an algebraic relation which can be expressed as h = f(V). Since most cans have straight sides, we expect that this relation can be written in the simple linear form

$$h = \frac{V}{A} \qquad (1\text{-}5)$$

where A is the cross-sectional area of the tank. There are two simple ways to measure the cross-sectional area and we should use both to minimize the possibilities for error. The first is to measure the diameter of the can with the ruler and compute the cross-sectional area from the results. For our can this procedure yields $A = 75.3 \text{ cm}^2$. The second method is to take a known volume of water (using the graduated measuring cup) and pour it into the can with the hole plugged up, of course. Then measure the height of water in the can and compute A from $A = V/h$. Do this several times with different quantities of water. This method yields $A = 73.8 \text{ cm}^2$, so we will use $A = 74.5 \text{ cm}^2$ in further work.[†]

From our knowledge of fluid mechanics, we know that the flow through the hole will be a function of the height of liquid in the tank, $Q_{out} = f(h)$. To find this function, we can perform the following experiment:

1) With the hole unplugged, turn the input water on.
2) Wait until the water level in the tank has stabilized.
3) Using the graduated measuring cup and the second hand of a watch, find Q_{out} by measuring the time for a given amount of water to accumulate, or the accumulation in a given time.
4) Plot this point on a curve of h vs Q_{out}, change the setting of the water source and do it again until the curve has points for the full range of h's.

Following this procedure, we generate the experimental points (designated by circles) in Fig. 1-5. The standard formulation for flow through an orifice is $Q = k\sqrt{h}$. With $k = 10.7$, we see that this relation fits the experimental data very well (solid line, Fig. 1-5). Substituting this result and Eq. (1-5) into Eq. (1-4) yields

$$h = \frac{1}{A}\int_0^t (Q_{in} - 10.7\sqrt{h})\,dt \qquad (1\text{-}6)$$

By differentiating both sides, we can write this in the form of a first order differential equation

$$\frac{dh}{dt} = -\frac{10.7}{A}\sqrt{h} + \frac{Q_{in}}{A} \qquad (1\text{-}7)$$

We can now use this result to test how good our modeling procedure has been by running a dynamic test and comparing the prediction of Eq. (1-7) to

---

† The differences resulting from redundant measurements of the same property give us a feeling for the precision that can be expected in the final results.

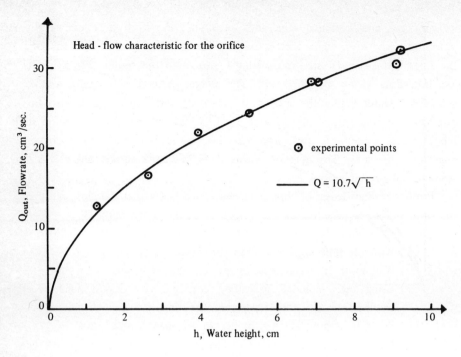

Fig. 1-5 Flow Characteristic of Hole

the experimental results. We will take the case of a *step response*; that is, at time zero the input water flow is turned on and then held at a constant value throughout the test. We start with the can empty. Using the watch and measuring cup technique, we can measure the flow. After starting the test, the water height is measured with a ruler every ten seconds. The experimental results for Q_{in} = 35.4 cm^3/sec are shown by the circled points in Fig. 1-6. To get a theoretical result, we must solve Eq. (1-7) with Q_{in} = constant and $h(0) = 0$. First, we can rearrange the differential equation into the integral

$$A \int_0^h \frac{1}{Q_{in} - 10.7\eta^{1/2}} \, d\eta = \int_0^t \, d\tau \tag{1-8}$$

where η and τ are dummy variables of integration. Making the substitution $z = \eta^{1/2}$, this can be transformed into a form appearing in standard integral tables.[†] The solution with $h(0) = 0$ is

---

†   No. 30 in the 20th edition of the CRC *Standard Mathematical Tables*

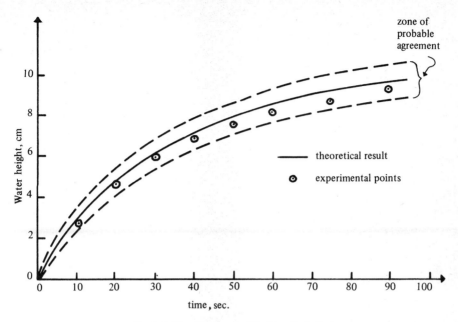

Fig. 1-6 Step Response of Leaking Tank System

$$\frac{2\,A}{10.7^2}\left[-10.7\,h^{\frac{1}{2}} - Q_{in}\,\ln\left(\frac{Q_{in} - 10.7\,h^{\frac{1}{2}}}{Q_{in}}\right)\right] = t \qquad (1\text{-}9)$$

Because of algebraic complexity, even for this simple problem, we cannot solve Eq. (1-9) for h explicitly. However, using the form given, we can plot an h versus t curve by putting in values of h and get corresponding values of t. This curve is shown as the solid line in Fig. 1-6. Noting that the errors in measuring and regulating the water flow are probably as high as ±5% and that there is an uncertainty in the area measurement as shown above, we can substitute the extreme possible values of the system parameters into Eq. (1-9) and get solutions that define the probable accuracy of the predicted results. These bounds are shown as the dashed lines in Fig. 1-6 and we see that the experimental points all fall within this zone. The results of these experiments give us confidence that the analytical solution we have derived in the form of the differential equation (1-7) can be used to predict the performance of this system under other operating conditions (different functions of time for Q_{in}, different initial conditions). Of course, we must always be aware of the limits of precision determined by the accuracy of our measurements and other approximations that might be made when using the results as an aid to decision making.

SUMMARY

We can now proceed to the next chapter, which examines the concept of the *state* of a system. Bear in mind while reading the remainder of the book that the concepts of causality, dynamics, feedback and system decomposition are fundamental to all of the material that is presented.

PROBLEMS

1-1 A bomb explosion is an *unstable process*. If a movie of an explosion is run backwards, does it appear to be unstable or stable?

1-2 World population in the year 1960 and thereafter is approximated by $N(t) = e^{0.02t}N_0$, where t is in years and N_0 is the initial population when $t = 0$, say the population in 1960 (3.01 billions). Obtain the time, t_d (years), that is required for the population to double. (In general, such a time interval t_d is called the *doubling time* and is constant for a given exponential function with a positive exponent.)

1-3 A cup of coffee was too hot ($90°C$) to drink when it was first served. It took 6 minutes (while stirring but not pouring in the cold cream) for the coffee to cool down to $55°C$ in a room at $20°C$ temperature. Assume that the *cooling curve* of the difference temperature (coffee temperature minus room temperature) is an exponential and obtain an expression for the cooling curve. Is 6 minutes in this example related to the doubling time of the preceding problem? (Times like the 6 minutes in this problem are generally called *half-lives*, especially in radioactive decay problems.)

1-4 If an automobile steering system, discussed in Sec. 1.2, has backlash in the linkage between the steering wheel and the front wheel, is the system still static?

1-5 Discuss what will happen if a light sensing switch (that turns a light on at dusk and turns it off at dawn the next morning) is facing a light bulb to which the switch is connected. Test this system by using your eye-hand combination as the switch. Is this a feedback system? Investigate the causality involved in the system.

1-6 Consider a system that is composed of two subsystems: a self-supporting commuter bus (or train) company and commuters who may use the transit system or drive their own cars. Suppose that fare and the number of paying riders are the two main variables of the system. Assign these two variables as the input and output of each subsystem and come up with a feedback structure for the entire system. If the transit company (or authority) is obliged to hike its fare due to inflation, and lose customers as a consequence, is the overall behavior of the system "stable" in the sense of our terminology?

1-7 Headway of a commuting train or bus system (i.e., time between train or buses) is scheduled to be a constant, such as 4 minutes, for instance, in rush hours. Suppose something causes a small delay in the schedule. Does this deviation tend to grow (meaning, is the transit system schedule inherently unstable in rush hours)?

1-8 Suppose head (or depth), H, versus outflow, Q, is related as shown in Fig. P-1-8(a) for an orifice in a tank-bottom. Is it possible to design a tank, as in Fig. P-1-8(b), for example, that has a cross-section A(H) as a function of depth H, such that the time rate of level drop due to the leak will remain constant? Can we expect the same result by changing A as indicated in Fig. P-1-8(c)? In the last case, does A at each depth, H, agree with the value of A(H) in Fig. P-1-8(b)? Are the systems shown in (b) and (c) of the figure autonomous?

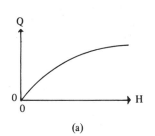

(a)

(b)

Fig. P-1-8

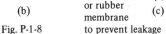

movable side-wall of a square tank

plastic or rubber membrane to prevent leakage

(c)

1-9 The variable x is level and Q_1 and Q_2 are flow variables in Fig. P-1-9(a), which is schematic so that the variables may apply to population, a thermal process, etc. Flow variables are related to the level of the single storage (tank) as shown by straight lines in Fig. P-1-9(b) (by some mechanism indicated only by dashed lines

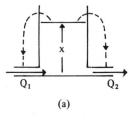

(a)

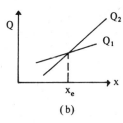

(b)

Fig. P-1-9

in (a)) so that x_e is an equilibrium state. Is this state stable or not? Let $\Delta x = x - x_e$ be a small deviation from the equilibrium state which is not zero at time zero. Sketch a response curve on a Δx versus t graph. Is this curve exponential?

1-10 Layer thickness is controlled by a linkage in a conveyor system for powder materials. Desired layer thickness is adjusted by vertically moving the pivot point of the lever mechanism as indicated in Fig. P-1-10. Suppose the system is at an equilibrium state (uniform layer thickness all over the belt) at time zero when the pivot point is pushed down. Discuss what will happen. How does the lever ratio affect the response?

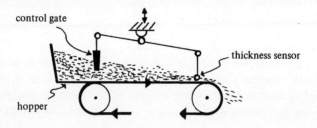

Fig. P-1-10

CHAPTER 2
STATE
VECTORS

To deal constructively with the dynamics of a system for purposes of either design or analysis, it is essential that there be available a mathematical model which reasonably well describes the behavior of that system. In this chapter, we lay the groundwork for such mathematical modeling by examining the behavior of individual elements from a particular perspective — the concept of the *state* of that element. The keynote of this chapter is input-output causality and the choice and definition of system state variables. Energetic systems are discussed in some detail, with attention to generalized resistive, capacitive and inductive elements and the concepts of analogy. The constitutive relations for a number of such elements are developed, utilizing the concept of effort and flow variables, whose product is power. Power and energy relations are then derived in terms of these variables. The chapter ends with a discussion of state variables, including an introduction to the concept of the state vector and a consideration of the necessity of having linearly independent state variables to describe a system.

2.1 STATE

If the motion of a system is recorded on movie film or videotape, then each single frame *freezes* that motion and presents a record of that motion, i.e., describes the instantaneous state of the system. We use a set of variables, called *state variables*, to identify a system and describe that motion. If a dynamic system is simple, then a single state variable will be sufficient to describe the state of the system completely. This was the case for the population $(N(t))$ and level $(h(t))$ problems in Chapter 1. However, in most cases, a set of state variables will be necessary to describe the state of a system completely at any instant. Thus, for example, two levels are necessary to model the two-tank system of Fig. 2-1.

A system which can be described by a finite number of (scalar) state variables is called a finite order system or a *lumped parameter system*. The term lumped parameter is used to express the concept that each point in a system *embodies* the properties of the region immediately surrounding it. Normally, scalar variables describe the state of a system at single points in space. When used as state variables, however, they are assumed to represent the average of the distribution around each point. That is, the properties of the surrounding region are *lumped* into each point the scalar state variables describe. The dynamic equations describing a lumped parameter system can be written as finite order, ordinary differential equations.† In this book, we have chosen to discuss mainly finite order systems because they are mathematically simple, flexible and well adapted to linear systems theory.

In this chapter and the next one on modeling state equations, we examine some procedures for designing the state variable model of a system to best fulfill the goals of the study. For example, design engineers ordinarily consider the state of a power generating plant to include various temperatures, pressures, speeds, voltages, etc. However, for a pollution prevention study, the plant state would likely be described by quite a different set of variables. For an economic

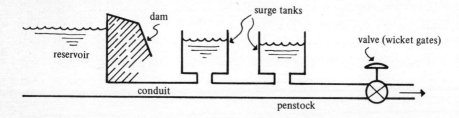

Fig. 2-1 Hydro-electric Power Plant with Double Surge Tanks

---

† Systems whose state is described by functions (like a hot steel ingot where the ingot temperature is a function of time *and* space dimensions) are generally called *distributed parameter systems*; the dynamical equations describing these systems are partial differential equations.

optimization study, the state would be different still.

Choosing state variables for a system is part of the *art* of engineering. The guidelines suggested below and elsewhere are no more than indications of where to start — none of them can take account of that most important aspect of the situation, the *purpose* of the whole project. They can only suggest an approach. Even after the goals of the project have been well defined and the structure of the model has been established, we will see that many equivalent sets of state variables will describe that same model. The engineer's intuition and "feel" for the situation must provide the major guidance.

2.2 ENERGETIC SYSTEMS

Some systems, by their actual structure, make the choice of state variables easy. Such is the case when a system's primary energy (or material) storage modes are associated with parts of the system that are physically separated, like the water tank system in Fig. 2-1. It is then customary to assign one state variable to each independent storage element (cases with dependent storage elements will be discussed in Chapter 3).

Consider the hydraulic system shown in Fig. 2-1, a schematic of a typical hydroelectric power plant. The two energy storage elements are the surge tanks, so one state variable is assigned to each; the height of water in each tank would be a good choice.† The assumptions used in making this choice are that 1) the system energy content is entirely potential energy as measured by liquid height, 2) contributions due to fluid velocities in the tank can be neglected and 3) variations in the height at the surface due to waves and surface ripples are small relative to the heights being measured. The reservoir (left end in the figure) is considered to be *infinite* in extent; that is, its surface level does not change appreciably because of water used for power generation. We thus view the reservoir as a source of stored energy in this problem.

The need to consider any other energy storage elements in this system depends both on the time duration we are interested in and the physial dimensions of the actual unit. For modest time durations, in normal operation with the wicket gates opening or closing slowly, we must decide if it is important to include the kinetic energy due to water velocity in the conduits and penstock.

---

† Water height is not the only choice — we could use liquid volumes in each tank as state variables also, for example.

If the conduits are very long, the kinetic energy will make an important contribution to the system dynamics. If, however, the problem is to understand the operation of the system when the wicket gate is being opened or closed rapidly, the compressibility of the water cannot be neglected. For these short time durations, the surge tanks can be treated as energy sources since their water level hardly changes at all. State variable assignments in the conduit and penstock can be made by lumping sections of pipe into a concentrated *inertia* to account for the mass of the liquid and into a concentrated *compliance* to account for its compressibility. The number of such sections required depends on the actual speed of the wicket gates. If a large number of lumps are required, it will probably be more efficient to regard the conduit and penstocks as distributed parameter systems.

Simple models of an automobile suspension system offer another opportunity to look at the process of choosing state variables. The two-state variable model (Fig. 2-2(a)), one for the kinetic energy of the moving mass and the other for the potential energy in the spring, is the least complex. The road is viewed as a vertical velocity input source to the system. The velocity of the mass and the force in the spring would be a good set of state variables for this model. A more sophisticated model (Fig. 2-2(b)) derives from considering the car as a *sprung* and *unsprung* mass. The unsprung mass is that part of the car below the main springs: the wheels, axles, wheel frames, etc. and the sprung mass is the rest: the body, engine, passengers. The motion leads to a four variable model and a separation of energies more representative of the real system.

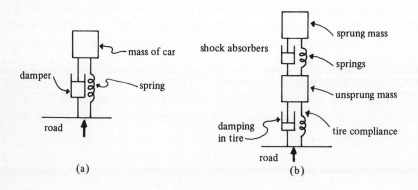

Fig. 2-2 Models of an Automobile Suspension

Yet another, completely different model is needed if we wish to study the dynamics of the tire-road interaction since the tire has a far more complex behavior than can be described by just a spring and damper.

2.3 ANALOGY IN ENERGETIC SYSTEMS

Energetic systems in many media (thermal, electrical, etc.) are governed by a common set of physical laws, although the widely differing notations and conventions often obscure this fact. In the following material, we exploit the common ground to derive a structure applicable to a wide variety of energetic systems and thus establish analogous relationships and variables for different physical systems. Use of such a common structure is particularly useful in the transfer of knowledge from one type of system to another. It is also useful in the development of general purpose computer programs for analysis or design of dynamic systems.†

The physics of individual elements in energetic systems are described by the constitutive relations of the elements. Constitutive relations are empirically based algebraic relationships between the variables of an element, like the relation between

    force and deflection for a spring
    velocity and momentum for a mass
    pressure and quantity of liquid in a liquid tank
    charge and voltage in a capacitor
    voltage drop and current for a resistor, etc.

All of the possible constitutive relations for lumped parameter models of energetic systems appear on H. M. Paynter's tetrahedron (Ref. [1]). The variables e and f in the tetrahedron are thought of as generalized *effort* (or *level*) and generalized *flow* (or *rate*) variables, such that instantaneous power usage at a point in a system is described by the product e·f. Commonly used pairs that fit this description are

    voltage and current in electrical systems
    pressure and flow in fluid systems

---

† A computer-based system of this sort, the bond graph system, is described in Ref. [2], and a series of applications of bond graphs is given in Ref. [3]. Refs. [1] and [4] also contain relevant material.

velocity and force in mechanical systems[†]

Most systems can store energy in two forms, as, for example, kinetic and potential or capacitive and inductive. On the upper left side of the tetrahedron generalized *capacitance* is diagrammed (Φ_C in Fig. 2-3) and on the lower right side generalized *inductance* is shown by Φ_I. Note that only generalized capacitance, Φ_C, applies to thermal systems. The center part of Fig. 2-3 shows energy *dissipation*, or resistance, by Φ_R. The Φ's are the constitutive relations and are static functions, that is, they include no dynamic operator like integration. The variables p and q in Fig. 2-3 are defined as the integrals with respect to time of e and f, respectively. For example

> flux, p, the integral of voltage in electrical systems
>
> quantity, q, the integral of flow in fluid systems
>
> displacement, x, the integral of velocity in mechanical systems, etc.

Note that the energy storage elements are identified by the presence of *integrators* in their computational path, whereas dissipation in a resistor is a purely static function. We present some examples of analogous storage and dissipation elements below.

Capacitive Elements

The constitutive relation

$$e = \Phi_C(q) \qquad \text{where} \quad q = \int f \, dt \qquad\qquad (2\text{-}1)$$

for a *liquid*-filled *tank*, is simply a matter of volumetric balance, an application of the conservation condition for an incompressible fluid (see Section 1.4). The flow variable is volume flow Q (cm^3/sec), so that the q variable stands for the

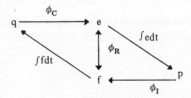

Fig. 2-3 The Tetrahedron

[†] And temperature and entropy flow in thermal systems, although *entropy flow* is not tempting for engineering usage; use of heat flow is generally more convenient.

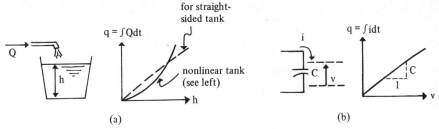

Fig. 2-4 Some Capacitive Elements

volume of liquid in the tank which, when divided by the cross-sectional area A
(cm^2) of a straight sided tank, gives the liquid height H (cm) in the tank. Thus

$$H(t) = H_0 + \frac{1}{A} \int_0^t Q \, dt \qquad (2\text{-}2)$$

where H_0 is the initial value of H(t). The engineering unit system, metric or
British, must be carefully applied to convert H into an effort variable for power
computation. The (static) relation (2-1) becomes *nonlinear* when a tank does
not have straight sides (Fig. 2-4(a)).

Another example is an *electrical* parallel-plate *capacitor*, where effort is voltage V (volts) and flow is current i (amp.). The integral of the current gives
charge q, in coulombs. The constitutive relation is

$$V(t) = V_0 + \frac{1}{C} \int_0^t i \, dt \qquad (2\text{-}3)$$

where V_0 is initial charge and C is the capacitance in farads, that is, coulombs/
volt, (Fig. 2-4(b)).

Inductive Elements

The constitutive relation is

$$f(t) = \Phi_I(p) \quad \text{where } p = \int e \, dt \qquad (2\text{-}4)$$

where e is voltage V and f is current i in an electrical system and

$$i(t) = i_0 + \frac{1}{I} \int_0^t V \, dt \qquad (2\text{-}5)$$

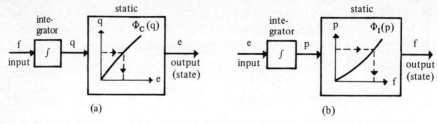

Fig. 2-5 $\Phi_C(q)$ and $\Phi_I(p)$

for an inductor of I (henry) with an initial current i_0. In the two dynamic elements, capacitive and inductive, Eqs. (2-1) and (2-4), we see that the relations Φ_C and Φ_I are both static, linear or nonlinear (Fig. 2-5) and coupled with an integrating action, respectively.

Where mechanical systems are concerned, there is general agreement that the proper signal variables are force F and velocity V (their product is power). A common procedure is to assign force as the e variable and velocity as the f variable. By Newton's second law

$$V(t) = V_0 + \frac{1}{m} \int_0^t F \, dt \tag{2-6}$$

we see that mass m plays the same role as does inductance I in Eq. (2-5). Hooke's law for a spring is

$$F(t) = F_0 + k \int_0^t V \, dt \tag{2-7}$$

so that spring constant k plays the role of (1/C) in Eq. (2-3) where C is capacitance.

Causality

In reviewing Fig. 2-5 and the relations so far derived, it appears that for pure capacitive elements f is always the input and e the output,[†] whereas for inductive elements the reverse is always true. This natural *causality* (cause and

---

[†] The output may or may not be identical with the state of the system, depending upon the dictates of the analysis. In some cases, the system output may be a function of some of the system state variables. This distinction is further explored in Chapter 5.

effect or input and output relationship) is not accidental. Note further that this causality provides additional information (or constraints) beyond the constitutive relations. The source of this causal information lies in the constraints of the physical world being modeled. Some counter-examples will perhaps suffice to clarify this point:

In Eq. (2-6) where a pure mass is acting as an inductive element and velocity V is an f variable, let us consider what might happen if V were to play the role of an arbitrary input: an arbitrary step change in velocity would require instantaneous infinite force since the force as an output would equal the derivative of the velocity — clearly an impossible situation because an infinite force acting at a finite velocity requires infinite power. In Eq. (2-7) where a pure spring is acting as a capacitive element, taking the force as an arbitrary input leads to the situation where the velocity depends upon the derivative of the force and must be instantaneously infinite to explain step changes in force, again a physically impossible situation. Similar arguments apply to the electrical elements of Eqs. (2-3) and (2-5). Thus, attempting to input a step change in voltage to a pure capacitance would theoretically lead to infinite currents. However, for large currents, lead wire resistance (no matter how small) must not be ignored.

Study of many diverse energetic elements leads to the conclusion that they all behave with natural *integral causality*. In all cases, the output level of an element is an accumulation (or integration) of the input, so we note that the arrowheads of Fig. 2-5 have a special significance. Furthermore, this concept is usually carried over to the modeling of nonenergetic elements (the usual case in social systems) where integral causality is always assigned, as will be clear in subsequent examples.

As another counter-example, let us assume that differential causality is feasible. In Fig. 2-5, this would mean that q and p as inputs might be differentiated to yield f and e as outputs. If we think of the differentiation process in its limiting form, $\lim_{\Delta t \to 0} \frac{\Delta q}{\Delta t}$ or $\lim_{\Delta t \to 0} \frac{\Delta p}{\Delta t}$, and attempt to apply this form to evaluate the *present* value of f or e, we note that this differential causality would require us to extrapolate into the *future* (e.g., $f_i = (1/\Delta t) \cdot [q_{i+1} - q_{i-1}]$) and use as yet unavailable information (q_{i+1}). On the other hand, integral causality is realizable in that it always sums up *past* system behavior to yield information about the present sytem state.

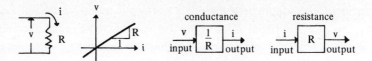

Fig. 2-6 Linear Electrical Resistor

Resistive Elements

The constitutive relation

$$e = \Phi_R(f) \tag{2-8}$$

is static, linear or nonlinear. Ohm's law is the simplest example where

$$V = Ri \tag{2-9}$$

where R (ohms) is the resistance. Since the relation is static, its causality is reversible (see Section 1.1) and 1/R (or the inverse function $\Phi_R^{-1}(e) = f$) may also give an input to output relation (Fig. 2-6).

A very common nonlinear electrical resistor, which is often introduced into a circuit intentionally, is the *diode*. Its resistance is strongly dependent on the directions of the current flow through it, as shown in Fig. 2-7(a). In many cases

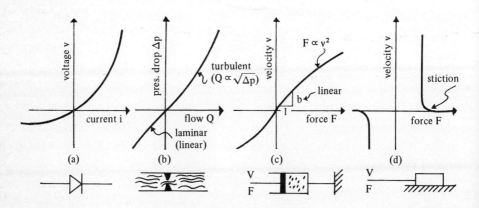

Fig. 2-7 Some Nonlinear Resistors

of practical interest, the resistance is nearly infinity for flow in one direction (like a check valve in a fluid line) and nearly zero for flow in the other direction.

A similar relation holds for fluid resistors (orifices, Sec. 1.1) but the static relation $e = \Phi_R(f)$ becomes nonlinear when the flow is turbulent (Fig. 2-7(b)). Such was the case in the leaking hole of the water tank experiment.

A static relation between force F and velocity V holds in a *mechanical resistor* or damper. The relationship is linear

$$F = bV \quad b = \text{constant} \tag{2-10}$$

for ideal *viscous friction*, valid only at low velocities when laminar flow will prevail in the lubricant. It is more likely that the force is proportional to V^2 (Fig. 2-7(c)) for appreciable velocities. To allow for a change in the sign of the force when the velocity changes sign, the equation for the V^2 resistor must be written as an *ab-squared* relation

$$F = BV|V| \tag{2-11}$$

where B is an empirical constant. *Dry friction* (also called Coulomb friction) has the interesting property that force is nearly constant, regardless of the velocity, except that it changes sign (i.e., its direction) with the direction of motion (i.e., the sign of velocity). Thus

$$F = B \, \text{sign}(V) \tag{2-12}$$

The effect known as *stiction* (stick friction) is also shown in Fig. 2-7(d). The friction force decreases as the velocity is increased from zero when stiction is involved. In the linear formulation, Eq. (2-10), this yields a negative value for b which may lead to the unstable equilibrium situation described as a stick-slip limit cycle.

2.4 ENERGY AND POWER

Three components for energetic systems, R, C and I, were discussed in the preceding section. We saw that C and I are dynamic elements: they act as integrators when causality is assigned to the constitutive relationships, whereas R is static. In the following, we shall briefly discuss the energy relation in R, C and I in terms of the two key variables, effort and flow, introduced in Section 2.3. We shall see that the energy is conserved in C and I elements (reversible energy flow) while it is dissipated in R elements (irreversible energy flow).

Since e and f variables are defined (Sec. 2.3) in such a way that

$$ef = p = \text{power} = \text{energy/time} \tag{2-13}$$

the product e(t)f(t) in a resistor will give an instantaneous rate of *power dissipation*. For instance, in a linear electrical resistor (Fig. 2-6) where e is V (volts) and f is i (amp.), V = iR, hence ef = iV = i^2R is Joule heating.

The change in energy due to a flow of power is the time integral of power

$$\Delta E = \int e(t)f(t)dt \tag{2-14}$$

The energy *stored* in capacitive and inductive elements can be computed from Eq. (2-14) using the definitions of the elements we made in the preceding section.

Capacitive Energy Storage: Inductive Energy Storage:

q is defined by   p is defined by

  $q = \int f\,dt$ or $dq = f\,dt$ $p = \int e\,dt$ or $dp = e\,dt$

so that   so that

  $\Delta E = \int e\,dq$ $\Delta E = \int f\,dp$

These integrals are shown in Fig. 2-8 schematically. In the case of *linear* constitutive relations, the integrals can be evaluated:

If Φ_C is such that   If Φ_I is such that

  $q = Ce$ $p = If$

then   then

  $\Delta E = \frac{1}{2}Ce^2 = \frac{q^2}{2C}$ $\Delta E = \frac{1}{2}If^2 = \frac{p^2}{2I}$

Note that only the positive sides (i.e., first quadrant) of e, f, p and q are shown in Fig. 2-8. Note also that E is always a positive quantity (called *positive definite*).

The two modes of energy storage in mechanical systems are the kinetic energy

$$E = \frac{1}{2}mV^2 \quad \text{where m is mass and V is velocity} \tag{2-15a}$$

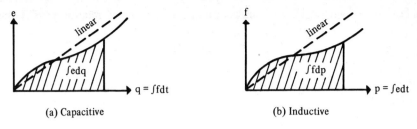

(a) Capacitive   (b) Inductive

Fig. 2-8   Energy Storage Modes

and potential energy

$$E = \frac{1}{2}kx^2 \quad \text{where k is the spring constant and x is the spring deflection}$$
(2-15b)

A single e-f pair is sufficient to describe the elements discussed above which are characterized by one power flow and are called *one-port* elements. Two pairs of e-f variables are necessary to describe the dynamics of a *two-port* element. Transforming and transducing elements are generally two-port. The simple (ideal) *transformer* is a static element which neither stores nor dissipates energy. Its two power flows are therefore equal, $P_1 = P_2$ and thus $e_1 f_1 = e_2 f_2$, and the constitutive relation for the ideal transformer has a single parameter, a modulus (turns ratio or gear ratio) r, such that

$$e_1 = re_2 \qquad f_1 = \frac{1}{r}f_2$$
(2-16)

If P_1 and P_2 are both power flows in the same medium, the above relations describe the common electrical transformer, the mechanical lever or the gear and pinion. If P_1 and P_2 are in different media, the element is usually called a *transducer*. The piston-cylinder pair for fluid to mechanical conversion and the solenoid for electrical to mechanical conversion are common examples of transducing elements.

2.5 STATE VARIABLES

The discussions of energetic systems in the last two sections suggest that the *number of state variables* necessary and sufficient to describe the system dynam-

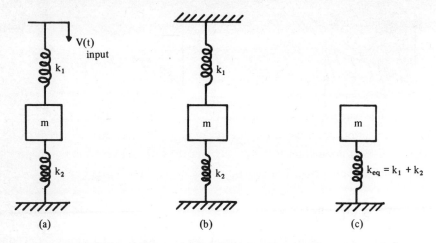

Fig. 2-9 Checking for Independence of Dynamic Elements

ics is either equal to or less than the number of C and I elements in the system. This number, in turn, is equal to the order of the system (or the number of integrators in the system). In many common energetic systems, the number of C's and I's will be the same as the number of necessary and sufficient state variables. In Fig. 2-9(a), for example, there are three dynamic elements, one mass and two springs and it takes three state variables to describe that system. If the velocity of the input is set to zero, however, that is equivalent to a system with grounds at both ends, as in Fig. 2-9(b). Although this system still has the same three dynamic elements, for modeling purposes it can be replaced by the equivalent system of Fig. 2-9(c) because the two springs acting in parallel can be replaced with a single spring having the spring constant shown. This equivalent system only requires two state variables; thus we can make a model of a system having three dynamic elements but only use two state variables for the model.

Besides being very useful for analyzing and simulating physical systems, dynamic systems theory is proving to be applicable to wide varieties of non-physical systems, among them urban dynamics, population dynamics and economics. Different methods of investigation use different parts of the theory and some or all of the techniques used to analyze physical systems. In order for any such use of dynamic system theory to succeed, it seems necessary to identify, at the very least, the state variables, constitutive relations and causality. Causality is the explicit identification of the input and output. In other words, the independent and dependent variables.

Let us consider, for example, a problem of population movement. The population flow between two regions, A and B, is assumed to be proportional to the difference in population density between the areas. The logical choices of state variables are N_1 (the total population in region A) and N_2 (that in region B), or population densities in the two regions, $n_1 = N_1/A_1$ and $n_2 = N_2/A_2$, or the overall total population $N = N_1 + N_2$ and the flow between the two regions, f, for which a simple empirical rule (proportionality "law") may apply

$$f = \frac{1}{R}(n_1 - n_2) \tag{2-17}$$

where R is a system parameter analogous to the resistance.

In this example the assumption that population density is the driving potential for migration establishes the need for two types of constitutive relations: 1) density is defined as the ratio of population to area, $n = N/A$ and 2) migration rate depends on the difference in densities, leading to the resistive type of relation for population flow of Eq. (2-17). Since there are two population storage elements (regions A and B), two state variables are necessary to characterize this system. They can be chosen from among several possibilities such as the populations in each region, the population densities, the differences or sums of populations, etc.

2.6 STATE VECTOR

A convenient notation for keeping track of system state variables, especially for high order systems with many state variables, is listing them as elements of a (column) *vector*

$$\underline{x}(t) = \begin{bmatrix} x_1(t) \\ x_2(t) \\ \cdot \\ \cdot \\ \cdot \\ x_n(t) \end{bmatrix} \tag{2-18}$$

where $\underline{x}(t)$ indicates a vector and $x_1(t)$ through $x_n(t)$ are the n state variables.

As noted in the preceding section, choosing a state vector or set of state variables is not a unique process. For a given system there is more than one possible set of state variables, all valid. However, all possible sets must have the same *number* of state variables and each set, to be valid, must consist of *independent* quantities. Independence requires that initial values for each of the state variables can be set arbitrarily. For example, in a system containing two water tanks we would not choose the water heights in each tank and the total volume of liquid (h_1 and h_2 and V_{tot}) as state variables because V_{tot} depends on h_1 and h_2. ($V_{tot} = V_1 + V_2 = \Phi_1(h_1) + \Phi_2(h_2)$. If the tanks had straight sides the volumes could be computed from $V = ah$ or $V_{tot} = A_1 h_1 + A_2 h_2$. This is linear dependence.) It is clear, however, that any *two* of these variables would make a valid set of state variables because there are no constraints on setting their initial values.

It is possible to construct a new state vector $\underline{x}(t)$ from any given state vector $\underline{x}^*(t)$ by applying the convenient linear transformation

$$\underline{x} = \underline{T}\,\underline{x}^* \tag{2-19}$$

where $\underline{T}$ is a square, nonsingular (i.e., $\det \underline{T} = |\underline{T}| \neq 0$) matrix of constant coefficients. Explicitly, the relation is

$$\begin{aligned} x_1 &= t_{11}x_1^* + t_{12}x_2^* + \cdots + t_{1n}x_n^* \\ x_2 &= t_{21}x_1^* + t_{22}x_2^* + \cdots + t_{2n}x_n^* \end{aligned} \tag{2-20}$$

and

$$\underline{T} = \begin{bmatrix} t_{11} & t_{12} & \cdots & t_{1n} \\ \cdots & \cdots & \cdots & \cdots \\ t_{n1} & t_{n2} & \cdots & t_{nn} \end{bmatrix} \tag{2-21}$$

The restriction that $\underline{T}$ be nonsingular guarantees that if the original state variables are independent, the new state variables will also be independent. If in some instance $\underline{T}$ were singular, the new set of state variables would be linearly dependent even if the original set were independent.

In the population movement system, for example, let

$$x_1^* = N_1 \qquad x_2^* = N_2$$

for a first choice of state variables and

$$x_1 = N = N_1 + N_2 = x_1^* + x_2^*$$
$$x_2 = f = \frac{1}{R}(n_1 - n_2) = \frac{1}{R}(\frac{x_1^*}{A_1} - \frac{x_2^*}{A_2})$$

for another choice. Then the $\underline{T}$ matrix will be

$$\underline{T} = \begin{bmatrix} 1 & 1 \\ \dfrac{1}{A_1 R} & \dfrac{-1}{A_2 R} \end{bmatrix} \qquad (2\text{-}22)$$

and the linear transformation is valid; that is, $\underline{T}$ is not singular so that its inverse $\underline{T}^{-1}$ (such that $\underline{T}\,\underline{T}^{-1} = \underline{T}^{-1}\,\underline{T} = \underline{I}$) will exist as long as

$$|\underline{T}| = -(\frac{1}{A_2 R} + \frac{1}{A_1 R}) \neq 0 \qquad \text{i.e., } A_1 \neq -A_2$$

Since land areas are constrained to be positive, A_1 can never equal $-A_2$, the state variables x are valid for any realistic set of parameters.

To continue our exploration of independent state variables and linear transformations, let us consider the automobile suspension of Fig. 2-2(a). In Section 2.2, it was suggested that the velocity of the mass and the force in the spring would be a good choice of state variables. Could we have chosen instead the force in the spring and the displacement of the mass? The independence requirement clearly rules this out: we cannot arbitrarily set independent initial values for both the spring force *and* the spring displacement. They are dependent.[†] However, an alternate reasonable and independent set of state variables might be the velocity of the mass (V_m) and the displacement of the mass (x_m). If we call the spring constant k and let the original set of state variables be the velocity of the mass (V_m) and the force in the spring (F_s), then Eqs. (2-20) and (2-21)

[†] In this case, the displacement of the mass is equal to the deflection of the spring, which, by Hooke's law for linear springs, is related to the spring force, $x_m = x_s = F_s/k$. The proposed new set of state variables can thus be written in terms of the old set by

$$\begin{bmatrix} F_s \\ x_m \end{bmatrix} = \begin{bmatrix} 1 & 0 \\ \frac{1}{k} & 0 \end{bmatrix} \begin{bmatrix} F_s \\ V_m \end{bmatrix} \qquad \underline{T} = \begin{bmatrix} 1 & 0 \\ \frac{1}{k} & 0 \end{bmatrix}$$

Since det $\underline{T} = 0$, we know that the new set cannot be independent.

become

$$V_m = V_m \qquad (x_1 = x_1^*)$$
$$x_m = \frac{1}{k} F_s \qquad (x_2 = \frac{1}{k} x_2^*)$$

and
$$\underline{T} = \begin{bmatrix} 1 & 0 \\ 0 & \frac{1}{k} \end{bmatrix}$$

In general, the $\underline{T}$ matrix will not be diagonal and for more complex cases each new (unstarred) state variable will be equal to a linear combination of all of the old (starred) state variables. It should be clear from this discussion that the application of the linear transformation of Eq. (2-19) is a tool we have at our disposal to change over from one to another of equally valid and independent sets of arbitrary state variables.

SUMMARY

The main theme of this chapter has been choosing variables to describe appropriately the dynamics of a system under study. With experience, one learns to apply the generalized system concepts introduced here to determine when and how to lump a system, how to choose system state variables and how to utilize the ideas of analogy in energetic relations. The concept of the state vector of a system is fundamental to system modeling. Much of the rest of the text builds on this concept of a system state vector.

REFERENCES

1. H. M. Paynter, *Analysis and Design of Engineering Systems*, MIT Press, 1961

2. D. Karnopp and R. C. Rosenberg, *Analysis and Simulation of Multiport Systems*, MIT Press, 1968

3. *ASME Quarterly Transactions Journal of Dynamic Systems, Measurements and Control*, Series G, Vol. 94, No. 3, "Bondgraph Modeling for Engineering Systems," September, 1972

4. Y. Takahashi, M. Rabins and D. Auslander, *Control*, Addison Wesley, 1970, Chap. 6

PROBLEMS

2-1 Consider a mass constrained to move in a straight line, for instance, a trolley car on a straight and horizontal rail section. How many state variables are necessary (and sufficient) to describe the state of its linear (i.e., straight) motion? Discuss the energy forms involved in the streetcar system.

2-2 Consider a system described by Newton's 2-nd law of motion

$$\text{(force)} = \text{(mass)} \times \text{(acceleration)}$$

where it is understood that

$$\frac{d}{dt}(\text{displacement}) = (\text{velocity}) \qquad \frac{d}{dt}(\text{velocity}) = (\text{acceleration})$$

and $\frac{d}{dt}$ (acceleration) is sometimes called *jerk*

Is it allowable to assign a three dimensional state vector $\underline{x}(t)$ for this system, such that

$$x_1(t) = \text{displacement} \qquad x_2(t) = \text{velocity} \qquad x_3(t) = \text{acceleration}$$

and $\dfrac{dx_3(t)}{dt} = \text{jerk}$?

2-3 Consider a rigid body (for instance, a space ship) in flight. Name the state variables that are necessary and sufficient to describe the state of the system.

2-4 The upper ends of a U-tube mercury manometer are open to the atmosphere. List the modes of energy that are associated with the mercury column motion. Does the column oscillate? Is this system analogous to the spring-mass system of Fig. 2-9(c)?

2-5 A bathtub is being filled by a hot water supply. The water in the tub is agitated throughout the filling process. What kinds of energies are involved in the process? What should be selected as state variables?

2-6 Consider an agitated tank completely filled by water and having a constant water inflow and outflow (Fig. P-2-6), where inflow temperature θ_1 is an input. Outflow

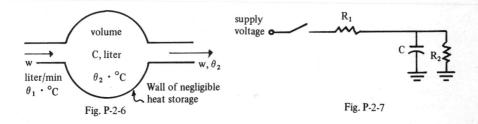

Fig. P-2-6

Fig. P-2-7

temperature θ_2 is equal to the temperature of the water in the tank. If the inflow is hot and the tank content is cold, there is a difference in heat flow carried by the water into and out of the tank. Where will this energy difference go? Is there any (qualitative) analogy between the tank temperature and the liquid level of a leaking tank in Chapter 1 (Fig. 1-4)?

2-7   Suppose that θ_1 and θ_2 in Fig. P-2-6 are concentrations of some chemical component dissolved in the water and measured by either parts per million or moles per liter. In what way is this system analogous to the thermal system of Problem 2-6? Is there any analogy between these systems and the electrical network shown in Fig. P-2-7?

2-8   Suppose that the heat storage effect of the tank wall in Fig. P-2-6 is not negligible but that the wall is thin so that its temperature $\theta_3°C$ is uniform all over. The ambient temperature surrounding the wall is $\theta_4°C$. Of the four temperatures (including θ_1 and θ_2 shown in the figure), which are candidates for state variables? Also indicate those that will represent inputs.

2-9   List the state variables that will best describe our comfort in an air-conditioned room. Identify the most important ones.

2-10   A computerized spinach farm tested in Osaka (Japan) is shown in Fig. P-2-10. One hundred thousand planter boxes are carried by seven rows of conveyor belts through a green house in which light, air temperature and humidity, and CO_2 content are maintained at an optimum level so that it will take only 3 weeks from seeding to harvesting (30% speed-up). List input and state variables of the green house and a goal function to be optimized by the computing control.

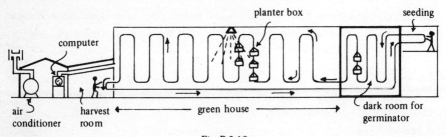

Fig. P-2-10

2-11   What kind of state variables would you choose to model a clear water pond used as a trout hatchery?

CHAPTER 3
STATE
EQUATIONS

In this chapter we deal with the problem of deriving the mathematical model of a system in state equation form. In Section 3.1 we survey various modeling techniques appropriate to the different problems at hand, whereas in Section 3.2 we start to focus on energetic system models. Section 3.3 considers the specific details of deriving the state equations for two different energetic systems. While the numerical and analytical solution of such equations is deferred to the next two chapters, Section 3.4 interprets the state equations from the perspective of motion through state space in order to better understand the nature of the state equations. For the same reasons, Section 3.5 deals with an interpretation of system stability. We conclude with a brief discussion of the linearization process in mathematical modeling.

3.1 DERIVING THE STATE EQUATION

Successful design or analysis of dynamic systems proceeds from a mathematical model derived by the system analyst to meet the goals of his study. This model must be predicated upon a full understanding of the system behavior. In the case of energetic systems, discussed in the next section, such understanding usually comes from application of natural laws (e.g., Newton's 2-nd law, Kirchhoff's current law, etc.). In the case of nonenergetic systems, where the "natural" laws, if they exist at all, are only poorly understood, the modeling problem is more challenging.

In attempting to derive a state equation for a system to which no known

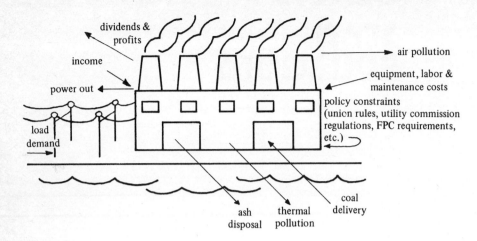

Fig. 3-1 Input/Output Pictorialization for a Power Plant

natural law applies, the keystone is full understanding of the mechanism by which the system operates. To facilitate development of this understanding, there are several alternative modeling techniques available: semipictorial representation of the system, flowcharting, block diagramming and detailed word description of the system relations. Most often, successful modeling will employ some sequential combination of these and other methods. The immediate aim is to develop a mathematical model of the system under study which suits the purpose of the study and which can be validated by comparison of the model's response to the response of the physical reality. In the absence of successful validation, the model must be continually improved through an iterative procedure.

To introduce the modeling procedure, we next examine several different approaches to a selection of problems. Since we wish to emphasize general approach techniques here rather than finished solutions, the problems have been simplified for demonstration purposes.

Let us first examine the problem of modeling the dynamic operation of a coal-fueled electric power generating station to optimize profit and minimize pollution. A simplified pictorial representation of the system is shown in Fig. 3-1. In this figure, key inputs and outputs have been identified. From such a figure, one might progress to the state equation, as was the case in going from

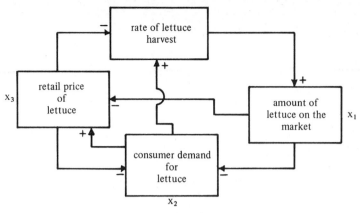

Fig. 3-2 Flow Charting

Fig. 1-4 to Eq. (1-4) after supplementary discussion. More often than not, and particularly in the case of nonenergetic systems, one or two intermediate steps are necessary.

A possible next step would be a flowcharting of the key variables in a problem along with their indicated relationships. Consider, for example, the problem of analyzing the fluctuations in the price of lettuce in order to better understand the dynamics of the lettuce industry. Some of the primary variables in this problem are indicated in Fig. 3-2 along with signed linkages. These links indicate which variables affect others. A plus or a minus sign in front of a variable designates deviation amplification or deviation counteraction, respectively. To check the sign on any link, the procedure is to assume a plus change in the variable at the tail of a link and then deduce the corresponding change in the variable output from the block at the arrowhead. If the resulting change is in the same direction as that assumed at the tail, then that link is assigned a positive sign. In some cases, the sign is obvious, as when an increase in lettuce harvest rate results in an increase in accumulated lettuce on the market. In other cases, deducing signs will require a detailed knowledge of the subtleties of the system operation. Thus, for example, to assign the minus sign between the lettuce price and lettuce harvest rate, one must know that farmers tend to ship less to market when prices are rising which tends to increase the price still further. (As alternatives the farmer might export his crop, delay its harvest or even plow some of it under.)

Fig. 3-2 now consists of several interlocking loops, where the product of the signs of all of the elements in a loop is positive for some loops and negative for others. At times, first one loop, then another dominates. Implicit in this model is the assumption that several other variables not included are of secondary importance. These might include, for example, the effect of government sub-sidies or the price of fertilizer. Whether or not to exclude a variable depends upon the purpose of the study and an estimation as to the importance of that variable. Our model must be continually refined to reflect reality more accurately. The refining process may not always complicate the system; on the contrary, very often some trivial effects or factors outside the time span of our interest (negligible short time or too slow and long range effects) may be deleted and moreover, some portion of a flowchart may be decoupled from the rest and treated independently.

At this point in the modeling process, clear choices should start emerging for the prime state variables of the problem. The number of state variables chosen to represent a nonenergetic system will depend upon the nature of the system, the amount of "lumping" to be permitted and the purpose of the study.

In Fig. 3-2, for example, these choices might be x_1, x_2 and x_3 as indicated. Note carefully that the rate of lettuce harvest is not an independent state variable but is the rate of change of x_1, i.e., dx_1/dt and, in general, will depend on x_1 and other state variables.

Now the question of integral causality, discussed in the previous chapter, must carefully be considered. The amount of lettuce on the market is the accumulation (integration) of the harvest rate. There may be arbitrary step changes in the latter to yield gradual responses in the former, but not vice versa. Thus, we wish to evolve a vector state equation which requires integration for solution. The required form of the state equation is

$$\frac{d}{dt}\underline{x} = \underline{f}(\underline{x},\underline{u},t) \quad \text{or} \quad \underline{x} = \underline{x}_0 + \int_0^t \underline{f}(\underline{x},\underline{u},t)dt \qquad (3\text{-}1)$$

where

$$\underline{x}(t) = \begin{bmatrix} x_1(t) \\ x_2(t) \\ x_3(t) \end{bmatrix}$$

and $\underline{u}$ is the input vector (including farming decisions and disturbances)
       t is time

The next step in the analysis is to investigate the vector function $\underline{f}$ in Eq. (3-1)

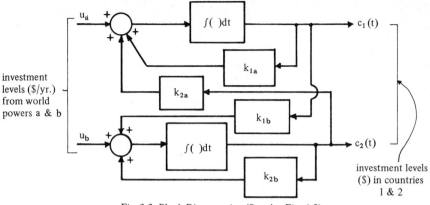

Fig. 3-3 Block Diagramming (See also Fig. 6-5)

by a careful study of the interrelationships of the state variables.[†]

In some cases, our flowchart may naturally evolve into a block diagram where integral causalities and functional relations are explicit and, in fact, for some problems we might start directly with such a block diagram. Consider, for example, the situation in which two world powers (a and b) are investing in two adjacent underdeveloped countries (1 and 2) for propaganda purposes. Letting c_i be the accumulated cash investment in country i, k_{ij} (may be + or − and may be a function of c_i) be the multiplicative effect of country i's investment level on the rate of expenditure by country j and u_j be the base investment rate by country j, then the state model for this simplified situation emerges directly from inspection of Fig. 3-3 as

$$\frac{dc_1(t)}{dt} = k_{1a}c_1(t) + k_{2a}c_2(t) + u_a(t)$$
$$\frac{dc_2(t)}{dt} = k_{1b}c_1(t) + k_{2b}c_2(t) + u_b(t)$$

(3-2)

or in vector form

$$\frac{d}{dt}\underline{c}(t) = \underline{K}\,\underline{c}(t) + \underline{u}(t)$$

(3-3)

_____

† A graphic example of this procedure of developing the state equation from flow charts may be found in Ref. [1] which deals with urban dynamic problems.

where

$$\underline{c}(t) = \begin{bmatrix} c_1(t) \\ c_2(t) \end{bmatrix} \qquad \underline{u}(t) = \begin{bmatrix} u_a(t) \\ u_b(t) \end{bmatrix} \qquad \underline{K} = \begin{bmatrix} k_{1a} & k_{2a} \\ k_{1b} & k_{2b} \end{bmatrix}$$

The next step in the analysis of this problem would be to evaluate numerically the elements[†] of the $\underline{K}$ matrix in consultation with knowledgeable political scientists who are familiar with the countries in question. Such consultation should take place at the earliest stages of the modeling process since this expert input helps determine the structure of the model.

As an example of possible structural changes in our model, consider the exogenous inputs u_a and u_b in Fig. 3-3. Further study might reveal that these "base" rates themselves are subject to change depending upon the perceived economic level in countries 1 and 2 as well as the political and economic situation in country a or b. Interpretation of this latter statement leads to a differently structured model and a new set of equations.

In some fortunate cases, our knowledge of the system may be at a sufficiently advanced stage to permit us to go directly to the state equation via a word description of the system relations. Consider, for our final modeling example, the problem of methylmercury (CH_3Hg) in fish and its toxic effects on man (Ref. [2]), where the sequence of events following the deposition of a chemical in the human body constitutes a dynamic process. For this purpose the human body may be divided into compartments: like a tissue compartment, the kidneys, the liver and an excretion reservoir where urinary and fecal mercury accumulate. It will be assumed that complete mixing occurs instantaneously in each compartment and that the rate of transport or transfer of material out of a compartment is proportional to the total amount of concentration within a compartment. The model can be further simplified if the toxic effect of methylmercury is our main concern. Approximately 15 to 22% of the total amount of methylmercury in the body is in the head and it is this fraction which is responsible for the toxic effect. More than 95% of the ingested methylmercury is absorbed from the gastrointestinal tract and its distribution speed is rapid compared to the rate of excretion (the excretion rate of methylmercury from the body is approximately 1% of the body level per day). Hence a simplified state model

$$\frac{dx}{dt} = ax + u \qquad \text{(state equation)} \tag{3-4}$$

---

† This may involve a linearization procedure. See Section 3.6.

where x(t), the state, is the total amount of methylmercury in the body, "a" (which, for this case, is $-(1/a) = 70$ days) is a constant determined by excretion and u(t) is the absorbed dose (an *impulse* for each fish meal). Depending on the purpose of the study, another equation, the *output equation*, may be needed for mathematical modeling to relate the state x(t) to an output y(t), which is the intensity of some biological effect (level of "sickness," perhaps)

$$y = h(x), \text{ a nonlinear function "h" of x} \quad \text{or } y = Cx \qquad (3\text{-}5)$$

where C = a constant if the state to output relation is linear.

The population system (Eq. (1-1)) and the leaking tank (Fig. 1-4) are both described by a state equation in the linear form of Eq. (3-4) or in the nonlinear form of

$$\frac{dx}{dt} = f(x,u) \qquad (3\text{-}6)$$

The population system was characterized by an isolated total population N(t) and the state equation was derived by population count (births minus deaths). The level system, with its height of level h(t) as state variable, was described by Eq. (1-7) which is based on a mass balance (or continuity) in the mass storage tank.

3.2 ENERGETIC SYSTEMS

Since engineering energetic systems, such as those presented in Chap. 2, are governed by known physical laws, they tend to be easier to deal with than systems for which the fundamental laws are not known (ecological or social systems, for example). Once the state variables of an energetic system are assigned for each energy storage element (C and I or mass and spring), they can be related to each other by applying the appropriate fundamental laws.

Two other operations are performed at this stage in the derivation of the system equation: verification that consistent natural causality exists throughout the system and assignment of *sign conventions*. We have already discussed the meaning of causality with respect to an individual element — to determine which of a pair of variables (e and f) is independent (input) and which is dependent (output) for that element. We must now check the overall system as elements are put together to make sure that there are no conflicts in causal assignment between connected elements. For example, were we to build a system model which contains an effort source (voltage source, pressure reservoir, etc.) connected directly to a capacitor, a causal conflict would result because the *output* from the source would be its effort value e, but the causal assignment demanded by a capacitor is that flow must be *input* and e output. This causal assignment is impossible. If the model configuration is not changed, the causality assignment must be reversed. We cannot reverse the causality on the source because its very definition specifies that e must be the output variable. Also, reversing the causality of the capacitance results in a differentiator. Differentiation is not a feasible operation (except an *approximate* differentiation which we shall study later in Chapter 6) because knowledge of the future is required to compute the derivative of an arbitrary function of time correctly. Moreover, it is extremely difficult to differentiate a signal with any significant noise content (most signals). The conclusion we draw from this is that the model, Fig. 3-4(a), is poorly formulated. A more logical formulation will account for whatever resistance exists in the connections and wires, Fig. 3-4(b). The natural causality is then satisfied, as shown in Fig. 3-4(c).

The operation that causes more trouble than any other in the process of deriving a set of system equations is keeping track of the signs. Any error is usually serious because stability of the system may be misinterpreted by an error in sign. Reduction of this problem from a major headache to a routine part of the process requires careful bookkeeping, explicit sign conventions (or notation) throughout the derivation process and application of a few consistency checks to the resulting equations. Note that sign conventions are usually ignored when writing constitutive relations; it is assumed that the correct sign will be applied when the combined system equations are derived. In electrical systems, signs for voltages are clear. One may define a current to be positive (+) when it flows from left to right. The same convention may apply to fluid

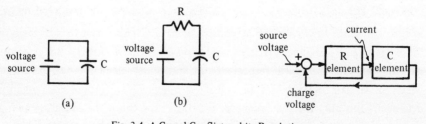

Fig. 3-4 A Causal Conflict and its Resolution

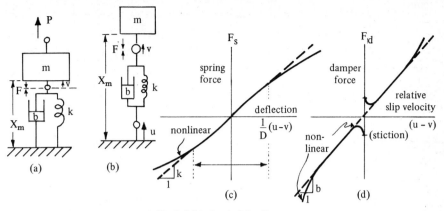

Fig. 3-5 Mechanical Oscillator

systems, where there is no problem with pressure and flow from left to right may be defined as positive. In mechanical elements for linear motions, we may define force positive for springs or dashpot links in compression (negative for tension) and mass velocity positive for the left to right direction. We shall treat some examples in the next section.

3.3 STATE EQUATIONS OF ENERGETIC SYSTEMS

Let us first derive the state equation for the spring-mass-damper system of Fig. 3-5(a). The input force P is defined to be positive in the upward direction. The velocity v for the mass is positive when the mass is moving upwards. Force F acting on the mass is positive when the link is in compression, as shown by the forces acting on the small circle in the figure. The constitutive relation for the spring is given in Fig. 3-5(c). The static relation between the spring force (plus for compression) and net deflection is normally nonlinear as indicated by the solid line in the figure. The relation is approximated over a limited range of deflection (Δ in the figure) of slope k (= spring constant) in Hooke's law, which is

$$F_s = \frac{1}{D} \left[k(v_0 - v) \right] \tag{3-7}$$

where D is the *derivative operator*, that is, D = d/dt, so that its inverse D^{-1} =

$1/D$ stands for integration in this shorthand notation. v_0 is the ground velocity, taken as zero in this case. The linear approximation for the damper, ignoring stiction and squared velocity behavior in Fig. 3-5(d) and replacing the solid line actual curve by the dashed straight line, is

$$F_d = b(v_0 - v) \tag{3-8}$$

where b is the damper constant. The three forces combined, $F = F_s + F_d + P$, will act on the mass, for which Newton's 2-nd law will apply

$$mDv = F \tag{3-9}$$

Since two energy storage elements (m and k) are involved in the system, the system must have two integrators and thus two state variables. We may choose the two as

x_1 = spring deflection: plus for compression ($= \frac{1}{D}(v_0 - v)$ in Fig. 3-5(a))

x_2 = velocity of the mass: plus for upwards ($= v$ in Fig. 3-5(a))

Then, from Eqs. (3-7) through (3-9), we obtain the following pair of state equations (with v_0 set equal to zero):

$$\begin{aligned} Dx_1 &= -x_2 \\ Dx_2 &= \frac{k}{m} x_1 - \frac{b}{m} x_2 + \frac{1}{m} P \end{aligned} \tag{3-10}$$

The format of these equations follows a well established and convenient pattern which will constantly reappear. This pattern will yield n (the system order) coupled first order differential equations with the derivatives of the n state variables appearing on the left hand side of the equations.

As noted in Sec. 2.6, the choice of state variables is not unique. For instance, a different pair, such as the velocity (v) and absolute displacement (x) of the mass, is also possible. If our interest is mainly in the absolute displacement of the mass x_m, which, because the ground velocity is zero, is equal to the spring displacement x_1, we can eliminate x_2 from Eq. (3-10) and obtain (instead of the two scalar first order differential equations of Eq. (3-10)) a scalar second order differential equation

$$D^2 x_m + \frac{b}{m} D x_m + \frac{k}{m} x_m = \frac{1}{m} P \tag{3-11}$$

This is a well known equation in the classical theory of mechanical vibrations. As we shall see in the next few chapters, this form of differential equation is not as appropriate for analytical and computational applications of dynamic systems theory as the state variable form of coupled first order differential equations (as in Eq. (3-10)).

If instead of a force input, the system is driven by a velocity input u (for example, a bumpy road) as shown in Fig. 3-5(b), an interesting change occurs in the system model. All of the above discussion concerning the constitutive relations for the spring, mass and damper still apply with v_0 replaced by u, and the following two matrix equations can be derived by the same steps we followed to get Eq. (3-10):

$$Dx_1 = -x_2 + u$$
$$Dx_2 = \frac{k}{m} x_1 - \frac{b}{m} x_2 + \frac{b}{m} u$$

However, as noted above, our interest in this system often centers on the displacement of the mass. Because this system, with a velocity input, has no direct attachment to the ground, there is no way that the displacement of the mass can be computed from x_1 and x_2. Instead, the mass displacement x_m must be computed by integrating the velocity v_m, giving us a *third* state equation

$$Dx_m = v_m$$

and a third state variable, x_m. Although for some problems we have no need to know the displacement and can thus use a second order model, a complete description of the system requires three state variables.

Before leaving this mass-spring-dashpot example, we note intuitively that in the absence of damping (i.e., b = 0 and, accordingly, no energy dissipation) the system will oscillate without any input. The *oscillation* occurs due to the surging between the kinetic mode of energy storage (maximum when the mass moves through the spring equilibrium position) and the potential mode of energy storage (maximum when the spring is either fully compressed or extended and the mass velocity is zero).

The second example of energetic system formulation, that of the power plant in Fig. 3-6 (first seen in Fig. 2-1), is more involved than the mechanical

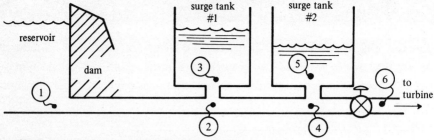

(Circled numbers are for position identification only.)

Fig. 3-6 The Surge Tank System

oscillator. We will view the water in the two main conduits as lumped inertias, hence kinetic energy storage elements. The surge tanks are capacitive storage elements, storing potential energy. Since the system involves four energy storage elements, we need four state variables, the choice of which is not unique. A most natural choice could be

$$x_1(t) \Rightarrow Q_{12} = \text{volume flow rate in line } 1-2, \text{ m}^3/\text{sec}$$
$$x_2(t) \Rightarrow P_3 = \text{pressure at point 3, N/m}^2$$
$$x_3(t) \Rightarrow Q_{24} = \text{volume flow rate in line } 2-4, \text{ m}^3/\text{sec}$$
$$x_4(t) \Rightarrow P_5 = \text{pressure at point 5, N/m}^2$$

$$(3\text{-}12)^\dagger$$

Let us write the constitutive relations from left to right in Fig. 3-6.

1) First consider the *momentum* or inertia effect of the fluid in the conduit 1–2 for the mass of fluid $m_{12} = \rho A_{12} L_{12}$ (kg), where

A_{12} = cross-sectional area of the conduit, m^2

L_{12} = its length, m

ρ = fluid mass density, kg/m^3

The force exerted on that mass is $(P_1 - P_2)A_{12}$, where P_1 and P_2 (N/m^2) are the pressures at points 1 and 2, respectively. The volumetric flow rate Q_{12} (m^3/sec) is related to the fluid velocity v_{12} (m/sec) by $v_{12} = Q_{12}/A_{12}$ (both assumed at average constant values in conduit 1–2) so that, by Newton's 2-nd

---

† For the reader accustomed to working in kgf rather than Newtons (N), divide force in N by 9.80665.

law, we obtain

$$DQ_{12} = \frac{A_{12}}{\rho L_{12}} (P_1 - P_2) \tag{3-13}$$

where the derivative operator D has inverse time dimensions (1/sec).

2) Surge tank no. 1 is connected to the main line via a restriction (*resistive* element) and the turbulent flow through it is given by

$$Q_{23} = \eta_1 \, SST(P_2 - P_3) \tag{3-14}$$

where η_1 is a semi-empirical coefficient as in Eq. (1-6) and SST is the *signed square root* operator, i.e.

$$SST(x) = SIGN\,(x)\sqrt{|x|}$$

This operator is needed because of possible flow reversals (such was not the case in the leaking tank, Sec. 1.4).

3) The *capacitive* effect for surge tank No. 1 is next considered. The level height h_1(m) is equal to (liquid volume V_1 in the tank)/(area of the tank A_1), where $V_1 = Q_{23}/D$ (m^3), so that $h_1 = (Q_{23}/D)/A_1$ where A_1 is in (m^2). Therefore the pressure P_3 at point 3 in Fig. 3-6 is

$$P_3 = \rho g h_1 = (\rho g Q_{23})/(A_1 D) \quad N/m^2$$

or

$$DP_3 = (\rho g Q_{23})/A_1 \tag{3-15}$$

where fluid density ρ was defined in 1) and g (m/sec^2) is the local value of the acceleration of gravity.

4) As in Eq. (3-13), the fluid inertia in line 2—4 is represented by

$$DQ_{24} = \frac{A_{24}}{\rho L_{24}} (P_2 - P_4) \tag{3-16}$$

Since the law of continuity applies to the three flows at the T-junction, at position 2

$$Q_{23} = Q_{12} - Q_{24} \tag{3-17}$$

5) For the resistor to tank no. 2

$$Q_{45} = \eta_2 SST(P_4 - P_5) \tag{3-18}$$

and for the second tank

$$DP_5 = (\rho g Q_{45})/A_2 \tag{3-19}$$

just like Eqs. (3-14) and (3-15), respectively.

6) The gate valve (wicket valve) as a resistor yields

$$Q_{46} = \eta_3 SST(P_4 - P_6) \tag{3-20}$$

where the valve opening is assumed to be kept constant. The continuity condition at point 4 is

$$Q_{45} = Q_{24} - Q_{46} \tag{3-21}$$

7) Boundary conditions or *sources*. At the upstream end of the system the reservoir can be treated as a pressure source; thus $P_1(t)$ is an independent variable, i.e., an input to the system. For simplicity we shall assume that the region just downstream of the valve (at point 6 in the figure) has a fixed pressure (which is not true in real systems), i.e., P_6 = constant = input.

8) For sign conventions we define flow as positive for left to right and upwards in Fig. 3-6 and we number the points of interest consistently so that the order of the subscripts denotes the positive direction.

9) Causality. Algebraic complexity in Eqs. (3-13) through (3-21) makes it difficult to eliminate the intermediate variables and reduce the set into the four state equations in terms of the state variables defined in Eq. (3-12). This is a typical situation in system modeling and simulation. In order to simplify the model and the analysis at this stage, let us linearize the static nonlinear relations for flow through the resistors and construct a block diagram. The linearized relations are

$$Q_{23} = \frac{1}{R_{23}}(P_2 - P_3) \tag{3-14'}$$

$$Q_{45} = \frac{1}{R_{45}} (P_4 - P_5) \qquad (3\text{-}18')$$

and $\quad Q_{46} = \frac{1}{R_{46}} (P_4 - P_6) \qquad (3\text{-}20')$

where the R's are equivalent linear resistances. Since other parts of the system are already linearized, we obtain the block diagram shown in Fig. 3-7. It consists of four dynamic blocks (which involve 1/D and hence are *integrators*) for the C and I type elements and three linearized static dissipative elements. Small circles (O) are for signal additions/subtractions as indicated by + and − signs. Pertinent equation numbers (primed for linearized versions) are indicated in parentheses. The four state variables, x_1 through x_4 defined in Eq. (3-12), are assigned at the output side of each integrator. The boxed set of equations in Fig. 3-7 are the linearized state equations resulting from algebraic manipulation of Eqs. (3-13) through (3-21). It is helpful to note that these four equations represent signals at the input side of the four integrators in Fig. 3-7.

3.4 MOTION IN STATE SPACE

The state equations of a dynamic system offer a wealth of insight into its dynamic behavior even before we solve them. The n state variables may be associated with separate axes in an n dimensional (Euclidian) space called the *state space*. The path or motion of a system's state in its state space is called the *state trajectory* and is the subject of this section. We will return to this same topic in Chapter 5 on a more analytical basis. Here our aim is to understand in a graphical sense the meaning of the rate of change of a state variable in the state equation. For ease of visualization, we will restrict our examples to two or three dimensional state spaces (n = 2 or 3).

To illustrate the idea of the state trajectory, let us consider a simplified model of an ecological problem: the competition of two species of population $N_1(t)$ and $N_2(t)$ (which are the state variables) isolated from the environment. We assume that the parameter r in Eq. (1-2) is now a function of N_1 and N_2 because of internal population pressure as well as pressure from the competition. Therefore the state equations are

$$\frac{dN_1}{dt} = (A_1 - k_{11}N_1 - k_{12}N_2)N_1$$

$$\frac{dN_2}{dt} = (A_2 - k_{21}N_1 - k_{22}N_2)N_2 \qquad (3\text{-}22)$$

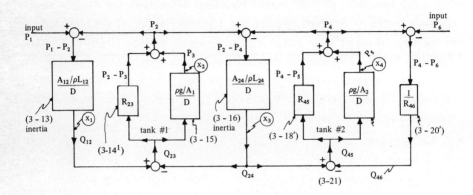

Fig. 3-7 Causality and the State Equations in the Surge Tank System
(Resistors are linearized)

where A_1, A_2 and all the k_{ij}'s are positive constants.† To facilitate the discussion, we assign numbers for the coefficients and consider the equations

$$DN_1 = (18 - 3N_1 - N_2)N_1$$
$$DN_2 = (10 - N_1 - N_2)N_2 \qquad (3\text{-}23)$$

Since our example system is second order (two state variables), the N_1-N_2 plane is the state space (or state plane); for first order systems the space reduces to a line. A pair of arbitrary values, $N_1 = 6$ and $N_2 = 9$ in Eq. (3-23), for instance, represents a point (or a *state*) in the state plane, as shown by P in Fig. 3-8, where, by Eq. (3-23)

$$DN_1 = -54 \qquad DN_2 = -45$$

and the two, DN_1 and DN_2 combined as a vector in the plane, represent the velocity vector of the motion of state at P in the state space. If the system were started at t = 0 at point P, it would move initially in the velocity vector direction. The state moves with time, leaving a trace which is called the *trajectory*, except at equilibrium points where the velocity is zero: $DN_1 = 0$ and $DN_2 = 0$. Time is an implicit variable along a trajectory, changing in nonlinear fashion. The equilibrium states of the system of Eq. (3-23) are easily found to be

$$\begin{bmatrix} N_1 \\ N_2 \end{bmatrix} = \begin{bmatrix} 0 \\ 0 \end{bmatrix}, \quad \begin{bmatrix} 0 \\ 10 \end{bmatrix}, \quad \begin{bmatrix} 6 \\ 0 \end{bmatrix} \text{ and } \begin{bmatrix} 4 \\ 6 \end{bmatrix} \qquad (3\text{-}24)$$

The directions of the velocity vector at various points in the state plane (other than the equilibrium points) are easily computed in the same fashion as was done for P. The velocity direction at P, which must be tangent to the trajectory at P, is given by

$$dN_2/dN_1 = DN_2/DN_1 = 45/54$$

---

† The A_1 and A_2 constants involve natural birth/death rates for each species when isolated. The k_{ij} involve nonlinear cross effects. See Refs. [3] and [4].

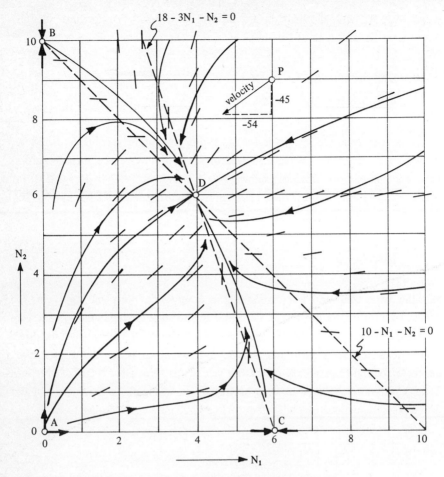

Fig. 3-8 State-Plane Trajectories of Two Competing Species

Note that D here is a derivative operator, d/dt, and thus dt drops out when the ratio is taken. Applying this principle to various points in the state plane, the resulting directions are indicated by short segments in Fig. 3-8. It is easy to construct various trajectories graphically by piecing together the segments, where the direction of state motion is indicated by arrows; we find these by recalling the sign of DN_1 and DN_2 in Eq. (3-23) at various points. The trajectory pattern shows that all the motions converge to equilibrium point D (which is the last pair in Eq. (3-24)) while all other equilibrium states are *unstable*. However, such a "peaceful" (i.e., *stable*) coexistence of the two species is not always assured; the trajectory pattern will drastically change as the parameter values of Eq. (3-22) are changed.

Graphical construction of the trajectories is instructive rather than practical and it applies only for the second order case where the state space is a plane. Projection of a three dimensional trajectory onto a plane, for instance, is practically meaningless. Fortunately, many systems exhibit a predominant second order response, making the technique shown in Fig. 3-8 generally applicable and illuminating. The concept of trajectory patterns in general closely ties into the concept of system *stability*, as we shall next see.

3.5 STABILITY

We all have our own heuristic understanding of what we mean when we use the word *stable* in some engineering context. However, it will be helpful if we can agree here on a working definition. We will attempt this by first defining what we mean by *unstable*. Let the state of the system be at rest at some equilibrium point at some instant of time and let us imagine it disturbed (perturbed) by some arbitrary disturbance (however small and/or short). If the state of the system diverges from its equilibrium point as a result of that disturbance, then we call the system unstable at that equilibrium point. If the system converges back to its equilibrium point, we call it asymptotically stable at that equilibrium point. If the system goes through a linear harmonic oscillation about an equilibrium point as in the example below, it is called limitedly stable at that point.

In common usage the words stable and unstable are often used to modify the word *system*, as in *stable system*. This usage should be interpreted as implying that the system is stable (unstable) at an equilibrium point of interest. With these definitions in mind, we can proceed with further interpretations of the state equations.

In the previous section, we saw that point D in Fig. 3-8 is a stable equilibrium point. Perturbations away from it will result in a trajectory converging back to point D. However, the equilibrium points A, B and C (first three of Eq. (3-24)) in Fig. 3-8 are unstable. For small arbitrary perturbations,[†] trajectories diverge from these three unstable equilibrium points. Point D is the only stable equilibrium point in this example. This system would be called stable in the region around point D.

---

† One purely vertical set of perturbations at point B in Fig. 3-8 and one purely horizontal set at point C do in fact converge. This, however, is not stable equilibrium because any other disturbance will cause divergence from the equilibrium point.

A different trajectory pattern will appear when two species form a predator-prey pair. Let us focus our attention on *small deviations* $n_1(t)$ and $n_2(t)$ of the two species' total populations $N_1(t)$ and $N_2(t)$ from an equilibrium state N_{1s}, N_{2s}

$$N_1(t) = N_{1s} + n_1(t) \qquad N_2(t) = N_{2s} + n_2(t) \tag{3-25}$$

and assume that the following relations will apply to the deviations:

$$Dn_1 = an_2 \qquad Dn_2 = -bn_1 \tag{3-26}$$

where a and b are positive constants and $DN_1 = Dn_1$ and $DN_2 = Dn_2$ since N_{1s} and N_{2s} are constants. The predator-prey relation is expressed in Eq. (3-26) by the rule that the rate of predator population increase is proportional to an excess in prey (i.e., food) population and the rate of decrease of the prey population is proportional to the increase of its enemy population.

The trajectory pattern of the system in the state plane can be graphically determined by making use of the principle applied in the preceding section, that is

$$dn_2/dn_1 = -(b/a)(n_1/n_2)$$

which reduces to a simpler form

$$dn_2/dn_1 = -c/r \qquad c = b/a = \text{constant} \tag{3-27}$$

and

$$r = n_2/n_1 = \text{slope of a radial line through the origin} \tag{3-28}$$

The radial line (r = constant) is called an *isocline* because the slope dn_2/dn_1 is constant on such a line. Once c is known, the slope of the trajectory tangent, dn_2/dn_1, can be easily determined on various isoclines such as r = 0 (n_1 axis), r = 1 (45° line), etc. The graphical method is called the *isocline method*, which generally is easiest to apply when a second order system is linear.

As shown in Fig. 3-9(a), the trajectory pattern for this system is an ellipse. This can be confirmed by noting that the following pair

$$n_1(t) = n_1(0) \cdot \sin \omega t \qquad n_2(t) = n_2(0) \cdot \cos \omega t \tag{3-29}$$

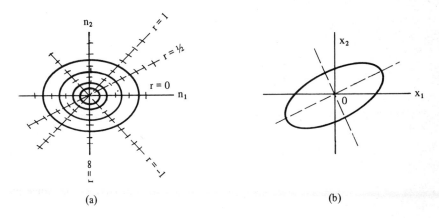

Fig. 3-9 Trajectory Pattern of a Linear Harmonic Oscillator

will satisfy Eq. (3-26) for an arbitrary pair of initial values $n_1(0)$ and $n_2(0)$, provided that $\omega = \sqrt{ab}$. An analytical expression for an ellipse will follow when t is eliminated from Eq. (3-29) by the relation $\sin^2 \omega t + \cos^2 \omega t = 1$. Except in an extremely simple case like this, however, any attempt to derive an analytical expression for a trajectory is generally futile.

Fig. 3-9 indicates that the predator-prey relationship is limitedly stable, yielding bounded and sustained oscillations. Let us interpret these oscillations physically. As predator population deviates slightly and positively from some nominal predator-prey population balance, the prey population will fall off (as more are eaten!). Eventually, as food supply decreases, the predator population will eventually decrease. But this will remove pressure on the prey population, permitting it to begin growing again. Now the loop is closed and the oscillation continues as the predator population can once again grow due to increased food supply. Since the recuperative process is slow, delays may occur as the oscillating signals travel around this loop.

Systems that exhibit limited stability can eventually become stable or unstable. In the predator-prey example, for instance, some exogenous input like unlimited hunting by a third species could wipe out the predator population, permitting the prey population to grow (assuming unlimited food and space) without bound.

The motion of a linear spring-mass system (b = 0 in Fig. 3-5(a)) is also simple harmonic. Since there is no energy dissipation when b = 0, energy surging between the two forms (kinetic energy and potential energy) will produce an undamped oscillation. The trajectory for an undamped oscillation is an ellipse, although the major axes may not coincide with the state variable axes (Fig. 3-9(b)).

Is this system stable? Since its state does not diverge away from the equilibrium point (the origin in Fig. 3-9), the system might be called stable, as Lyapunov did in the last century, but the stability is marginal or *limited*; on the other hand, the equilibrium state D in Fig. 3-8 is said to be *asymptotically stable*. It is asymptotically stable because the trajectory converges to the equilibrium point. If the mechanical oscillator (Fig. 3-5(a)) has a damping action (b ≠ 0), energy will dissipate and the oscillation amplitude will decay; the trajectory for this case is a spiral, converging to the origin, and the system is then asymptotically stable at the origin. As we shall see later, an oscillation of increasing amplitude can occur when the control gain is too high in a feedback control system; its trajectory will be a spiral diverging away from an equilibrium state in an unstable fashion.

The stability concept, introduced in this section for second order systems for which the state space reduces to a plane, also applies to systems of an arbitrary order.

3.6 LINEARIZATION

As we saw in the previous section, one motivation for approximating a nonlinear function with its linearized version is that this procedure facilitates a straightforward analysis. We can use digital or analog computers to obtain numerical solutions for one set of system parameters; however, to obtain solutions with more generality, some form of analysis is necessary. Because there are precious few analytical solutions available for nonlinear differential equations, to analyze we must linearize!

Moreover, if we wish to apply one of the most powerful analytical tools available — superposition — our system must be linear. The concept of superposition is illustrated as follows: if an input u_1 applied to a linear system produces an output y_1 and u_2 produces y_2, then input $(u_1 + u_2)$ will produce output $(y_1 + y_2)$. Fig. 3-10 shows a linear, static function to which superposition applies and a nonlinear one to which it does not.

A general form for a two state variable system, like Eq. (3-22), is

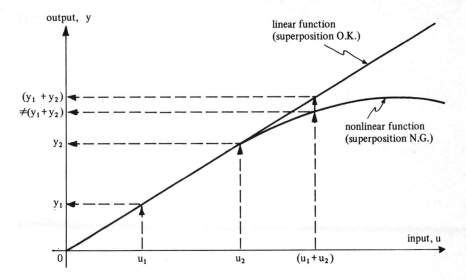

Fig. 3-10   Linearization and Superposition

$$Dx_1 = f_1(x_1,x_2) \qquad Dx_2 = f_2(x_1,x_2) \qquad (3\text{-}30)$$

A further generalization into an n-state variable system (see Eq. (2-18)) with r number of inputs u_1, u_2, . . ., u_r will yield n scalar first order differential equations in the form

$$Dx_i = f_i(x_1, \ldots, x_n; u_1, \ldots, u_r) \qquad i = 1, \ldots, n \qquad (3\text{-}31)$$

The set of n equations may be expressed by a compact vector form

$$D\underline{x}(t) = \underline{f}(\underline{x},\underline{u}) \qquad (3\text{-}32)$$

where

$$\underline{f}(\underline{x},\underline{u}) = \begin{bmatrix} f_1(\underline{x},\underline{u}) \\ f_2(\underline{x},\underline{u}) \\ \cdot \\ \cdot \\ \cdot \\ f_n(\underline{x},\underline{u}) \end{bmatrix} \qquad \underline{x} = \begin{bmatrix} x_1 \\ x_2 \\ \cdot \\ \cdot \\ \cdot \\ x_n \end{bmatrix} \qquad \underline{u} = \begin{bmatrix} u_1 \\ u_2 \\ \cdot \\ \cdot \\ u_r \end{bmatrix}$$

are, respectively, a vector function of order n, a *state vector* of order n and an *input vector* of order r. Since $D\underline{x}(t) = \underline{0}$ at an equilibrium state, it is generally convenient to choose the origin ($\underline{x} = \underline{0}$) of the state space to be an equilibrium state, that is

$$\underline{f}(\underline{x}, \underline{u}) = \underline{0} \quad \text{at } \underline{x} = \underline{0} \text{ and } \underline{u} = \underline{0} \tag{3-33}$$

The vector function $\underline{f}(\underline{x},\underline{u})$ is *static* (i.e., algebraic) in the sense that $\underline{f}$ is instantaneously determined for a given set of $\underline{x}$ and $\underline{u}$. Consider, for example, the static nonlinear relation shown in Fig. 3-11 between the force acting on a spring and the spring deflection. Let $F = (F_s + u)$ and $X = (X_s + x)$, whereby we have performed a transformation from the F-X axes with origin at point 0 to the u-x axes with origin at point $0'$. Here u is the deviation in force about the constant force level F_s and x is the deviation in displacement about the constant displacement X_s caused by F_s. The variables x and u are the scalar equivalents of $\underline{x}$ and $\underline{u}$ in Eq. (3-33) and represent the deviations about a nominal operating point ($0'$) caused by the constant force F_s. The nonlinear function $F = g(x)$ goes through both points and is continuous (all derivatives exist) everywhere in the figure. Now consider the Taylor series expansion of F =

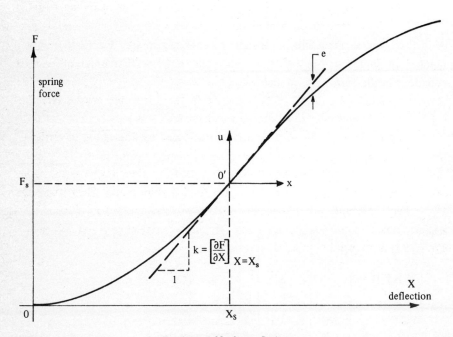

Fig. 3-11 A Nonlinear Spring

g(X) about point $0'$

$$F = g(X_s) + \left[\frac{\partial g(X)}{\partial X}\right]_{X=X_s} \frac{x}{1!} + \left[\frac{\partial^2 g(X)}{\partial X^2}\right]_{X=X_s} \frac{x^2}{2!} + \cdots \qquad (3\text{-}34)$$

where
$$g(X_s) = F_s$$
$$F - F_s = u$$
and
$$\left[\frac{\partial g(X)}{\partial X}\right]_{X=X_s} = k \quad \text{(see Fig. 3-11)}$$

Thus, Eq. (3-34) becomes (neglecting second and higher order derivatives)

$$u = kx \qquad (3\text{-}35)$$

which is recognized as Hooke's law for a linear spring. Throughout this analysis, we have assumed that the force-deflection curve of Fig. 3-11 is stationary, that is, the curve doesn't change with time.

Several observations should emerge from this linearization exercise:

1) Drawing a tangent to a nonlinear curve at an operating point is equivalent to using only the linear term of the Taylor series expansion of the nonlinear function,

2) The linearized version of the nonlinear function (the tangent here) is only valid for limited variations about the operating point $0'$. The larger the excursion from point $0'$ the larger the error e (see Fig. 3-11) introduced by the linearization, and

3) Mathematically, the error e is introduced by truncating the series of Eq. (3-34).

The vector function of Eq. (3-32) is scalar for a first order system as we saw, for example, in Sec. 1.4 and Fig. 1-5 for a leaking tank. When its inflow Q_1 is kept constant, the corresponding equilibrium level h_1, for which $Q_1 = \eta\sqrt{h_1}$ holds, is an equilibrium state. The state variable $x(t)$ that will satisfy Eq. (3-33) is a deviation of level h from h_1

$$x = h - h_1$$

and the state equation, from Eq. (1-7), is

$$Dh = Dx = \left(\frac{\eta}{A}\right)\left(\sqrt{h_1} - \sqrt{h_1 + x}\right) = f(x) \qquad (3\text{-}36)$$

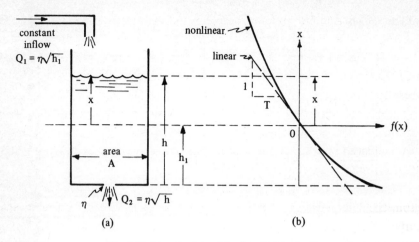

Fig. 3-12 Linearization of Outflow Resistance

The nonlinear relation between $f(x)$ and x, shown in Fig. 3-12(b), may be approximated by a linear (i.e., straight line) relation for small values of x. Eq. (3-36) for the linear approximation will take the following form:

$$Dx = ax \quad a < 0 \tag{3-37}$$

Since a constant inflow Q_1 is needed for an equilibrium point h_1 to exist, input u for this system must be defined as a deviation of inflow measured from a fixed Q_1

arbitrary inflow rate $= Q_1 + u(t)$

and the general form of Eq. (3-37) is

$$Dx(t) = ax(t) + bu(t) \quad b = 1/A \quad A = \text{surface area}$$

Like the linear population dynamics given by Eq. (1-3), the analytical solution of Eq. (3-37) is

$$x(t) = e^{at}x(0) \quad \text{or} \quad x(t) = e^{-t/T}x(0) \tag{3-38}$$

where x(0) is an arbitrary initial deviation and the negative slope (shown in Fig. 3-12(b)) of the linear relation is represented by a = $-1/T$. The exponential decay is thus represented, for the linearized version of the problem, by a constant parameter T, which is called the *time constant*. In Chapter 5, on the analytical solutions of linear differential equations, we shall further discuss the significance of this time constant T. We wish to emphasize here that inconsistencies in the time constant may result from discrepancies between the linearized and nonlinear versions of the system function as well as excessive deviations from the operating point of the system.

The linearization of a scalar function f(x,u) into ax + bu has the following geometric interpretation: f(x,u) in a three dimensional space f-x-u represents a surface that passes through the origin under the condition of Eq. (3-33); this surface is replaced by a plane (which is tangent to the surface at the origin as in Fig. 3-12(b)) when the relation is linearized into the form ax + bu, a and b constant.

Generalizing the principle to the system of Eq. (3-32), we obtain the following linear form for a vector state equation:

$$D\underline{x}(t) = \underline{A}\,\underline{x}(t) + \underline{B}\,\underline{u}(t) \tag{3-39}$$

This is equivalent to n scalar equations

$$Dx_i = \sum_{j=1}^{n} a_{ij}x_j + \sum_{k=1}^{r} b_{ik}u_k \qquad i = 1, \ldots, n \tag{3-40}$$

$\underline{A}$ and $\underline{B}$ in Eq. (3-39) are thus constant coefficient matrices, where $\underline{A}$ is nxn and $\underline{B}$ is nxr

$$\underline{A} = \begin{bmatrix} a_{11} & a_{12} & \cdots & a_{1n} \\ \cdots \cdots \cdots \cdots \\ a_{n1} & \cdots \cdots \cdots & a_{nn} \end{bmatrix} \qquad \underline{B} = \begin{bmatrix} b_{11} & \cdots & b_{1r} \\ \cdots \cdots \\ b_{n1} & \cdots & b_{nr} \end{bmatrix} \tag{3-41}$$

The matrix $\underline{A}$ is an array of linearized constants and it plays the role of the Jacobian array (see Ref. [5]) in mathematical analysis of nonlinear systems.

Since there is no general theory for the solution of nonlinear equations, one must usually rely on a computer to solve Eq. (3-32). We shall present one such approach in the next chapter. When a system has been linearized and is represented by Eq. (3-39), there is a general theory for the solution, as we shall see in Chapter 5.

SUMMARY

This chapter has treated more complex systems than those previously examined and has considered various initial modeling approaches such as flow-charting and block diagramming. The problems of state variable assignment, constitutive relations, sign conventions, causality and the like were reviewed in this chapter from the perspective of deriving the state equations of a complex system made up of various integrating and static elements. As an introduction to later analytical and simulation work, the dynamic behavior of these complex systems was studied by viewing the motion of the system state in state space. The graphical trajectory of this motion was developed and investigated for its stability characteristics and for its behavior around the equilibrium points of the trajectory. Finally, the importance of viewing linear system dynamics as a local-ized subset of the global nonlinear system behavior was emphasized.

REFERENCES

1. J. Forrester, *Urban Dynamics*, MIT Press, Cambridge, Mass., 1969 and *World Dynamics*, Wright-Allen Press, Cambridge, Mass., 1971

2. R. C. Spear and E. Wei, "Dynamic Aspects of Environmental Toxicology," *ASME Quarterly Transactions Journal of Dynamics Systems, Measurement, and Control*, Vol. 94, Series G, No. 2, June 1972

3. E. C. Pielou, *An Introduction to Mathematical Ecology*, J. Wiley, New York, 1969

4. N. Keyfitz, *Introduction to the Mathematics of Population*, Addison-Wesley, Reading, Mass., 1968

5. S. M. Shinners, *Modern Control System Theory and Application*, Addison-Wesley, Reading, Mass., 1972, p. 366

PROBLEMS

3-1 Replace the lettuce in Fig. 3-2 by a manufactured product (canned food, soap, elec-

tric bulbs, etc.), the harvest by a production process and insert a warehouse inventory between the manufacturing (or production) process and the amount on the
(wholesale and retail) market. Construct a flowchart and assign state variables.

3-2   Since electrical energy cannot be stored without energy conversion once it is generated, schemes for "warehousing" energy must be devised. A high reservoir is used as
an "inventory" to which water will be pumped up when power generation exceeds
demand and the flow is reversed to drive hydraulic-turbine generator sets when
demand exceeds generation. For instance, there is a reservoir in Luxembourg with a
6.6 million cubic meter capacity at a 380 meter head. Assuming a steam power plant
to be independent (i.e., no tie-line to other power stations), three major storage
elements meaningful for a time span of from several hours to several weeks are
shown in Fig. P-3-2. Designate input variables and write a state equation in a general,
conceptual form.

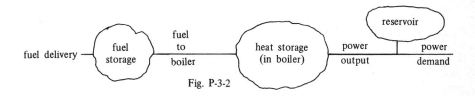

Fig. P-3-2

3-3   Waste heat in a power plant (and some other processing plants) is often dissipated
into the atmosphere by a vertical spray over a cooling pond. Assuming water temperature in the pond to be uniform (i.e., lumping the heat capacitance of the pond)
and taking it as a state variable, write (a general form of) the state equation and also
define important inputs.

3-4   A thermal pollution problem in river water is expressed by a simplified model in Fig.
P-3-4 where the bulk of water is lumped into two agitated tanks and the water temperatures in the two tanks are taken as state variables, x_1 and x_2. Let

w = product of flow rate and specific heat of water, kcal/($^\circ$C·hour)
C_1, C_2 = heat capacitance of the water in the tanks, kcal/$^\circ$C
u = temperature of upstream water, $^\circ$C

and obtain state equations by applying a heat balance. Under what conditions are the

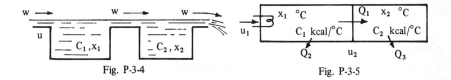

Fig. P-3-4   Fig. P-3-5

equations time invariant (i.e., the coefficients in the equation are not affected by time)? Does an analogy apply for chemical component concentration in place of temperature?

3-5 Temperatures and heat capacitances of two chambers separated by a conducting wall (Fig. P-3-5) are x_1, C_1, x_2 and C_2, respectively. The first chamber has heat supplied at a rate of $u_1(t)$ kcal/min. Newton's law of cooling applies to the heat flows Q_1, Q_2 and Q_3 (kcal/min). These are shown in the figure with arrows indicating the direction of positive flow

$$Q_1 = \frac{x_1 - x_2}{R_1} \qquad Q_2 = \frac{x_1 - u_2}{R_2} \qquad Q_3 = \frac{x_2 - u_2}{R_3}$$

where
    u_2 = ambient temperature

and
    R_i = resistance of i-th wall (assumed to be three different constants in (°C·min)/kcal

Obtain the $\underline{A}$ and $\underline{B}$ matrices for the vector state equation, Eq. (3-39). Also discuss the analogy of this system with an electrical system, a diffusion system of some chemical component and a population system.

3-6 Discuss the equilibrium state(s) and the stability of a mass attached to a pivoted link in a gravity field (Fig. P-3-6). Derive linearized state equation(s) in the vicinity of the equilibrium state(s).

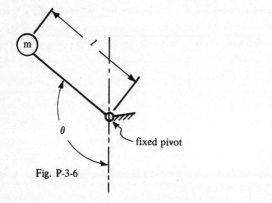

Fig. P-3-6

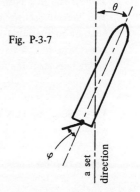

Fig. P-3-7

3-7 The deviation angle θ (radians) of a boat from its prescribed direction is detected by a compass. The error angle is then fed into a power amplifier which, in turn, adjusts the rudder angle (φ in Fig. P-3-7) in such a way that the restoring torque generated by the rudder will be proportional to the error angle; hence

    restoring torque = $k\theta$ k = constant

Let I be the moment of inertia of the boat, $\theta = x_1$ be the first state variable and obtain a state equation. Is this feedback control system stable?

3-8 According to the Malthusian equation, $dN(t)/dt = rN(t)$, a population $N(t)$ will "explode" when r is a positive constant. P. F. Verhulst (a Belgian mathematician) modified this equation in 1838 by making r a linear function of $N(t)$

$$r = k_1(1 - \frac{N(t)}{N_1})$$

where k_1 and N_1 are positive constants. Determine the equilibrium state(s). Using the idea of the isocline graphical technique given for the state plane in Fig. 3-8, obtain a $N(t)$ response curve in the N-t plane for an initial state $N(0) \ll N_1$. Is this system stable?

3-9 Let $n(t) = N(t) - N_1$ = a small deviation in the Verhulst equation (see the preceding problem) and derive a linear equation in $n(t)$. What behavior does this linearized equation predict?

3-10 In place of Eq. (3-23) for a pair of species in competition, consider that the following equations apply:

$$DN_1 = (10 - N_1 - N_2)N_1$$
$$DN_2 = (18 - 3N_1 - N_2)N_2$$

Construct state-plane trajectories by the graphical method and discuss the stability at an equilibrium point where the two species might coexist.

3-11 The *biotic potential* r in the Malthusian equation of a single population, $dN(t)/dt = rN(t)$, was considered as a linear function of N by Verhulst (Prob. 3-8). The linear form for r was generalized for two species in competition by G. F. Gause (1934) and that is Eq. (3-22). In the famous Volterra-Lotka equation for predator-prey dynamics (A. J. Lotka, 1920, V. Volterra, 1926), the r's for predator and prey are also linear in population

$$\frac{dN_1(t)}{dt} = r_1 N_1(t) \text{ for prey} \qquad \frac{dN_2(t)}{dt} = r_2 N_2(t) \text{ for predator}$$

where $\quad r_1 = A_1 - k_1 N_2 \qquad r_2 = -A_2 + k_2 N_1$

and where A_1, A_2, k_1 and k_2 are positive constants. Linearize these equations for small deviations n_1 and n_2 about an equilibrium state.

CHAPTER 4
COMPUTER SOLUTION OF SYSTEM EQUATIONS

Once the analyst has obtained the system equations, he can choose to:
- Stop there — the information gained just in deriving the equations and clarifying the system interconnections is sometimes enough to answer the questions asked in starting the analysis;
- Apply analytical techniques to solve the equations or to manipulate them for purposes such as optimization or sensitivity analysis;
- Obtain a numerical solution, either manually or with a computer.

The greatest incentive for using a computer is its potential for accelerating the design process by providing fast, efficient solutions. Moreover, the computer solution technique is the only one known that applies to both linear and nonlinear systems.

On the other hand, the technique provides no global answers. Direct computer solutions are limited to simulating the behavior of systems for which the parameters and initial conditions have been hypothesized by the analyst. The analyst alone can make the inferences necessary to improve his system based on the numerical results he obtains from the computer.

Two entirely different classes of equipment can be used to solve the system equations we are discussing here: *digital computers*, which can perform simple numerical operations in microseconds, and *analog computers*, which can solve differential equations by analogy with electronic circuits. We turn our attention first to digital computers.

4.1 USE OF DIGITAL COMPUTERS

The easiest of the digital computer numerical techniques is *Euler's method*. To apply it, we first integrate the state equation of the system (Eq. (3-32))

$$\frac{d}{dt}\underline{x} = \underline{f}(\underline{x}, \underline{u})$$

to get

$$\underline{x}(t) = \underline{x}(t_0) + \int_{t_0}^{t} \underline{f}(\underline{x},\underline{u}(\tau))d\tau \tag{4-1}$$

where t is running time, t_0 is the initial time, τ is a dummy integration variable, $\underline{x}(t_0)$ is specified and the input $\underline{u}(\tau)$ is known for the interval of computation. If a set of intermediate variables $\underline{w}$ is involved, as in the example of Section 3.3, then

$$\underline{x}(t) = \underline{x}(t_0) + \int_{t_0}^{t} \underline{F}(\underline{x},\underline{w},\underline{u}(\tau))d\tau$$

and the auxiliary equation is

$$\underline{w} = \underline{g}(\underline{x},\underline{u})$$

Euler's method is applied by examining the system's response as it changes over a small time increment Δt as time goes from t to $(t + \Delta t)$. We make the approximation that over this small time period $\underline{f}$ (or $\underline{f}$ and $\underline{g}$) are constant and, thus, can be taken outside of the time integral. Evaluation of the integral then becomes trivial, giving the result at $(t + \Delta t)$ as (assuming Eq. (4-1) without any auxiliary equations)

$$\underline{x}(t + \Delta t) = \underline{f}_{av}\Delta t + \underline{x}(t) \tag{4-2}$$

For Euler's method the average $(\underline{f}_{av})$ is evaluated solely on the basis of information available at the beginning of the time increment; that is

$$\underline{f}_{av} = \underline{f}(\underline{x}(t),\underline{u}(t)) \quad \text{for t to } (t + \Delta t) \tag{4-3}$$

where t is the time at the start of the calculation and $\underline{x}(t)$ and $\underline{u}(t)$ are the values of the state vector and the input vector at that time, $\underline{x}(t)$ being given by the computation at the end of the previous step.

A variant of this method is to use the newly calculated state variables on the righthand side of Eq. (4-3) as they become available. When f_1, the first element of $\underline{f}$, is calculated, there is no information available about the state variables other than $x_1(t)$, $x_2(t)$, etc. After calculating f_1, however, $x_1(t + \Delta t)$ can be calculated immediately and used instead of $x_1(t)$ in approximating f_2, the second element of $\underline{f}$. In scalar form, the modified Euler equivalent to Eq. (4-3) for an n-th order system is

$$f_{1\ av} = f_1(x_1(t), x_2(t), \ldots, u_1(t), \ldots)$$
$$f_{2\ av} = f_2(x_1(t + \Delta t), x_2(t), x_3(t), \ldots, u_1(t), \ldots)$$
$$f_{3\ av} = f_3(x_1(t + \Delta t), x_2(t + \Delta t), x_3(t), \ldots, u_1(t), \ldots) \qquad (4\text{-}4)$$

$$\vdots$$

This variant requires no more computational effort than the standard Euler's method (in fact, it is slightly more efficient) and, as we will see in some examples, it is considerably more accurate.

To get a feeling for this easy method, let's consider a two-state variable (or second order) system for which

$$x_1(t) = x_1(0) + \int_0^t f_1(x_1, x_2, u)d\tau$$
$$x_2(t) = x_2(0) + \int_0^t f_2(x_1, x_2, u)d\tau \qquad (4\text{-}5)$$

where x_1 and x_2 are the state variables and u is the system input. We start by making the following definitions:

$\quad t_1 \Rightarrow$ time at the beginning of a time increment
$\quad t_2 \Rightarrow$ time at the end of a time increment
$\quad \Delta t \Rightarrow$ step size, equal to $(t_2 - t_1)$

At the start of the computation t_1 is zero, so $x_1(t_1)$ and $x_2(t_1)$ are just the initial conditions and are presumed known. In *any* solution technique, the initial conditions must be independently known. Noting t_2 is Δt, $x_1(t_2)$ is calculated in the same manner for the Euler and the variant method

$$x_1(t_2) = x_1(t_1) + f_1(x_1(t_1), x_2(t_1), u(t_1))\Delta t \qquad (4\text{-}6)$$

(Note that for a system with only one state variable, the Euler and the variant methods are the same.) For the Euler method, $x_2(t_2)$ is

$$x_2(t_2) = x_2(t_1) + f_2(x_1(t_1), x_2(t_1), u(t_1))\Delta t \qquad (4\text{-}7a)$$

while for the variant, $x_2(t_2)$ is

$$x_2(t_2) = x_2(t_1) + f_2(x_1(t_2), x_2(t_1), u(t_1))\Delta t \qquad (4\text{-}7b)$$

In the case of both Eqs. (4-7a) and (4-7b), the righthand side is completely determined in terms of known quantities. After solving for $x_1(t_2)$ and $x_2(t_2)$, t_1 and t_2 can be incremented by Δt and the newly calculated values become the initial conditions for the next step in the computation. The entire algorithm, for a solution starting at time $t = 0$ and extending through time $t = t_{final}$ with a step size Δt, is illustrated below in Fortran† for the Euler variant. The input u is assumed constant over this entire period. Writing DT for Δt, the Fortran program is

```
        read in (or set) values for U, DT,
            TFINAL, X1ZERO, X2ZERO
        T=0                              — Initialize the time and
        X1=X1ZERO                          state variables here. Note
        X2=X2ZERO                          that since U does not
100     CONTINUE                           change in the course of
        print (or plot) T, X1, X2          the computations, its val-
                                           ue only has to be set
                                           once.
110     X1=X1+f1(X1,X2,U)*DT             — The actual functions for
120     X2=X2+f2(X1,X2,U)*DT               f1 and f2 must be used
                                           here.
        T=T+DT                           — Update the time variable.
        IF(T .LE. TFINAL) GO TO 100      — If t is less than or equal
        STOP                               to t_final, continue the
                                           calculation; otherwise stop.
```

† Fortran will be used here and in later sections because it is a convenient method for communicating algorithms. No attempt will be made to show complete computer programs. For this reason, most of the Fortran listings will not include input/output statements, dimension, etc. Words in lower case within listings have been substituted for the proper Fortran terminology for the sake of simplicity and are meant only as general descriptions.

Note that the nature of Fortran assures that the updated value of X1 will be used in the computation of X2, thus giving us the Euler variant algorithm. The standard Euler algorithm can be obtained by replacing statements 110 and 120 with the following four statements:

```
110  F1=f₁(X1,X2,U)
     F2=f₂(X1,X2,U)
     X1=X1+F1*DT
     X2=X2+F2*DT
```

The extra variables F1 and F2 had to be defined to make sure that only values of X1 and X2 from the beginning of the computation for that time step were used.

Example 4-1: Euler's Method and Euler Variant Applied to a Second Order System

We would like to obtain a digital solution for the time response of the system described by the following equations:

$$\frac{dx_1}{dt} = -290x_1 + 10{,}000x_2 \tag{4-8a}$$

$$\frac{dx_2}{dt} = -140x_1 - 300x_2 + u \tag{4-8b}$$

f_1 and f_2 are the righthand sides of (4-8a) and (4-8b), respectively. Following the pattern given above, we can write the Fortran program for the following conditions:

$$x_1(0) = 0.0 \qquad x_2(0) = 1.0$$
input u = constant = 1,000

The program to compute 100 points over a time interval of 0.01 is (for the Euler variant method)

```
U=1000.
X1ZERO=0.0
X2ZERO=1.0
TFINAL=0.01
DT=0.0001
T=0
X1=X1ZERO
```

```
    X2=X2ZERO
100 CONTINUE
    plot X1 and X2 versus T
110 X1=X1+(-290.0*X1+10000.0*X2)*DT
120 X2=X2+(-140.0*X1-300.0*X2+U)*DT
    T=T+DT
    IF(T .LE. TFINAL)GO TO 100
    STOP
```

As before, we can change this to the standard Euler algorithm by replacing statements 110 and 120 with

```
110 F1=-290.0*X1+10000.0*X2
    F2=-140.0*X1-300.0*X2+U
    X1=X1+F1*DT
    X2=X2+F2*DT
```

In solving this problem, a computer with a storage-type oscilloscope for output was used. The results of the computation are shown in Fig. 4-1; the curves shown are actual photographs of the oscilloscope screen. Because digital solu-

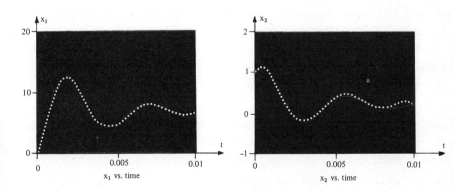

Fig. 4-1
Results of Digital Computer Solution

Solid line: exact solution
Dotted line closest to solid line: Euler-Variant
Dotted line furthest from solid line: Euler-Standard

tions are *discrete*, that is, answers are only produced at specific times, t = 0, Δt, 2Δt, 3Δt, etc., the response appears as a series of dots rather than a continuous curve. For purposes of comparison, results are shown for both the standard and variant Euler methods and for the "exact" solution, generated in this case by using a very small Δt.

4.2 TIME INCREMENT

The trickiest part of applying Euler's method is picking the right step size Δt. The choice of Δt is governed primarily by the accuracy required. The resolution we demand in the output determines the minimum number of data points required over the solution time and thus the maximum step size. A lower limit on the step size is set by the precision of the computer being used; if Δt is so small that the roundoff error becomes significant in comparison with F1*DT or F2*DT, the error accumulation at each step will be excessive. Somewhere between these limits lies the optimum choice for the step size. We define the optimum in this case to be that step size which meets the desired accuracy and resolution requirements and results in the minimum computing time cost. For most digital computers, the lower limit is so low that it represents no practical limitation. In the absence of any other information, the upper limit specified by the resolution requirement can be used as a starting point for the step size because minimum cost will be achieved by using the largest Δt that meets the accuracy requirement. This represents a good starting point because it is usually based on an intuitive feel for the nature of the expected output. Also, the conditions for minimum loss of information in the solution (i.e., resolution) and the general conditions for achieving an accurate numerical solution are the same, namely, the change in the system's state from step to step should be small.

How do you know if your choice of step size is appropriate? In other words, how can you tell if the solution is right? Usually, the only way is to "play" with the solution. The first set of results should be viewed as a trial solution. If these results look reasonable (which is often the only check), they probably are acceptable. For a check on the accuracy of the solution, however, a good procedure is to cut the step size in half and run another trial. If the change in the output is well within the accuracy requirement, then the step size is small enough. If it is not, keep halving the step size and rerunning the solution until it is. Verification of the model at a higher level than this self-consistency type of check requires use of independent information, for example, by comparison with an independent solution (perhaps an analog computer or an analytical solution) to confirm that the numerical analysis was correct or against experimental data to validate the modeling procedure.

If the results of the first trial don't look at all reasonable, the probable culprit is a step size that is much too large. In this case, there may be excessive *error accumulation* over all or part of the solution time of interest. Error accumulation describes the situation in which the error increases from step to step. This can cause very large errors to build up, even in situations in which the error caused by approximating the actual f's in the differential equation by some $f_{average}$ is modest for a single step. At times, the error gets so large that it swamps the solution and the result becomes nonsensical. The nature of error accumulation in a particular problem depends both on the type of integration algorithm used† and on the nature of the system. The step size affects the magnitude of error buildup over the time interval of interest. As a general rule of thumb, the more stable a system is, the less serious error accumulation problems tend to be. Since we are usually interested in the solution for only a finite time period, error accumulation problems can most often be solved by reducing the step size to the point at which the total error accumulation over this time period is acceptable. If this doesn't work or the step size grows so small that the solution becomes very expensive, it would be wise to investigate a different integration algorithm. (A common cause of this problem is the inclusion of both very fast and slow components in a system model. Even though their effect on the overall system behavior may be small, the fast elements can cause very large errors to accumulate unless very small step sizes are used.) Below, we study error accumulation using the familiar mass-spring-dashpot system.

Example 4-2: Digital Solution of Mass-Spring-Dashpot Response

We define velocities as positive in the upward direction and forces as positive in compression as shown in Fig. 4-2. For state variables, we take the velocity of the mass (V_m) and the force in the spring (F_s). By Newton's law

$$DV_m = \frac{1}{m} F_{total} \tag{4-9}$$

---

† Although only two integrating algorithms are discussed here, there are many others, for example, trapezoidal, backwards Euler, Runge-Kutta and predictor-corrector. A good compendium of numerical methods is given in [1]. Ref. [2] is an excellent source of information for digital and analog computer simulations.

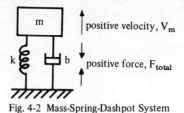

Fig. 4-2 Mass-Spring-Dashpot System

For a linear spring

$$DF_s = -kV_m \qquad (4\text{-}10)$$

(the relative velocity here becomes V_m because the spring is fixed between the mass and ground). If the force in the dashpot is proportional to the velocity across it, the total force, which is the sum of the forces in the dashpot and spring, becomes

$$F_{total} = F_s - bV_m \qquad (4\text{-}11)$$

Combining (4-9) through (4-11), we get the system equations

$$DV_m = -\frac{b}{m} V_m + \frac{1}{m} F_s \qquad (4\text{-}12a)$$

$$DF_s = -kV_m \qquad (4\text{-}12b)$$

For simplicity, we take m and k equal to 1. The error accumulation characteristics are shown in Fig. 4-3 as b varies over positive, negative and zero values. A "negative" frictional element, that is, b less than zero, does not make much sense physically in normal circumstances since such a device would constantly put energy into the system instead of dissipating energy! Under certain important circumstances, however, negative frictional elements appear to exist for short times (during the *break-free* period in a stiction system, for example). Because of the simplicity of this system, the analytical solution (see next chapter) was used to compute the error of the Euler approximation as shown in Fig. 4-3. The algorithm for the Euler numerical solution of these equations is shown below.

```
      REAL M,K                              — Declare M and K to be
                                              REAL variables.
      read in (or set) values for DT,      — Use FS and VM for the
          TFINAL,FSZERO,VMZERO,              state variables $F_s$ and
          M,K,B                              $V_m$.
      T=0
      FS=FSZERO
      VM=VMZERO
100   CONTINUE
      print (or plot) T,VM,FS
110   F1=-(B/M)*VM+(1.0/M)*FS              — With the statements in
115   VM=VM+F1*DT                            this order, this algorithm
120   F2=-K*VM                              describes the Euler vari-
125   FS=FS+F2*DT                            ant; rearrange them to
      T=T+DT                                 110, 120, 115, 125 for
      IF(T .LE. TFINAL)GO TO 100             standard Euler.
      STOP
```

One conclusion is inescapable from Fig. 4-3: the Euler variant method is far superior to the standard Euler method. More specifically, we can see some general trends in the array of results presented. The likelihood of error accumulation being a serious problem goes from least likely at the upper left, where the system is very stable and the step size very small, to most likely at the lower right, where the system is unstable and the step size very large. Four cases are shown clearly:

1) the error remains negligibly small over the entire solution interval,
2) the error builds up to a modest value and then dies away,
3) the error builds up to a more-or-less constant magnitude and appears to stay there and
4) the error gets larger and larger as the solution proceeds (sometimes so large that the solution becomes meaningless).

In short, the analyst must always be certain that a numerical solution to a set of system equations really reflects the system characteristics and not the errors accumulated during the solution process.

We next turn our attention to a basic circuit of electrical power supplies: an ac-to-dc rectifier circuit. This problem is a good example of how a very strongly nonlinear element like a diode can be treated in a digital computer simulation.

COMPUTER SOLUTION OF SYSTEM EQUATIONS

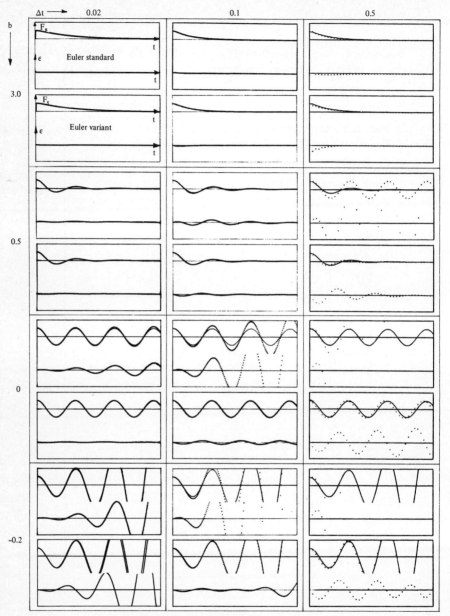

Fig. 4-3 Error Accumulation Characteristics for Mass-Spring-Dashpot System
(see next page for explanation of scales)

Explanation and Scales

Each box is for one parameter set (b,Δt). There are 12 boxes. Two types of curves are shown: Spring force v. time and error v. time. Scales for these are shown below. All F_s graphs have the same scale as do all error graphs. Each box contains four sets of axes, as shown below. The analytical solutions for F_s are shown as solid lines and the Euler solutions by dots (where the solutions have very good agreement, or where the dots are very close together (as in Δt = 0.02) the dotted lines may appear solid). The error v. time is shown directly below the corresponding F_s curve in each case.

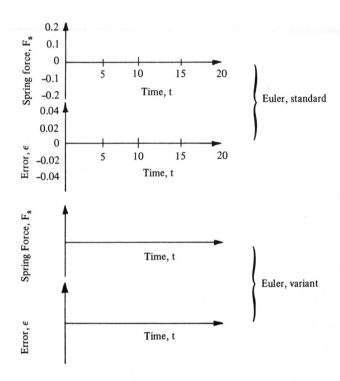

Fig. 4-3 Error Accumulation Characteristics for Mass-Spring-Dashpot System

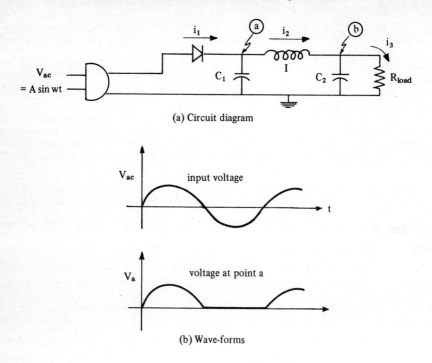

(a) Circuit diagram

(b) Wave-forms

Fig. 4-4 Half-Wave Rectifier

Example 4-3: Half-Wave Rectifier

Let us consider the simple ac-to-dc converter (rectifier) which uses a diode, as shown in Fig. 4-4. This is known as a half-wave rectifier because of the shape of the V_a voltage curve shown in Fig. 4-4(b). We shall neglect the transformer that is usually used on the input side and assume the load to be purely resistive.

For state variables we choose the voltages on the two capacitors, V_a and V_b, and the current through the inductor, i_2. Starting from the left and using the sign conventions shown in Fig. 4-4, we can derive the system equations

$$DV_a = \frac{1}{C_1}(i_1 - i_2) \qquad (4\text{-}13)$$

where i_1 is a function of the voltage drop across the diode

$$i_1 = \phi_{diode}(V_{ac} - V_a) \qquad (4\text{-}14)$$

For the inductor

$$Di_2 = \frac{1}{I}(V_a - V_b)$$ (4-15)

and for the capacitor C_2

$$DV_b = \frac{1}{C_2}(i_2 - i_3)$$ (4-16)

where

$$i_3 = \phi_{load}(V_b)$$ (4-17)

We will assume that the diode has a constitutive relation as shown in Fig. 4-5; that is, it acts like a linear resistor when the voltage drop across it is positive and it acts like an open circuit (R = infinity) when the voltage drop is negative. The linear resistance is meant to account for the series resistance in the wires and connections, transformer (if any), etc. as well as for the actual resistance of the diode itself. Note that in the case of the circuit shown in Fig. 4-4(a) with no transformer at the left end, we must include the series resistance to avoid causal conflict such as that mentioned in connection with Fig. 3-4.

This is the first example of a digital solution for which the input function, V_{ac} in this case, is not constant throughout the solution time. This means that the value of V_{ac} must be recomputed for each time step. Because we assume that the righthand sides of the state equations remain constant over a time increment, we must pick a single value to approximate the input for each time period Δt. This approximation of the input by a constant for each time incre-

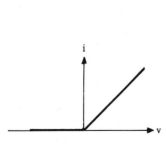

Fig. 4-5 Constitutive Relation
for the Diode

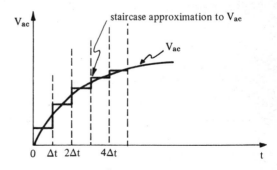

Fig. 4-6 Staircase Approximation

ment is called a *staircase approximation*. For $V_{ac} = A\sin(\omega t)$ the staircase approximation shown in Fig. 4-6 was arrived at by using a constant value for $V_{ac} = A\sin(\omega t + \Delta t/2)$ over the period t to $(t + \Delta t)$.

The algorithm, using the Euler variant method, is

```
       REAL I,I1,I2
       read in (or set) values for DT,
          TFINAL,I,C1,C2,RDIOD,
          RLOAD,W,A,VAZERO,
          VBZERO,I2ZERO
       T=0
       VA=VAZERO
       VB=VBZERO
       I2=I2ZERO
100    CONTINUE
       print (or plot) T,VB (and any
          other variables of interest)
       VAC=A*SIN(W*T+DT/2.0)
       VDIOD=VAC−VA


       IF(VDIOD .LT. 0.0)I1=0.0
       IF(VDIOD .GE. 0.0)I1=VDIOD/
          RDIOD
       VA=VA+((I1−I2)/C1)*DT
       I2=I2+((VA−VB)/I)*DT
       VB=VB+((I2−VB/RLOAD)/C2)*DT
       T=T+DT
       IF(T .LE. TFINAL)GO TO 100
       STOP
```

— Declare the variable I to be REAL so we can use it for the inductance value; I1 and I2 will be used for the currents i_1 and i_2.

— RLOAD is the load resistance, assumed to be linear. RDIOD is the linear part of the diode resistance.

— A and W are the amplitude and frequency (in rad/sec) of the input voltage.

— These statements compute the current through the diode; VDIOD is the voltage across the diode. If it is negative, i_1 is zero. If it is positive, i_1 = VDIOD/RDIOD.

The results of this simulation are shown in Fig. 4-7, where (a) shows a set of trials used to determine a suitable step size for one set of parameters and (b) shows the effect of some variations in C_1, C_2 and I of the filter circuit. If we measure the quality of an ac-to-dc converter by how much of the ac component gets through to the output (the less, the better since, ideally, we want a "ripple-free" output), we can see that the quality decreases as C and I get smaller. As C and I get larger, the amount of time it takes for the output voltage to

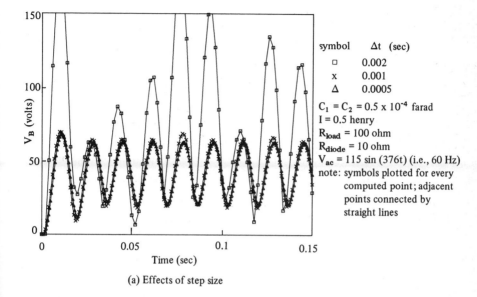

(a) Effects of step size

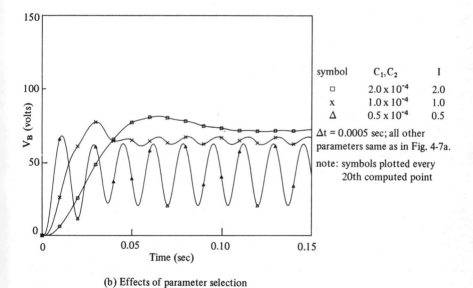

(b) Effects of parameter selection

Fig. 4-7 Response of a Rectifier Circuit

reach a steady-state increases. In general, we are interested in power supplies that put out constant dc voltages. We therefore would want C and I to be as large as practical.

4.3 PRINCIPLES OF ANALOG COMPUTING

Our discussions of digital computer simulation have shown how system equations can be manipulated numerically to derive an algorithm which approximates the solution to those equations. We will now examine a computer which operates on a different principle. An analog computer is used by manipulating a set of electronic components until a circuit is set up whose system equations have exactly the same form as the system equations we want to solve. When this is done, it remains to determine the relationship between the variables that describe the computer circuit so that, by running the computer, we can deduce by *analogy* the response of the system in question.

The heart of the analog computer is the *operational amplifier*, a dc voltage amplifier with very high gain, as high as 10^5 to 10^9. When wired as shown in Fig. 4-8(a), it has the unique property that the relationship between the input voltage V_1 and the output voltage V_2 is independent of the actual characteristics of the amplifier itself and depends only on the nature of the input and feedback circuit elements.

For example, if both the input and feedback elements are resistors, as in

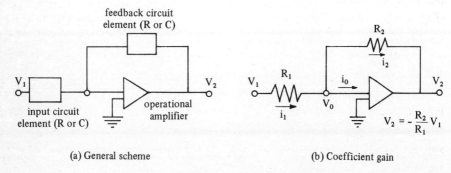

(a) General scheme   (b) Coefficient gain

Fig. 4-8 Wiring Diagram for Analog Computer

Fig. 4-8(b), the output voltage is equal to a *negative* constant times the input voltage, regardless of the gain or linearity of the amplifier. This unique situation can be quickly understood by looking at the equations describing the circuit: if V_2 is a modest voltage within the computer's operating range (±10 or ±100 volts are typical ranges), the voltage V_0 at the input side of the operational amplifier must be nearly zero because the gain of the amplifier is very high (i.e., $V_0 = (10^{-5}$ to $10^{-9})V_2$). Furthermore, since operational amplifiers are designed to draw very little current, i_0 (the current going into the amplifier from its input or primary side) is negligible. Therefore, the following equations will very nearly describe this circuit:

$$i_1 = i_2$$

where

$$i_1 = \frac{V_1 - V_0}{R_1} \qquad i_2 = \frac{V_0 - V_2}{R_2} \qquad V_0 = 0$$

so

$$\frac{V_2}{V_1} = -\frac{R_2}{R_1} \tag{4-18}$$

Note the minus sign well! It appears in all such relations involving operational amplifiers. It is desirable to make the resistances (R_1, R_2) large, in the order of megohms, so that they will not draw much current. Within its operating range, the amplifier is capable of accomodating whatever (positive or negative) current necessary to maintain the output voltage.

A set of basic configurations are shown in Fig. 4-9 along with equations and *computing diagrams*. The *integrators*, (d) and (e) in the figure, will be key elements for solving state equations of the type we have been using. By replacing the feedback resistor R_2 in the circuit of the coefficient gain element (Fig. 4-9(b)) with a capacitor, the input-output relation corresponding to Eq. (4-18) is

$$\frac{V_2}{V_1} = \frac{-1}{RC}\frac{1}{D}$$

where $1/D$ corresponds to integration. This relation is the description of the integrator, Fig. 4-9(d). Summers are constructed by inserting an additional input resistance for each input. The computing diagrams of Fig. 4-9 are very convenient for selecting appropriate analog circuits and component values because they are much easier to visualize than wiring diagrams yet are very easy to transform into wiring diagrams when the proper coefficients have all been computed.

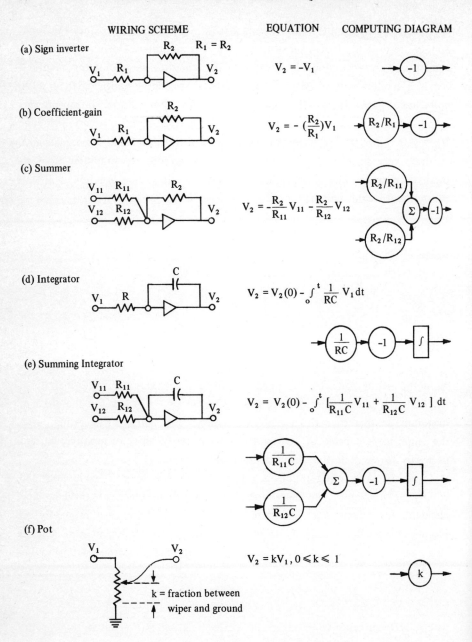

WIRING SCHEME   EQUATION   COMPUTING DIAGRAM

(a) Sign inverter

$$V_2 = -V_1$$

(b) Coefficient-gain

$$V_2 = - \left(\frac{R_2}{R_1}\right) V_1$$

(c) Summer

$$V_2 = -\frac{R_2}{R_{11}} V_{11} - \frac{R_2}{R_{12}} V_{12}$$

(d) Integrator

$$V_2 = V_2(0) - \int_0^t \frac{1}{RC} V_1 \, dt$$

(e) Summing Integrator

$$V_2 = V_2(0) - \int_0^t \left[\frac{1}{R_{11}C} V_{11} + \frac{1}{R_{12}C} V_{12} \right] dt$$

(f) Pot

$$V_2 = kV_1, \ 0 \leqslant k \leqslant 1$$

k = fraction between wiper and ground

Fig. 4-9 Common Analog Computing Elements

When converting from computing diagrams to wiring diagrams, pay careful attention to the ubiquitous sign reversals (see Eq. (4-18)) and insert inverters as necessary.

For ease of reading, initial conditions have been omitted from the diagrams; however, they appear in the equation column of Fig. 4-9. It is necessary to set an initial voltage on *all* integrators on an analog computer. This operation varies depending on the computer being used.

The importance of operational amplifiers extends well beyond analog computing circuitry — operational amplifiers are also used in nearly all systems to isolate the instrument from the recording or computing equipment and to do simple computing operations on signals.

4.4 ANALOG COMPUTER PROGRAMMING

Starting with system equations, an analog computer "program" can be generated by first converting the system equations into a computing diagram. The computing diagram must then be manipulated until groupings that correspond to the basic computing elements are obtained (the elements shown in Fig. 4-9). Since the variety of (R and C) components available is limited, as is the total number of operational amplifiers, the diagram must be adjusted and compressed to obtain a final match.

The elements presented in Fig. 4-9 enable us to compute solutions only for linear systems, that is, system equations of the form

$$Dx_i = a_{i1}x_1 + a_{i2}x_2 + \cdots + b_{j1}u_1 + \cdots \tag{4-19}$$

because all we have available in Fig. 4-9 are integrators, coefficient elements and summation. While a variety of nonlinear elements are available (see Sec. 4.6), the nature of the machine puts a premium on having the system equations in linear form.

As an example, assume that we have the same state equations as in Eqs. (4-8a) and (4-8b), repeated here

$$\begin{aligned} Dx_1 &= -290x_1 + 10000x_2 \\ Dx_2 &= -140x_1 - 300x_2 + u \end{aligned} \tag{4-20a}$$

or, in integrated form

$$x_1 = x_1(0) + \int_0^t (-290x_1 + 10000x_2)dt$$

$$\qquad\qquad\qquad\qquad\qquad\qquad\qquad (4\text{-}20b)$$

$$x_2 = x_2(0) + \int_0^t (-140x_1 - 300x_2 + u)dt$$

The computing diagram for this system is shown in Fig. 4-10. Fig. 4-10(a) shows the form of computing diagram that corresponds most closely to the original equations. The diagram of Fig. 4-10(b) has exactly the same mathematical representation but it has been deformed so that computing blocks can be grouped to correspond with analog computing elements as shown in Fig. 4-9.

The best way to construct these diagrams is to start with the integrators in Fig. 4-10(a), label their outputs as x_1 and x_2 and then work backwards from

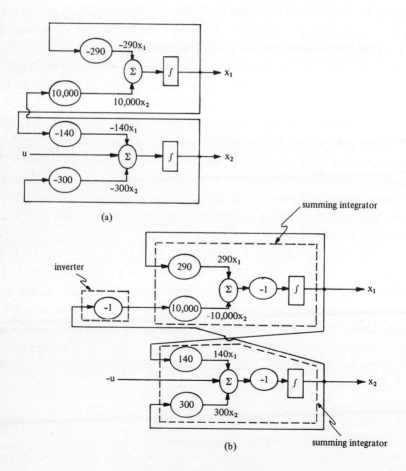

Fig. 4-10 Computing Diagram for Equation (4-20)

them. For the top integrator, for example, to construct the integrand $(-290x_1 + 10,000x_2)$, we must have a summer immediately preceding the integrator. Proceeding backwards from the summer along the top track, we insert a coefficient element for the -290 of the $-290x_1$, where x_1 is available as the output of the top integrator. We continue this process until no dangling lines remain. (The "u" line is not considered to be dangling because u is an input, hence a variable independent of x_1 and x_2, to be supplied from outside by a signal generator, for instance.)

The next step is to deform the diagram of Fig. 4-10(a) until the arrangement of computing elements resembles the forms shown in Fig. 4-9. In this example, the changes are minor and consist mainly of inserting -1 coefficients at the inputs of the integrators to account for the sign inversion that takes place as shown in Fig. 4-10(b). Since the coefficients at the input to a summing integrator must be positive (they are reciprocals of RC products in the actual circuit), a sign inverter must be used to maintain correct signs. The dashed lines in the figure outline the analog computing stages (or elements). Note that the internal quantities (e.g., $-290x_1$) are marked in for clarity of presentation only. There is no way to measure them on the computer.

The process described here is not unique; several alternate procedures and conventions can be used, particularly for deforming the original computing diagram (e.g., Fig. 4-10(a)) into an analog computing diagram (Fig. 4-10(b)). We have adopted the conventions shown above because they seem the most direct for analog computer programming.

We are now ready to go to the computer itself and use the computing diagram to generate the circuitry. Two problems face us at this point: first, analog computers have limited operating voltage ranges, usually -100 to $+100$ volts or -10 to $+10$ volts. Second, the circuit components (R and C) come only in fixed values. To circumvent the problem of fixed values, we usually use potentiometers (voltage dividers). These pots (Fig. 4-9(f)), as they are called, make it possible for the user to choose any coefficient in the range of 0 to 1. This, in combination with various fixed R_2/R_1 and $1/RC$ values, permits multiplication by a single coefficient between about 0.1 and 10.

4.5 SCALING

Transforming the system equations to be compatible with the conditions imposed by the analog computer hardware is called *scaling*. These conditions are:

> — all of the coefficients in the transformed equation should fall in the range from 0.1 to 10.0 (though a somewhat wider range is acceptable on some analog computers)
> — no voltage should exceed the ±10 or ±100 volt limit, depending on the particular machine.

We use a linear transformation from the original state variables and the independent variable (usually time) to a new set according to the relations

$$x_1 = k_1 V_1 \quad x_2 = k_2 V_2 \quad \ldots; \quad t = k_t T \tag{4-21}$$

where $V_1, \ldots, V_n$ are the new state variables and T is the new time variable. The state variable transformation can be expressed in matrix form as

$$\underline{x} = \underline{K}\,\underline{V} \tag{4-22}$$

This is exactly the same as the state variable transformations we saw in Chapter 2 except that here $\underline{K}$ has the special diagonal form

$$\underline{K} = \begin{bmatrix} k_1 & & & & 0 \\ & k_2 & & & \\ & & k_3 & & \\ & & & \cdot & \\ & & & & \cdot \\ 0 & & & & \cdot \end{bmatrix} \tag{4-23}$$

Input variables, if there are any, transform in the same manner

$$u_1 = k_{u1} V_{u1} \quad u_2 = k_{u2} V_{u2} \quad \cdots \tag{4-24}$$

or in matrix form

$$\underline{u} = \underline{K}_u\,\underline{V}_u \tag{4-25}$$

where $\underline{K}_u$ is

$$\underline{K}_u = \begin{bmatrix} k_{u1} & & & 0 \\ & k_{u2} & & \\ & & \cdot & \\ 0 & & & \cdot \end{bmatrix}$$

Scaling is accomplished by substituting the new variables into the system equations according to Eqs. (4-21) through (4-24) and then choosing values for all the k's. For system equations that are linear, the substitution yields an interesting result: using the matrix form of the system differential equation

$$\frac{d}{dt}\underline{x} = \underline{A}\,\underline{x} + \underline{B}\,\underline{u}$$

we get by substitution

$$\frac{1}{k_t}\frac{d}{dT}\underline{K}\,\underline{V} = \underline{A}\,\underline{K}\,\underline{V} + \underline{B}\,\underline{K}_u\,\underline{V}_u \tag{4-26}$$

Multiplying the left and right sides by $k_t \underline{K}^{-1}$ gives the final form of the transformed state equation

$$\frac{d}{dT}\underline{V} = k_t\underline{K}^{-1}\underline{A}\,\underline{K}\,\underline{V} + k_t\underline{K}^{-1}\underline{B}\,\underline{K}_u\,\underline{V}_u \tag{4-27}$$

$$= \underline{A}^*\,\underline{V} + \underline{B}^*\,\underline{V}_u$$

Because $\underline{K}$ is diagonal, we can easily invert it

$$\underline{K}^{-1} = \begin{bmatrix} 1/k_1 & & & 0 \\ & 1/k_2 & & \\ & & 1/k_3 & \\ 0 & & & \ddots \end{bmatrix}$$

and then perform the indicated multiplications to find $\underline{A}^*$ and $\underline{B}^*$

$$\underline{A}^* = \begin{bmatrix} k_t a_{11} & k_t a_{12}(k_2/k_1) & k_t a_{13}(k_3/k_1) & \cdots \\ k_t a_{21}(k_1/k_2) & k_t a_{22} & k_t a_{23}(k_3/k_2) & \cdots \\ k_t a_{31}(k_1/k_3) & k_t a_{32}(k_2/k_3) & k_t a_{33} & \cdots \\ \cdot & \cdot & \cdot & \cdot \\ \cdot & \cdot & \cdot & \cdot \\ \cdot & \cdot & \cdot & \cdot \end{bmatrix}$$

and

$$\underline{B}^* = \begin{bmatrix} k_t b_{11}(k_{u1}/k_1) & k_t b_{12}(k_{u2}/k_1) & k_t b_{13}(k_{u3}/k_1) & \cdots \\ k_t b_{21}(k_{u1}/k_2) & k_t b_{22}(k_{u2}/k_2) & k_t b_{23}(k_{u3}/k_2) & \cdots \\ k_t b_{31}(k_{u1}/k_3) & k_t b_{32}(k_{u2}/k_3) & k_t b_{33}(k_{u3}/k_3) & \cdots \\ \cdot & \cdot & \cdot & \cdot \\ \cdot & \cdot & & \cdot \\ \cdot & \cdot & \cdot & \end{bmatrix} \qquad (4\text{-}28)$$

where the a_{ij}'s and b_{ij}'s are the coefficients of the original (before transformation) system equation. The elements of $\underline{A}^*$ and $\underline{B}^*$ are the coefficients of the transformed equations, that is

$$\frac{dV_1}{dt} = k_t a_{11} V_1 + k_t a_{12}(k_2/k_1)V_2 + \ldots + k_t b_{11}(k_{u1}/k_1)V_{u1} + \ldots$$

$$\cdot$$
$$\cdot$$
$$\cdot$$

Although we have derived this result in matrix form, it can be verified by direct substitution into the nonmatrix form of the system equations.

Choosing Values for the k's

Since the coefficients with the simplest form are the diagonal elements of $\underline{A}^*$, we choose a value for k_t first. Note that it is generally most convenient to pick scaling factors that are "round numbers."

Bearing in mind the 0.1 to 10 restriction for coefficients of the transformed equation, we pick a k_t so that a_{11}^*, a_{22}^*, a_{33}^*, etc. all fall into this range. Once k_t is fixed, we are left with all possible ratios of the k's in $\underline{A}^*$ to juggle. Since all of the ratios are not independent (i.e., if both k_1/k_3 and k_2/k_3 have been chosen, k_1/k_2 is fixed) the juggling process is usually one of compromise and "eye-balling" to maneuver all of the remaining coefficients into the 0.1 to 10 range (this procedure can be automated for digital computer solution but, except for very complex problems, automation is rarely worth the trouble). The elements of $\underline{B}^*$ are fixed in the same way, except that there is considerably more freedom in the choice of ratios because both k's and k_u's are present.

Finally, now that we have chosen all of the ratios, we have to determine the actual values of the k's and k_u's. If there are any input variables in the problem being scaled, we begin our search for the actual values there. For each input variable, we pick a k_u such that when the maximum value of that input is applied, the corresponding value of V_u will be as high as possible without exceeding the voltage limitation of the analog computer being used In general, we are seeking a *golden mean* — if voltages exceed the machine limitation the results become nonsensical. On the other hand, as the operating voltages get lower and lower the accuracy of the solution decreases and the relative noise content increases. For example, if we are using a computer which has a range of ±10 volts and a particular input variable, say u_3, has a maximum value of 1,500,000, we should choose a value for k_{u3} so that $1.5 \times 10^6/k_{u3}$ is less than 10. In this case, $k_{u3} = 2 \times 10^5$ would probably be a good choice. Because of all of the ratios that were determined in the previous step, once all of the k_u's are chosen, the k's will also be fixed. If the problem has no input variables (i.e., if it is an autonomous system), it is necessary to guess the maximum value for any one of the state variables and fix its k. The rest of the k's are then determined from the ratios.

What if This Procedure Doesn't Work?

What if, despite your best efforts, no set of scaling constants brings all of the coefficients into the 0.1 to 10 range? This usually means that the problem has been poorly formulated. Typically, it means that some components which respond very rapidly have been included in a model which also has some very slowly responding components. A common way out of this dilemma is to break the system into a slow part and a fast part and solve the two sections separately. Similarly, in digital simulations, if you discover that you must use an unacceptably small step size in order to get reasonable accuracy, you are probably caught in the same situation and can maneuver out of it by dividing your system into component parts and solving each individually.

Example 4-4:   Scaling for a Linear System

We will continue the solution of the system described by Eq. (4-20). In matrix form we have

$$\frac{d}{dt}\underline{x} = \underline{A}\underline{x} + \underline{B}\underline{u}$$

where

$$\underline{A} = \begin{bmatrix} -290 & 10{,}000 \\ -140 & -300 \end{bmatrix} \qquad \underline{B} = \begin{bmatrix} 0 \\ 1 \end{bmatrix}$$

Using the results of Eq. (4-28), $\underline{A}^*$ and $\underline{B}^*$ are

$$\underline{A}^* = \begin{bmatrix} -k_t \cdot 290 & k_t \cdot 10{,}000(k_2/k_1) \\ -k_t \cdot 140(k_1/k_2) & -k_t \cdot 300 \end{bmatrix}$$

$$\underline{B}^* = \begin{bmatrix} 0 \\ k_t \cdot 1(k_{u1}/k_2) \end{bmatrix}$$

$k_t = 0.002$ will bring the a_{11}^* and a_{22}^* elements into the desired range (any round number for k_t near 0.002 will probably work just as well — as an exercise, try rescaling the problem with slightly different choices for all the scaling constants). $\underline{A}^*$ then becomes

$$\underline{A}^* = \begin{bmatrix} -0.58 & 20(k_2/k_1) \\ -0.28(k_1/k_2) & -0.6 \end{bmatrix}$$

$k_2/k_1 = 0.1$ will bring all of the elements into the 0.1 to 10 range

$$\underline{A}^* = \begin{bmatrix} -0.58 & 2.0 \\ -2.8 & 0.6 \end{bmatrix}$$

With this choice of k_t, $\underline{B}^*$ is

$$\underline{B}^* = \begin{bmatrix} 0 \\ 0.002(k_{u1}/k_2) \end{bmatrix}$$

where

$$\frac{k_{u1}}{k_2} = 500 \text{ gives } \underline{B}^* = \begin{bmatrix} 0 \\ 1 \end{bmatrix}$$

So far we have not required information about the maximum values of any of the variables or the computer voltage range. This information now becomes necessary: if $u_{max} = 1{,}000$ and we are programming for a ten volt computer, we want $1{,}000/k_{u1}$ (from Eq. (4-24)) to be approximately equal to ten. $k_{u1} = 100$ satisfies this need. Back substituting $k_{u1}/k_2 = 500$ and $k_2/k_1 = 0.1$ yields $k_2 = 0.2$ and $k_1 = 2$. The scaling is now complete.

The Final Step — Putting the Problem on the Computer

We now need a little more information about our computer. Let us presume it has resistors of 0.1 and 1 unit, and capacitors of 0.1 and 1 unit available on its summing integrators.[†] This means that we can obtain coefficients of 1, 10 and 100 directly without the use of pots. Any other coefficient values will require potentiometers. The computing diagram (Fig. 4-10(b), for example) must be deformed further at this point to reflect the scaling we have just completed and the R and C values available. The actual analog circuit can be drawn from this latest computing diagram with very little difficulty. The computing diagram and circuit for the sample problem are shown in Fig. 4-11.

We compute the initial conditions for the state variables from the initial values of the original problem variables by dividing the scaling constants. Next, we set these conditions, along with the voltages for the input variables, on the computer's integrators according to the instructions supplied with the computer. After setting the pots to their proper values, we can run the solution by moving the computer mode switch to "operate" or "repetitive operation" ("rep-op"), depending on the computer. It may be necessary to make some adjustments of the scale factors at this point, primarily to account for any bad guesses for maximum values. If major changes are required, however, it is likely that a mistake was made somewhere in the scaling or setup process.

Interpreting the Results

Most analog computers use X-Y plotters or oscilloscopes as output devices. In the most usual mode, the time variable is plotted as the abscissa (x axis) and the values of the state variables as the ordinate (y axis). Converting from voltage to the units of the original problem is very easy for the voltages corresponding to the state variables: simply apply Eq. (4-21) with the scale factors computed above. The interpretation of the time variable depends on the computer being used. If the computer has its own automatic "time-base generator," it will generally be calibrated to agree with our definition of T. It is then only necessary to establish the correspondence between time units, as calibrated on the computer console, and distance on the x axis of the output plot. If there is no time-base generator, one can be made by wiring up an integrator using unit values for R and C and a one volt input. The output of that integrator, meas-

---

[†] Many analog computer manufacturers use arbitrary units for resistance and capacitance; see the instruction manual.

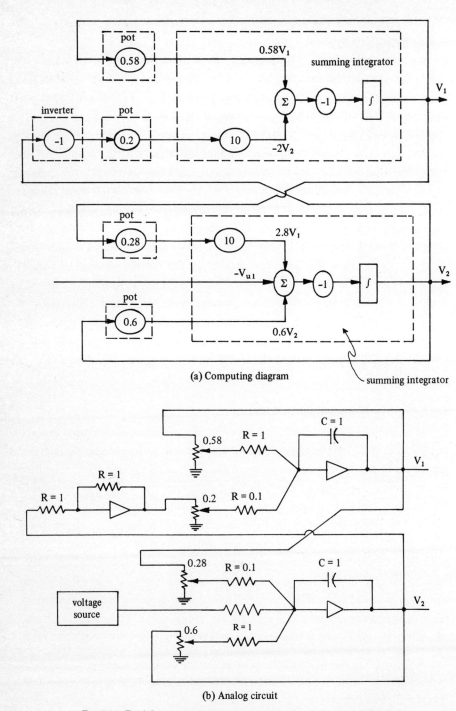

(a) Computing diagram

(b) Analog circuit

Fig. 4-11 Final Computing Diagram and Analog Circuit for Sample Problem

ured in volts, is T.[†] (In either case, to convert back to the original time variable t just multiply T by k_t.)

The computer output for Example 4-4 is shown in Fig. 4-12 with all variables shown both in volts and in the units of the original problem. The state-plane trajectory (Fig. 4-12(b)) is generated by plotting one state variable against the other. For second order systems whose state space is two dimensional, this operation provides a very good "feel" for the nature of the system's behavior.

Having shown from the analog computer solution that the system is stable and does have a steady state solution, we can use the original system equations to compute the steady-state value for $\underline{x}$ (i.e., $\underline{x}(\infty) = \lim_{t \to \infty} \underline{x}(t)$). For very large time with u = constant as it is in this case, $(d/dt)\,\underline{x}$ will approach zero, so we can write

$$\underline{A}\,\underline{x}(\infty) + \underline{B}\,\underline{u} = \underline{0}$$
or $$\underline{x}(\infty) = -\underline{A}^{-1}\,\underline{B}\,\underline{u}$$

For low order systems this is easily done by hand (above third order a computer is usually necessary) and we find that $x_1(\infty) = 0.195$ and $x_2(\infty) = 6.67$. These values are in agreement with the apparent final values of the curves in Fig. 4-12.

4.6 ANALOG SIMULATION OF NONLINEAR SYSTEMS

Multipliers, diodes, function generators, digital logic elements, etc. are all available for use in the analog computer simulation of *nonlinear* relations. Diodes are especially versatile for constructing piecewise linear relations, such as saturation or discontinuous control actions, or for approximation of nonlinear functions. However, nonlinear components are not as easy to use as the linear components discussed in the preceding sections since, in general, they are not as stable or as accurate as the linear elements and cause more scaling difficulties.

---

† If we know the R and C values in real engineering units rather than in arbitrary units as used on some analog computers, T can be related to time as we measure by the clock on the laboratory wall. If the resistors are calibrated in megohms and the capacitors are in microfarads, T is equivalent to normal clock time. When in doubt, the safest approach is to construct a time-base generator as described above.

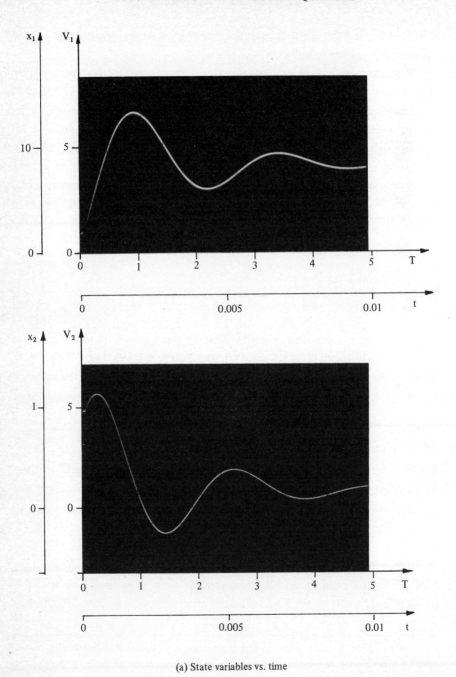

(a) State variables vs. time

Fig. 4-12 Output for Sample Problem (continued on next page)

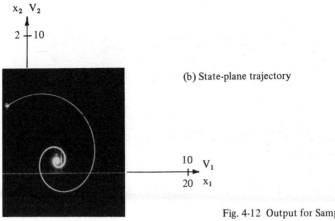

(b) State-plane trajectory

Fig. 4-12 Output for Sample Problem

Example 4-5:   The Leaking Tank Problem

Let us take the leaking tank problem (Sec. 1.4) as an example again. Eq. (1-4) restated in differential form with $V = Ah$

$$A\frac{dh}{dt} = Q_1 - Q_2 \tag{4-29}$$

relates inflow Q_1 and leaking flow Q_2 (both in units of volume/time) to level height h. A (area) is the free surface area in the tank, assumed to be constant. If the flow is turbulent, the constitutive relation for the leaking flow is given by

$$Q_2 = \eta\sqrt{h} \quad h > 0 \tag{4-30}$$

As discussed in Sec. 3.4, the system parameter η includes the orifice area, flow coefficient, density of the fluid and local gravitational acceleration. Substituting Eq. (4-30) into (4-29), we get Eq. (1-7) restated

$$A\frac{dh}{dt} = Q_1 - \eta\sqrt{h} \tag{4-31}$$

We will do the analog solution for the following parameter set:

$$\eta = 0.1 \quad A = 10 \quad Q_1 = 2.0 \text{ (constant)}$$

Let's begin by scaling this equation. Unfortunately there are no general rules for scaling nonlinear problems as there are for linear systems. We start in a similar manner, however, by defining scaling coefficients

$$h = k_1 V_1 \qquad Q_1 = k_{u1} V_{u1} \qquad t = k_t T$$

Substituting into Eq. (4-31) and dividing through by A, we get

$$\frac{1}{k_t} \frac{d(k_1 V_1)}{dT} = \frac{k_{u1}}{A} V_{u1} - \frac{\eta}{A} \sqrt{k_1 V_1}$$

Putting in numerical values for the parameters and generally cleaning up

$$\frac{dV_1}{dT} = \frac{k_{u1} k_t}{10 k_1} V_{u1} - 0.01 \frac{k_t}{\sqrt{k_1}} \sqrt{V_1} \qquad (4\text{-}32)$$

Eq. (4-32) is the scaled equation with V_1 the state variable and V_{u1} the input, both measured in volts. Since we know the value of Q_1, the input flow, a good place to start the scaling coefficient selection is with k_{u1}. We will use the same analog computer as in Example 4-4; thus we are restricted to ±10 volts and summing integrator coefficients of 1, 10 and 100. To give V_{u1} a value of 10 volts with $Q_1 = 2.0$, we need $k_{u1} = 0.2$. To proceed further, we have to look at a general principle of scaling that was implicit in scaling for linear systems; that is, we adjust the scaling coefficients so that for each term of a system equation (i.e., each input to a summing integrator or summer), if the variable voltage reaches a magnitude of 10 volts (or whatever the machine limit is), the whole term will have a value of about 10 volts. Since it is rare that all of the variables reach their maximum voltage at the same time and since there are positive and negative voltages usually present, the sum of the terms will probably stay within 10 volts if we follow this rule for scaling. In the event that an amplifier does attempt to go beyond its voltage limit, modest adjustments in the scaling coefficients will usually solve the problem.

Turning to Eq. (4-32) and looking at the term with $\sqrt{V_1}$ in it, we obtain the following relation between k_1 and k_t by letting $V_1 = 10$ volts and applying the above guideline:

$$0.01 \frac{k_t}{\sqrt{k_1}} \sqrt{10} = 10$$

or

$$\frac{k_t}{\sqrt{k_1}} = 350$$

We get another relation between k_t and k_1 by substituting the value of k_{u1} already selected into the first term on the righthand side of Eq. (4-32). Again applying the guideline, $(0.2/10) \cdot (k_t/k_1) = 1$ (since this is a linear term, we want the coefficient to have a value of about 1), or $k_t/k_1 = 50$. Solving these two relations together, we obtain (round numbers have been chosen) $k_t = 2500$ and $k_1 = 50$. The scaled equation thus becomes

$$\frac{dV_1}{dT} = V_{u1} - 3.54\sqrt{V_1} \tag{4-33}$$

Next problem — how to generate the square root function on an analog computer. There are two common methods: one is to use a multiplier as a squarer and put it in a feedback loop (see Ref. [2] or a manufacturer's guide to analog computing for the circuit details); the other is to use a diode function generator to obtain an approximation to the square root with a series of straight lines. In order to preserve the full accuracy of the computer, we always want to operate over the widest voltage range possible; for a square rooter on a 10 volt computer, merely taking the square root would mean that for the maximum voltage in, the maximum voltage out would be $\sqrt{10} = 3.16$ volts, which is too low to achieve good accuracy. For this reason a factor of $\sqrt{10}$ is included so that a 10 volt signal will result in a 10 volt output, as shown in Fig. 4-13(a). When drawing the computing diagram for our system, we must be careful to include that extra coefficient in our calculations. Fig. 4-13(b) shows the square root function, a straight line approximation as generated by a diode function generator, and a possible linear approximation, the secant approximation. Fig. 4-13(c) shows the computer implementation of the square root function generated by using a squarer in a feedback loop and using a diode function generator.[†] The computing diagram and circuit diagram are shown in Fig. 4-14 (note the inclusion of the $\sqrt{10}$ factor in the computing diagrams) and the time response shown in Fig. 4-15 (using the diode function generator). For purposes of comparison, a linear response using a *secant approximation* chosen so that the final states will be the same is shown plotted on the same scale. Note the significant difference in dynamic behavior.

[†] All analog outputs are photographs of oscilloscope traces.

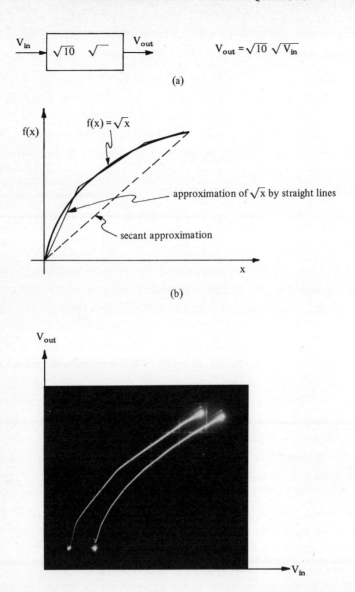

$$V_{out} = \sqrt{10}\ \sqrt{V_{in}}$$

(a)

(b)

Square-root by multiplier-in-feedback (right curve) and diode function generator using three segments (left curve). Curves have been separated for clarity.

(c)

Fig. 4-13 Analog Square-root Generation

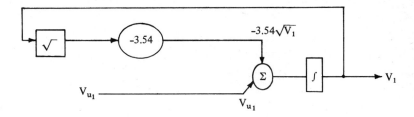

(a) Basic computing diagram

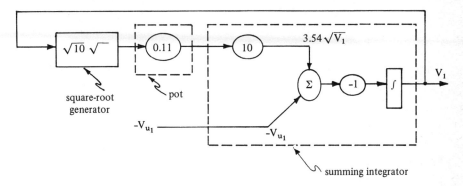

(b) Deformed computing diagram

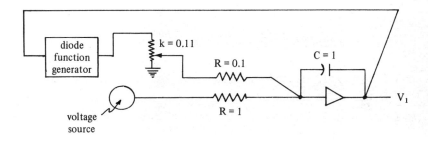

(c) Circuit diagram

Fig. 4-14 Computing and Circuit Diagrams for Leaking Tank Problem

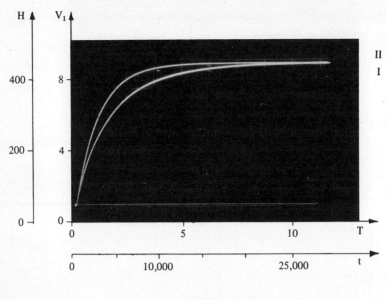

I – Nonlinear, diode function generator (lower curve)
II – Linear, secant (upper curve)

Fig. 4-15 System Response—Leaking Tank

SUMMARY

The key to really learning the material in this chapter is to try it out! Skill in applying digital and analog computers comes with experience, like playing a musical instrument, and study must be liberally supplemented with practice.

Effective digital simulation depends on proper application of the integration algorithm. A good intuitive understanding of the role of step size is crucial. For simple systems, the methods of the next chapter provide exact analytical solutions which may be quantitatively compared to the numerical analyses discussed here. By varying the step size, you can observe how close your numerical solution is getting to the exact analytical solution. However, for complex systems we must usually rely on digital or analog simulation, since analytical techniques are largely unavailable for such problems.

No two models of analog computers operate quite the same way. Thus, the first step in becoming proficient in analog simulation is to become intimately familiar with the buttons and knobs on your computer. Then experiment with each of the basic computing elements in Fig. 4-9, making sure that all of the input-output relations work exactly as stated. Finally, start simulating, beginning with first order linear systems and moving to higher order systems and nonlinear sysems.

REFERENCES

1. B. Carnahan, H. Luther and J. Wilkes, *Applied Numerical Methods*, John Wiley, New York, 1969

2. R. J. Kochenburger, *Computer Simulation of Dynamic Systems*, Prentice-Hall, Inc., Englewood Cliffs, N. J., 1972

PROBLEMS

4-1 Using the Euler variant method, develop a digital simulation for the leaking tank problem of Sec. 1.4 and Example 4-5.

4-2 Consider a leaking, spherical tank of radius r shown in Fig. P-4-2, where the outflow rate is expressed by

$$Q = f \sqrt{h} \quad \text{(volume/time)}$$

Initially the tank is completely full and it is desired to compute the leaking process. The inlet and outlet pipes are both of diameter $D = r/10$, so that when the tank is either nearly full or nearly empty, the free surface area is not zero. The upper limit on h is accordingly equal to $2r - f(D/r)$. Utilizing trigonometric relations, develop a program which computes the response in level h. What difficulty is encountered as D/r gets very small?

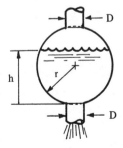

Fig. P-4-2

4-3 Consider a simple model for commuting traffic accumulation in which we use a single state variable N to account for all of the cars on the highway at any instant of time. Assume that the number of cars leaving for work and entering the highway system

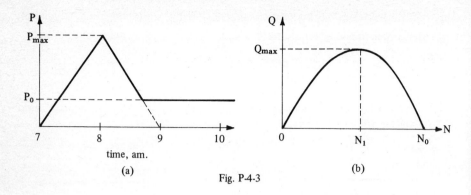

Fig. P-4-3

can be approximated by the curve in Fig. P-4-3(a), where P is measured in cars/hr. Because of the possibility of traffic jams, highways have the kind of through-flow capacity characteristics shown in Fig. P-4-3(b), where Q represents the number of cars per hour leaving the highway because they have arrived at their destination. The drop-off in carrying capacity past N_1 is caused by traffic jam slowdowns. (Note that we have not explicitly taken account of travel time in this approach.)

Assume that the Q versus N curve can be described by a parabola and that P_{max} = 18,000 cars/hr, P_0 = 5,000 cars/hr, Q_{max} = 12,000 cars/hr, N_1 = 4,500 cars and N_0 = 9,000 cars. Compute the number of cars on the highway as a function of time, N(t), from 7 A.M. to 10 A.M.

4-4 Assume that a city is served by two highway systems of the sort described in Prob. 4-3. Compute the number of cars in the city as a function of time, $N_{CITY}(t)$, if one highway has the same characteristics and input as the above highway, and, for the other, P_{max} = 21,000 cars/hr, P_0 = 4,000 cars/hr and the input curve has the shape shown in Fig. P-4-4. All other characteristics are the same. Assume no cars are leaving the city during this time interval.

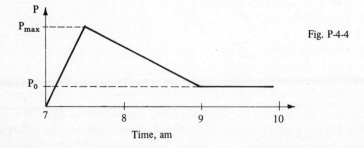

Fig. P-4-4

4-5 Derive the input-output relation for the integrating analog computing element of Fig. 4-9(d).

4-6 Derive the input-output relations for the summing analog computing elements of Figs. 4-9(c) and (e).

4-7 Is it possible to add two signals (i.e., voltages) V_{11} and V_{12} by the connection shown in Fig. P-4-7? If not, what will the voltage V_2 be?

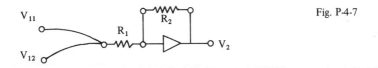

Fig. P-4-7

4-8 Generate an analog computer program for the following input-output relations:

$$\frac{dx}{dt} = \frac{u}{T_i} \qquad y = k_c(x + u)$$

where u is input, y is output, x is an internal variable (state variable), and k_c and T_i are adjustable parameters. (This is a PI controller action; see Chap. 7.)

4-9 It is desired to simulate a linear process whose unit step input response (with zero initial state) has a negative dip as shown in Fig. P-4-9. The process is called a *reverse reaction process* and is further discussed in Chapter 6. Assuming an equation

$$y(t) = 1 - 2e^{-t} + e^{-4t}$$

for the response, construct an analog computer network for the process.

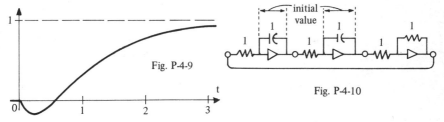

Fig. P-4-9

Fig. P-4-10

4-10 What do you expect to get from the wiring shown in Fig. P-4-10? What do you really get if you let the computer run a while?

4-11 Show that Fig. P-4-11 acts like a derivative network. Test it to see whether it will really work to check out what was said about causality in preceding chapters (a step input could be a severe test). Is it possible (and advisable) to build an approximate derivative stage using an integrating stage?

4-12 Test the system shown in Fig. P-4-12 and plot the (static) input-output relation.

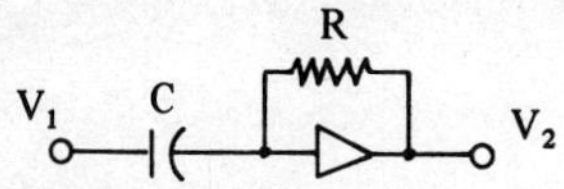

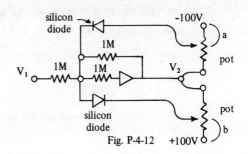

Fig. P-4-11

Fig. P-4-12

CHAPTER 5

ANALYTICAL SOLUTION OF THE LINEAR STATE EQUATION

The application and development of computational methods, as presented in the previous chapter, is most effective when based on a firm understanding of the underlying theory. Indeed, theoretical analysis should precede new computational schemes to justify them or, at least, to give us confidence and insight into the meaning of the numerical results. Further, theoretical analysis often leads both to new design approaches and to the development of yet additional theoretical extensions. In this chapter, we will discuss the analytical solution of the stationary, linear state equation which was introduced in Chapter 3 and numerically solved in Chapter 4. We start with the simplest case of a first order, unforced system and then continue on with the matrix solution to n-th order systems, forced responses with emphasis upon linearity, impulse and step responses, graphical interpretation of the analytical solution and, finally, discussion of the modes of a system's response. The following two chapters in particular, and the remainder of the book in general, will build upon the analytical foundation of this chapter.

5.1 FREE SYSTEMS

While the computer method of solution discussed in the previous chapter can be used to obtain the response of fairly complex mathematical models rather quickly, the results are not general; they apply only to a particular set of initial conditions and system parameters. Far more general properties of a mathematical model can be deduced by an analytical approach. Unfortunately, most of the known analytical techniques are applicable only to linear systems, but even with this restriction, we shall be able to build a substantial body of theory which will help us deal with real world problems.

Although a general solution is possible only for linear systems, there are also some analytical methods which can be used to deal with nonlinear models. These, however, are applicable to only certain properties of specific types of nonlinearities. Therefore, the analytical approach and numerical methods (i.e., computer approach) generally complement each other; for instance, a solid background in linear systems theory greatly helps to plan meaningful computer use and to draw pertinent information from numerical analyses. For this reason we shall next present some of the basic material on the analytical treatment of linear, time invariant (i.e., stationary) finite order (i.e., lumped parameter) systems. It should be kept in mind, however, that such systems are abstract, in the sense that any real system is never truly linear or finite order! To properly interpret analytical results and apply them to real systems requires intuition, experience and a good feeling for one's subject and the object of the analysis or design.

We begin the analytical approach with the simplest case: free motion of a first order system described by

$$\frac{dx(t)}{dt} = ax(t) \quad x(0) = x_0 \text{ at } t = 0 \tag{5-1}$$

where a is a real constant: positive, zero or negative. The equation can be solved by noting that

$$\int \frac{dx}{x} = \int a \, dt$$

and the solution is

$$x(t) = e^{at}x_0 = e^{-t/T}x_0 \tag{5-2}$$

where $T = -1/a$. This result is the same as Eq. (3-38). Note that if $x_0 = x_{01} + x_{02}$, the solution is

$$x(t) = e^{at}(x_{01} + x_{02}) = e^{at}x_{01} + e^{at}x_{02}$$

This *superposition* (i.e., linear summation) of solutions due to independent initial conditions is equivalent to the static superposition condition discussed in connection with Fig. 3-10 and is the condition which a free dynamic system must satisfy to be linear. This condition can only be satisfied if the coefficient "a" is not a function of x. Further, we will limit our development to those cases for which "a" is not a function of time either and is just a scalar constant.

Eq. (5-2) represents an exponential growth if a is positive, as in Fig. 1-2; an exponential decay if a is negative. If a is zero

$$x(t) = x_0 = \text{constant for all } t$$

which means complete memory of a past value x_0; this is the case of the integrating circuit of an analog computer (Fig. 4-9(d)) with no input, thus holding its initial value.

From Eq. (5-2) it follows that

$$\log_e \left[\frac{x(t_1)}{x(t_2)}\right] = -\frac{1}{T}(t_1 - t_2)$$

where $\log_e x = 2.3026 \log_{10} x$ so that

$$\Delta t = t_2 - t_1 = 2.3026T$$

for a one decade drop of x (that is, $x(t_2)/x(t_1) = 1/10$) when x(t) is plotted on semi-log paper, as in Fig. 5-1(b). In Fig. 5-1(a) the response of Eq. (5-2) is plotted for a $<$ 0 and two alternative interpretations of the time constant T are offered: it is the time (from direct substitution of t = T in Eq. (5-2)) at which

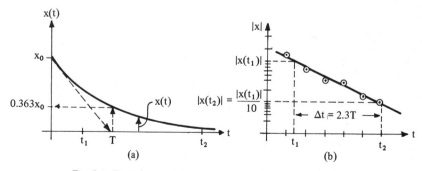

Fig. 5-1 Time Constant Estimation from an Exponential Decay

$(1/e) = 0.363$ of the free and transient response remains or, alternatively, it is the time at which the transient response would have been completed if it had continued on at its original rate.

The accuracy or validity of the linear model of Eq. (5-1) can be checked by inspecting the deviation of experimental data on $x(t)$ from the theoretical straight line plot of Fig. 5-1(b). Thus, in Fig. 3-12 for example, we would take $x(t) = (h_1 - h)$ and plot the absolute value of this exponential remainder to determine if Eq. (5-1) models the tank problem reasonably well.

Decoupled (Diagonal) Systems

To extend the first order solution to higher order systems, consider first a special case where the system is decoupled as in

$$\frac{dx_1^*(t)}{dt} = \lambda_1 x_1^*(t)$$

$$\frac{dx_2^*(t)}{dt} = \lambda_2 x_2^*(t)$$

$$\vdots$$

$$\frac{dx_n^*(t)}{dt} = \lambda_n x_n^*(t)$$

(5-3)

and where we are still considering a free system ($u(t) = 0$). We note in Eq. (5-3) that even though this model represents an n-th order system by a state vector with n elements, the resulting n first order differential equations for this choice of the state vector are independent (decoupled) and may be solved separately! Each such solution will be of the form of Eq. (5-2), each with its own separate time constant T_i equal to $-(1/\lambda_i)$.

Let us recast Eq. (5-3) into matrix format as

$$\frac{d}{dt} \underline{x}^*(t) = \underline{\Lambda}\, \underline{x}^*(t)$$

(5-4)

where

$$\underline{x}^*(t) = \begin{bmatrix} x_1^*(t) \\ x_2^*(t) \\ \vdots \\ x_n^*(t) \end{bmatrix} \qquad \underline{\Lambda} = \begin{bmatrix} \lambda_1 & & & 0 \\ & \lambda_2 & & \\ & & \ddots & \\ 0 & & & \lambda_n \end{bmatrix}$$

(5-5)

$\underline{\Lambda}$ is a diagonal matrix with elements λ_1 of Eq. (5-3). Note carefully the equivalence of decoupled differential equations in Eq. (5-3) and a diagonalized system matrix $\underline{\Lambda}$ in Eq. (5-5). The scalar differentiation operation on a vector implies differentiation on each scalar element of the vector.

We next define the matrix exponential as

$$e^{\underline{\Lambda}t} = \sum_{m=0}^{\infty} \frac{(\underline{\Lambda}t)^m}{m!} = \underline{I} + \underline{\Lambda}t + \frac{1}{2!}\underline{\Lambda}^2 t^2 + \frac{1}{3!}\underline{\Lambda}^3 t^3 + \cdots \tag{5-6}$$

where each scalar element of this nxn square matrix exponential will be an infinite series. We note that this matrix series can be shown to be a solution to Eq. (5-4) by direct substitution. For our starting special case of a diagonal matrix, it is easily checked by a few multiplications that

$$\underline{\Lambda}^m = \begin{bmatrix} \lambda_1^m & & & 0 \\ & \lambda_2^m & & \\ & & \ddots & \\ 0 & & & \lambda_n^m \end{bmatrix} \tag{5-7}$$

Recalling the Taylor series expansion of a scalar exponential and using Eq. (5-7) in Eq. (5-6), we get

$$e^{\underline{\Lambda}t} = \begin{bmatrix} e^{\lambda_1 t} & & & 0 \\ & e^{\lambda_2 t} & & \\ & & \ddots & \\ 0 & & & e^{\lambda_n t} \end{bmatrix} \tag{5-8}$$

But we know by inspection of Eqs. (5-3) and (5-2) that each scalar element of the state vector will have a solution of the form

$$x_i^*(t) = e^{\lambda_i t} x_i^*(0) \tag{5-9}$$

where $x_i^*(0)$ is the initial value of that element of the state vector. Thus, by defining an initial state vector as

$$\underline{x}^*(0) = \begin{bmatrix} x_1^*(0) \\ x_2^*(0) \\ \cdot \\ \cdot \\ \cdot \\ x_n^*(0) \end{bmatrix}$$

(5-10)

we can immediately write the solution to Eq. (5-4) as

$$\underline{x}^*(t) = e^{\Delta t}\underline{x}^*(0)$$

(5-11)

Eq. (5-11) is dimensionally consistent, with n dimensional vectors appearing on both sides of the equation, as long as the order of postmultiplying the matrix exponential by the initial state column vector is observed. Since the matrix exponential $e^{\Delta t}$ governs the transition of the system from its initial state to its state at time t, $e^{\Delta t}$ is often called the modal *transition matrix*.

Nondiagonal Systems

The results so far are valid only for the case when the system matrix is diagonal. To extend the solution to the nondiagonal case (but still for a free system), let us next rewrite the system equations in general coupled form as

$$\frac{d}{dt}\underline{x}(t) = \underline{A}\,\underline{x}(t)$$

(5-12)

where the system matrix $\underline{A}$ takes on the general form

$$\underline{A} = \begin{bmatrix} a_{11} & a_{12} & \cdots & a_{1n} \\ a_{21} & a_{22} & \cdots & a_{2n} \\ \cdot & & & \cdot \\ \cdot & & & \cdot \\ a_{n1} & a_{n2} & \cdots & a_{nn} \end{bmatrix}$$

(5-13)

For a free system to be linear and stationary, all of the elements of $\underline{A}$ must be constants. Because the elements of $\underline{A}$ are not functions of any of the x's, a free linear system can be scaled, i.e., if the entire state vector $\underline{x}$ is multiplied by a scalar factor k, the k cancels out in Eq. (5-12), leaving the solution unchanged in its fundamental properties. Eqs. (5-12) and (5-13) are equivalent to

$$\frac{d}{dt}\begin{bmatrix} x_1(t) \\ x_2(t) \\ \vdots \\ x_n(t) \end{bmatrix} = \begin{bmatrix} a_{11} & a_{12} & \cdots & a_{1n} \\ a_{21} & a_{22} & \cdots & a_{2n} \\ \vdots & & & \vdots \\ a_{n1} & a_{n2} & \cdots & a_{nn} \end{bmatrix} \begin{bmatrix} x_1(t) \\ x_2(t) \\ \vdots \\ x_n(t) \end{bmatrix}$$

$$= \begin{bmatrix} a_{11}x_1(t) + a_{12}x_2(t) + \cdots + a_{1n}x_n(t) \\ a_{21}x_1(t) + a_{22}x_2(t) + \cdots + a_{2n}x_n(t) \\ \vdots \\ a_{n1}x_1(t) + a_{n2}x_2(t) + \cdots + a_{nn}x_n(t) \end{bmatrix}$$

or

$$\frac{dx_i(t)}{dt} = \sum_{j=1}^{n} a_{ij}x_j(t) \quad i = 1, 2, \ldots, n$$

The resulting n first order differential equations are now coupled (i.e., each state variable appears in each scalar equation) and they can not be solved independently. However, if we can show that Eqs. (5-3) and (5-12) are equivalent ways of describing the same system with two different but algebraically related sets of state variables, then the previous solution will be seen as a solution to this general case as well. In order to show this equivalence, we utilize the concept of a linear transformation from one valid state vector $\underline{x}^*(t)$ to another $\underline{x}(t)$ by the linear algebraic transformation of Eq. (2-19), restated here as

$$\underline{x} = \underline{T}\,\underline{x}^* \tag{5-14}$$

where the square nxn matrix $\underline{T}$ is an array of constants and is assumed to be nonsingular (i.e., det $\underline{T} \neq 0$). The scalar expansion of Eq. (5-14) and the format of the matrix $\underline{T}$ are given in Eqs. (2-20) and (2-21), respectively.

Substituting Eq. (5-14) into Eq. (5-12) and premultiplying both sides of the resulting equation by the inverse of $\underline{T}$ (= $\underline{T}^{-1}$, where $\underline{T}\,\underline{T}^{-1} = \underline{T}^{-1}\,\underline{T} = \underline{I}$; the inverse exists since det $\underline{T}$ is assumed nonzero), we get

$$\frac{d}{dt}\underline{x}^*(t) = \underline{T}^{-1}\,\underline{A}\,\underline{T}\,\underline{x}^* = \underline{\Lambda}\,\underline{x}^* \tag{5-15a}$$

Eq. (5-15a) indicates that

$$\underline{T}^{-1} \underline{A} \underline{T} = \underline{\Lambda} \tag{5-15b}$$

from which a nondiagonal system matrix $\underline{A}$ is expressed in terms of the diagonal system matrix $\underline{\Lambda}$ by

$$\underline{A} = \underline{T} \underline{\Lambda} \underline{T}^{-1}$$

Let us momentarily assume that a matrix $\underline{T}$ exists that performs this transformation and can be computed (we will discuss this shortly). If such be the case, then for any arbitrary choice of the system coordinates (i.e., state vector $\underline{x}$) we are able to convert the system back to a starred set of state variables in decoupled form, similar to Eq. (5-3), by application of the linear transformation $\underline{x}^* = \underline{T}^{-1} \underline{x}$. The intent here is not to show a computational scheme, but to indicate a path from the known solution for the diagonal system (Eq. (5-4)) and the as yet unknown solution for a system described by an $\underline{A}$ matrix which is not diagonal (Eq. (5-12)). Once this path is established, the nature and existence of the general system solution will be known. We continue on this path.

Since the solution of Eq. (5-4) was given by Eq. (5-11), the remaining problem would be the evaluation of the λ_i's that appear in Eq. (5-8). The λ_i's are called the system *eigenvalues*. We will discuss the eigenvalue problem below. From Eqs. (5-11) and (5-8), we see that the solution in the modal coordinates is

$$
\begin{bmatrix}
x_1^*(t) \\
x_2^*(t) \\
\cdot \\
\cdot \\
\cdot \\
x_n^*(t)
\end{bmatrix}
=
\begin{bmatrix}
e^{\lambda_1 t} x_1^*(0) \\
e^{\lambda_2 t} x_2^*(0) \\
\cdot \\
\cdot \\
\cdot \\
e^{\lambda_n t} x_n^*(0)
\end{bmatrix}
\tag{5-16}
$$

We note that each modal coordinate response $x_i^*(t)$ consists of only one exponential term $e^{\lambda_i t}$ multiplied by an initial value $x_i^*(0)$ (i.e., $e^{\lambda_j t}$ terms do not enter the response of $x_i^*(t)$ terms, where $i \neq j$). We describe this special case of the modal coordinate as being made up of pure *eigenmodes*, the $e^{\lambda_i t}$ terms. In order to find the system response solution in the original coordinates, we note from Eqs. (5-14) and (2-21) that for the usual case of systems with distinct eigenvalues[†] (i.e., $\lambda_i \neq \lambda_j$ for all $i \neq j$)

---

† A modification of this material results in cases of repeated eigenvalues; see Ref. [1].

$$
\begin{bmatrix} x_1(t) \\ \cdot \\ \cdot \\ \cdot \\ x_n(t) \end{bmatrix} = \begin{bmatrix} t_{11}e^{\lambda_1 t}x_1^*(0) + \cdots + t_{1n}e^{\lambda_n t}x_n^*(0) \\ \cdot \\ \cdot \\ \cdot \\ t_{n1}e^{\lambda_1 t}x_1^*(0) + \cdots + t_{nn}e^{\lambda_n t}x_n^*(0) \end{bmatrix} \tag{5-17a}
$$

$$
= \begin{bmatrix} t_{11}x_1^*(0) \\ \cdot \\ \cdot \\ \cdot \\ t_{n1}x_1^*(0) \end{bmatrix} e^{\lambda_1 t} + \cdots + \begin{bmatrix} t_{1n}x_n^*(0) \\ \cdot \\ \cdot \\ \cdot \\ t_{nn}x_n^*(0) \end{bmatrix} e^{\lambda_n t} \tag{5-17b}
$$

The response of Eq. (5-17) indicates the presence in each response term $x_i(t)$ of each eigenmode $e^{\lambda_j t}$ for which $t_{ij} \neq 0$. The initial values $x_i^*(0)$ in Eq. (5-17) are found in terms of the initial values $x_i(0)$ by noting from Eq. (5-14) that

$$
\underline{x}^*(0) = \underline{T}^{-1} \underline{x}(0) \tag{5-18}
$$

Eigenvalues and the Characteristic Equation

We will now consider the two problems left unsolved above: the determination of the system eigenvalues and the necessary transformation matrix $\underline{T}$. Considering the eigenvalue problem first, note in Eq. (5-17b) that the solution appears as a sum of exponential terms. Because this is a linear system, each of the exponential terms must be a solution and thus satisfy Eq. (5-12). Writing p for λ_i, we can derive the condition for determination of the λ_i's by substituting into Eq. (5-12)

$$
\frac{d}{dt} \underline{x}(t) = p\,\underline{x}(t) = p\,\underline{I}\,\underline{x}(t) = \underline{A}\,\underline{x}(t)
$$

or

$$
\left[p\,\underline{I} - \underline{A} \right] \underline{x}(t) = \underline{0} \tag{5-19}
$$

For a nontrivial solution ($\underline{x} \neq \underline{0}$) to exist

$$
\left| (p\,\underline{I} - \underline{A}) \right| = p^n + a_1 p^{n-1} + \ldots + a_{n-1}p + a_n = 0 \tag{5-20}
$$

This n-th order polynomial in p will yield n roots, called the *eigenvalues* of the system. These will be the λ_i described earlier. Equation (5-20) is called the *characteristic equation* of the system and will start appearing in this text with increasing frequency. One fundamental point about the system eigenvalues is that they are invariant — they will be the same no matter which choice of system coordinates we make. Thus, if we repeat the analysis of Eqs. (5-19) and (5-20), but start with Eq. (5-4) this time, we obtain

$$\left| p\,\underline{I} - \underline{\Lambda} \right| = 0 \tag{5-21}$$

But substituting Eq. (5-15b) into the last equation, we get

$$\left| (p\,\underline{I} - \underline{T}^{-1}\,\underline{A}\,\underline{T}) \right| = \left| (p\,\underline{T}^{-1}\,\underline{I}\,\underline{T} - \underline{T}^{-1}\,\underline{A}\,\underline{T}) \right|$$
$$= \left| \underline{T}^{-1} \right|\, \left| (p\,\underline{I} - \underline{A}) \right|\, \left| \underline{T} \right| = 0 = \left| (p\,\underline{I} - \underline{A}) \right|$$

The last line indicates that the eigenvalues of the two different descriptions of the same system are indeed the same.

Now let us address ourselves to the existence and nature of the transformation matrix $\underline{T}$. We start by premultiplying both sides of Eq. (5-15b) by the matrix $\underline{T}$ to get

$$\underline{A}\,\underline{T} = \underline{T}\,\Lambda \tag{5-22}$$

Let the matrix $\underline{T}$ be made up of n column vectors $\underline{v}_i$ (each n dimensional) and rewrite the previous equation using this format and the definition of $\underline{\Lambda}$ given by Eq. (5-5) to get

$$\underline{A}\,[\underline{v}_1\ \underline{v}_2\ \cdots\ \underline{v}_n] = [\underline{v}_1\ \underline{v}_2\ \cdots\ \underline{v}_n]\begin{bmatrix} \lambda_1 & & & 0 \\ & \lambda_2 & & \\ & & \ddots & \\ 0 & & & \lambda_n \end{bmatrix} \tag{5-23}$$

By equating the two sides of Eq. (5-23), a column at a time, we get

$$\underline{A}\,\underline{v}_i = \lambda_i\,\underline{v}_i = \lambda_i\,\underline{I}\,\underline{v}_i$$

or

$$[\underline{A} - \lambda_i\,\underline{I}]\,\underline{v}_i = \underline{0} \qquad i = 1, 2, \ldots, n \tag{5-24}$$

The vectors $\underline{v}_i$ in this equation are called the *eigenvectors*. Each eigenvector equation, corresponding to a particular eigenvalue λ_i, will consist of n simultaneous, homogeneous, algebraic equations which can be solved up to a proportionality constant. The directions of the eigenvectors are thus found (but not their magnitudes). Using these direction vectors as the columns, a transformation matrix $\underline{T}$ is obtained. The details will become clearer in the examples below.

Examples

Let us solve two numerical examples. First, recall the problem of two competing powers investing in two underdeveloped countries as described by Fig. 3-3 and Eq. (3-2). We will assume that the system is in equilibrium when it is disturbed by some exogenous changes in the levels c_1 and c_2. These changes will be taken as the initial conditions $c_1(0)$ and $c_2(0)$ of the state variables and we wish to ascertain the dynamic response of the system in the absence of any forcing input ($u_a(t)$ and $u_b(t) = 0$). To solve this problem numerically, let us suppose that the $\underline{A}$ matrix for the system is given by

$$\underline{A} = \begin{bmatrix} -1 & 0 \\ 1 & -2 \end{bmatrix}$$

for which, by Eq. (5-20)

$$\left|(p\underline{I} - \underline{A})\right| = \begin{vmatrix} p+1 & 0 \\ -1 & p+2 \end{vmatrix} = (p+1)(p+2) = 0$$

so that the eigenvalues (roots) are

$$\lambda_1 = -1 \qquad \lambda_2 = -2$$

Using this information in Eq. (5-24), we get for the first eigenvector

$$\begin{bmatrix} 0 & 0 \\ 1 & -1 \end{bmatrix} \begin{bmatrix} v_1^1 \\ v_1^2 \end{bmatrix} = \begin{bmatrix} 0 \\ 0 \end{bmatrix}$$

where v_i^j is the j-th row element in the i-th eigenvector. This last expression yields the algebraic relation

$$v_1^1 - v_1^2 = 0$$

which is valid as long as the two terms are equal. We shall arbitrarily assume their magnitude to be unity (we are only interested in the eigenvector directions), so that the first eigenvector becomes

$$\underline{v}_1 = \begin{bmatrix} 1 \\ 1 \end{bmatrix}$$

Using the second eigenvalue, $\lambda_2 = -2$, we get for the second eigenvector

$$\begin{bmatrix} 1 & 0 \\ 1 & 0 \end{bmatrix} \begin{bmatrix} v_2^1 \\ v_2^2 \end{bmatrix} = \begin{bmatrix} 0 \\ 0 \end{bmatrix}$$

from which v_2^1 must be zero and v_2^2 can be anything (again, we'll arbitrarily choose unity). Thus, the second eigenvector is

$$\underline{v}_2 = \begin{bmatrix} 0 \\ 1 \end{bmatrix}$$

and the transformation matrix $\underline{T}$ is

$$\underline{T} = [\underline{v}_1 \ \underline{v}_2] = \begin{bmatrix} 1 & 0 \\ 1 & 1 \end{bmatrix}$$

for which

$$\underline{T}^{-1} = \begin{bmatrix} 1 & 0 \\ -1 & 1 \end{bmatrix}$$

As a check, we compute that $(\underline{T}^{-1} \underline{A} \underline{T}) = \begin{bmatrix} -1 & 0 \\ 0 & -2 \end{bmatrix} = \underline{\Lambda}$ as it should.

We can immediately write the solution in modal coordinates $\underline{x}^*(t)$ from Eq. (5-16) as

$$\begin{bmatrix} x_1^*(t) \\ x_2^*(t) \end{bmatrix} = \begin{bmatrix} x_1^*(0)e^{-t} \\ x_2^*(0)e^{-2t} \end{bmatrix}$$

but we must still relate the original system coordinates $c_1(t)$ and $c_2(t)$ to these modal coordinates. To do this, we first apply Eq. (5-18) to find the initial values of the modal coordinates $\underline{x}^*(0)$ in terms of the initial values of the original coordinates $\underline{c}(0)$

$$\begin{bmatrix} x_1^*(0) \\ x_2^*(0) \end{bmatrix} = \underline{T}^{-1}\underline{c}(0) = \begin{bmatrix} 1 & 0 \\ -1 & 1 \end{bmatrix}\begin{bmatrix} c_1(0) \\ c_2(0) \end{bmatrix} = \begin{bmatrix} c_1(0) \\ -c_1(0) + c_2(0) \end{bmatrix}$$

Substituting the last equation into the preceding one and using Eq. (5-14) with $\underline{c}(t)$ defined as the system state $\underline{x}(t)$, we get for the solution

$$\begin{bmatrix} c_1(t) \\ c_2(t) \end{bmatrix} = \underline{T}\,\underline{x}^* = \begin{bmatrix} 1 & 0 \\ 1 & 1 \end{bmatrix}\begin{bmatrix} c_1(0)e^{-t} \\ [-c_1(0) + c_2(0)]\,e^{-2t} \end{bmatrix}$$

$$= \begin{bmatrix} c_1(0)e^{-t} \\ c_1(0)\,[e^{-t} - e^{-2t}] + c_2(0)e^{-2t} \end{bmatrix}$$

For our second example, we consider an undamped oscillator — the predator-prey problem of Chapter 3. From Eq. (3-26)

$$\frac{dn_1}{dt} = an_2 \qquad \frac{dn_2}{dt} = -bn_1$$

The relation can be *normalized* by changing the variables into a new set

$$x_1 = \frac{n_1}{\sqrt{a}} \qquad x_2 = \frac{n_2}{\sqrt{b}} \qquad \tau = \sqrt{ab}\;t$$

Since normalization contributes to generality, it is recommended for both analytical and numerical approaches. Now the normalized state equations for a free, undamped oscillator in time τ become

$$\frac{dx_1}{d\tau} = x_2 \qquad \frac{dx_2}{d\tau} = -x_1 \qquad \underline{x}(0) = \underline{x}_0$$

so that

$$\underline{A} = \begin{bmatrix} 0 & 1 \\ -1 & 0 \end{bmatrix}$$

for which the eigenvalues are

$$\lambda_{1,2} = \pm j$$

We next apply Eq. (5-24) to find the eigenvectors

$$[\underline{A} - \lambda_1 \underline{I}] \, \underline{v}_1 = \begin{bmatrix} -j & 1 \\ -1 & -j \end{bmatrix} \begin{bmatrix} v_1^1 \\ v_1^2 \end{bmatrix} = \begin{bmatrix} 0 \\ 0 \end{bmatrix}$$

from which the first complex eigenvector is found to be

$$\underline{v}_1 = \begin{bmatrix} 1 \\ j \end{bmatrix}$$

Similarly the second complex eigenvector is computed as

$$\underline{v}_2 = \begin{bmatrix} 1 \\ -j \end{bmatrix}$$

and the transformation matrix $\underline{T}$ and its inverse are

$$\underline{T} = \begin{bmatrix} 1 & 1 \\ j & -j \end{bmatrix} \qquad \underline{T}^{-1} = \frac{-1}{2j} \begin{bmatrix} -j & -1 \\ -j & 1 \end{bmatrix}$$

As a check on the work to this point, we compute $[\underline{T}^{-1} \, \underline{A} \, \underline{T}]$ to be $\begin{bmatrix} j & 0 \\ 0 & -j \end{bmatrix}$ as it should.

We now find the solution to the system equation in the modal coordinates by direct application of Eq. (5-16)

$$\underline{x}^* = \begin{bmatrix} x_1^*(0)e^{jt} \\ x_2^*(0)e^{-jt} \end{bmatrix}$$

To find the modal initial values in terms of the original initial values, we apply Eq. (5-18) as before

$$\underline{x}^*(0) = \underline{T}^{-1} \, \underline{x}(0) = \frac{-1}{2j} \begin{bmatrix} -j & -1 \\ -j & 1 \end{bmatrix} \begin{bmatrix} x_1(0) \\ x_2(0) \end{bmatrix}$$

from which

$$x_1^*(0) = [\frac{x_1(0)}{2} + \frac{x_2(0)}{2j}] \qquad x_2^*(0) = [\frac{x_1(0)}{2} - \frac{x_2(0)}{2j}]$$

Substituting these latter results into the solution for $\underline{x}^*$ above and applying the transformation equation (5-14), we get (after some algebraic rearrangements)

$$x_1(t) = x_1(0) [\frac{e^{jt} + e^{-jt}}{2}] + x_2(0) [\frac{e^{jt} - e^{-jt}}{2j}]$$

and

$$x_2(t) = x_1(0) [\frac{-e^{jt} + e^{-jt}}{2j}] + x_2(0) [\frac{e^{jt} + e^{-jt}}{2}]$$

By applying the Euler equations

$$\cos \theta = [\frac{e^{j\theta} + e^{-j\theta}}{2}] \qquad \sin \theta = [\frac{e^{j\theta} - e^{-j\theta}}{2j}] \tag{5-25}$$

the solution in the normalized coordinates is found to be

$$\begin{aligned} x_1(\tau) &= x_1(0) \cos \tau + x_2(0) \sin \tau \\ x_2(\tau) &= -x_1(0) \sin \tau + x_2(0) \cos \tau \end{aligned} \tag{5-26}$$

We have now developed the ability to find the solution to the free linear system by the modal method.

Direct Solution of the Matrix State Equation

Can we solve the state equation in the nondiagonal form (Eq. (5-12) — restated)

$$\frac{d}{dt} \underline{x}(t) = \underline{A} \, \underline{x}(t) \tag{5-12}$$

directly without going through the modal transformation? By inspection of the solutions of Eq. (5-2) for the scalar case and Eq. (5-11) for the modal case, we intuitively attempt a solution in the form

$$\underline{x}(t) = e^{\underline{A}t} \underline{x}(0) \tag{5-27}$$

where, similar to Eq. (5-6), the matrix exponential is defined by (Ref. [2])

$$e^{\underline{A}t} = \underline{I} + \underline{A}t + \frac{1}{2!}\underline{A}^2t^2 + \frac{1}{3!}\underline{A}^3t^3 + \cdots \qquad (5\text{-}28a)$$

The fact that Eq. (5-27) with (5-28a) does indeed constitute a solution to Eq. (5-12) may be confirmed by direct back substitution. Eq. (5-28a) is called the transition matrix or solution matrix of the system.

Because of the simple form of the $\underline{A}$ matrix in the oscillator example, we can use the matrix exponential of Eq. (5-28a) to find the solution directly. By successive multiplication, we find that

$$\underline{A}^2 = -\underline{I} \qquad \underline{A}^3 = -\underline{A} \qquad \underline{A}^4 = \underline{I} \qquad \text{and so on}$$

Therefore, by substituting these into Eq. (5-28a), the exponential matrix function $e^{\underline{A}t}$ is found to be

$$e^{\underline{A}t} = \begin{bmatrix} 1 - \frac{t^2}{2!} + \frac{t^4}{4!} - \cdots & t - \frac{t^3}{3!} + \frac{t^5}{5!} - \cdots \\ -t + \frac{t^3}{3!} - \frac{t^5}{5!} + \cdots & 1 - \frac{t^2}{2!} + \frac{t^4}{4!} - \cdots \end{bmatrix} = \begin{bmatrix} \cos t & \sin t \\ -\sin t & \cos t \end{bmatrix}$$

$$(5\text{-}28b)$$

By using this result in Eq. (5-27), we again arrive at Eq. (5-26), the same solution previously found by modal analysis.

In general, however, such a direct approach requires a computer, since the task of manual computation is prohibitive. In fact, the Euler method of the preceding chapter is an approximation of the transition matrix over a short time interval Δt, that is

$$e^{\underline{A}\Delta t} \approx \underline{I} + \underline{A}\Delta t$$

In simple systems, particularly of low order, the Laplace domain approach, which we shall present in the next chapter, may be conveniently applied to obtain a closed form, analytical expression for $e^{\underline{A}t}$.

5.2 FORCED SYSTEMS

The state equation for a first order, linear system with a forcing input u(t) is

$$\frac{dx(t)}{dt} = ax(t) + bu(t) \qquad x(0) = x_0 \tag{5-29}$$

where $u(t)$ is given for $t \geq 0$ and a and b are constants. To determine the general solution of Eq. (5-29), we make use of the unique property of linear systems discussed earlier — linear superposition. That is, we consider $x(t)$ to consist of two parts: 1) a free component x_{free} with initial state x_0 and $u = 0$ and 2) a forced component x_{forced} for "forcing" input $u(t)$ but with zero initial state. The free component is given by Eq. (5-2). To solve Eq. (5-29) for the forced component, it is convenient to combine the two terms, dx/dt and ax, into one by letting

$$e^{at}x_p = x_{forced} \tag{5-30}$$

where x_p is, as yet, an unknown function. Since $D(e^{at}x_p) = a(e^{at}x_p) + e^{at}(Dx_p)$, we have

$$(D - a)x_{forced} = e^{at}Dx_p$$

where D is a convenient shorthand operator notation for d/dt and Eq. (5-29) with $x(t) = x_{forced}(t)$ simplifies to

$$Dx_p = e^{-at}bu(t)$$

This can be integrated to obtain

$$x_p(t) = \int_0^t e^{-a\tau}bu(\tau)d\tau$$

where τ is the dummy variable of integration that will vanish when the integration limits are substituted in. The initial value of $x_p(t)$ is zero for the definite integral from time zero to a running time point t. Therefore, by Eq. (5-30), we find

$$x_{forced} = e^{at}\int_0^t e^{-a\tau}bu(\tau)d\tau = \int_0^t e^{a(t-\tau)}bu(\tau)d\tau \tag{5-31a}$$

and the total solution of Eq. (5-29) is

$$x(t) = x_{free} + x_{forced} = e^{at}x_0 + \int_0^t e^{a(t-\tau)}bu(\tau)d\tau \tag{5-31b}$$

An integral of a product of two functions, in the form of Eq. (5-31a), is called a *convolution integral*.

As a simple example, consider the linearized leaking tank which we have discussed in Sections 1.4 and 3.6, with a step change in inflow. We let

$$a = -\frac{1}{T}$$

where T is the time constant as indicated in Eq. (3-38), and consider u(t) to be a unit step input

$$u(t) = 0 \quad \text{for } t < 0 \qquad u(t) = 1 \quad \text{for } t \geqslant 0 \tag{5-32}$$

If the initial state x_0 is zero, $x(t) = x_{\text{forced}}$ and by Eq. (5-31)

$$x(t) = e^{-t/T} \int_0^t e^{(\tau/T)}b \, d\tau = (1 - e^{-t/T})bT \tag{5-33}$$

This response is plotted in Fig. 5-2(a). Now suppose the valve controlling the input flow rate is kept open for t' seconds and then closed. For the first t' seconds the solution would be as given by Eq. (5-33), and for $t > t'$ the solution would be given by

$$x(t) = e^{-(t - t')/T}x(t')$$

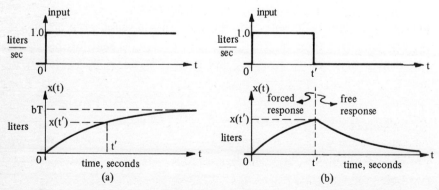

Fig. 5-2 Step (a) and Pulse (b) Responses for the Linearized Leaking Tank Problem

where $x(t')$ would be the numerical value of Eq. (5-33) at $t = t'$. For $t > t'$, it is seen that the free transient solution pertains with an initial value equal to the final value at the end of the forced response era. The total response is shown in Fig. 5-2(b).

Impulse Input

To introduce a new kind of forcing function, let us suppose that t' in the tank example gets very small so that the pulse input of Fig. 5-2(b) lasts for only a very short time, but the valve is opened wider (to a higher input flow rate) so that the same total amount of water is thrown into the tank. We note that the amount of water thrown into the tank is equal to the area under the input versus time plot, so that maintaining a constant amount of added water in the shorter time means that the height of the pulse grows proportionally larger. In the limit, as t' approaches zero, the ordinate value of the input must approach infinity. Such an input is called an *impulse* and differs from a pulse input in that the elapsed time of the input, t', must be significantly (at least an order of magnitude) smaller than the system time constant T. This does not distinguish between an *approximate impulse* (i.e., a very short pulse) and a theoretically defined impulse; we defer detailed discussion of this point to Chapter 6.

The area under the impulse input versus time plot is called the strength of the impulse, and a unit impulse will prove to be a versatile test signal. It is also known as the Dirac delta function and is usually denoted as $\delta(t - t_1)$, where t_1 is the instant of time at which the impulse is applied. In the case of our leaking tank example, a unit impulse could be physically realized by instantaneously dumping one liter of water into the tank.

Let us imagine that our tank is in equilibrium with $x(0) = 0$ when a unit impulse input is applied at $t = 0$. Applying the convolution integral of Eq. (5-31a), we get

$$x_{forced} = e^{at} \int_0^t e^{-a\tau} b\delta(\tau)d\tau \tag{5-34}$$

To evaluate Eq. (5-34), we note the integral of any function times a Dirac delta function is equal to the value of the function evaluated at the instant of time when the delta function argument is zero. This statement is heuristically understandable when we view integration as an area summing process. The forced solution thus becomes

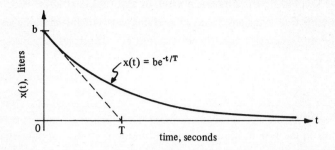

Fig. 5-3 Response of a First Order System to a Unit Impulse Input

$$x(t) = be^{at} = be^{-t/T} \tag{5-35}$$

and is plotted in Fig. 5-3. If the strength of the impulse is k rather than unity, then the constant k carries through from Eq. (5-34) to (5-35), yielding a response with the same dynamics as in Fig. 5-3, but just starting k units higher on the ordinate scale. It is important to note that an impulse response has the same nature as the system's free, transient response when excited by some equivalent initial condition. In the case of the first order linear system, the equivalent initial condition is (bk).

Convolution

Keeping the impulse input in mind, let us return to the convolution integral of Eq. (5-31a) to further investigate the nature of the forced response as found by convolution. One approach would be to consider the input $u(\tau)$ as being made up of a series of square pulses (i.e., the staircase approximation of Fig. 4-6). For a sufficiently small step size Δt in Fig. 4-6, the square pulses can be approximated by impulses. The strength of each impulse is equal to the area of the square pulse it replaces. In the limiting case, as Δt approaches dt, the term $bu(\tau)d\tau$ in Eq. (5-31a) may be interpreted as an impulse of that strength as shown by the cross-hatched area in Fig. 5-4(a). The term $e^{a(t-\tau)}$ in Eq. (5-31a) is the unit impulse response due to an impulse occurring at $\tau = \tau_i$. Fig. 5-4(b) shows the response due to the impulse of strength $bu(\tau)d\tau$ occurring at $\tau = \tau_i$. The total forced response at any instant of time t is the summation (superposition) of all such impulse responses, as shown in Fig. 5-4(c). Since super-

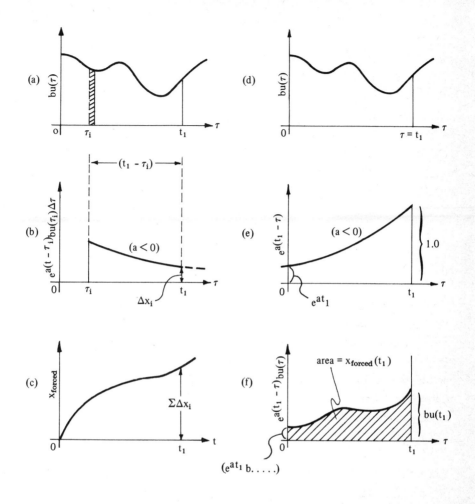

Fig. 5-4 Graphical Views of Convolution

position is involved, we are restricted to dealing with a linear system. This point of view of the convolution integral will be explored still further in Section 9.2 when we deal with discrete time systems.

Still another interpretation of the convolution integral is possible. In Fig. 5-4(d) an arbitrary forcing function $bu(\tau)$ is plotted versus τ. In Fig. 5-4(e), the backwards running response function $e^{a(t-\tau)}$ is plotted. The product of these two functions is plotted in Fig. 5-4(f) and the area under this curve is seen to be equal to the numerical value of the response x at this one instant of time,

t_1. This is seen to be true by examining Eq. (5-31a), repeated here for convenience

$$x_{forced} = \int_0^t e^{a(t - \tau)}bu(\tau)d\tau \qquad (5\text{-}31a)$$

and comparing the righthand side of the equation term by term to (d), (e) and (f) of Fig. 5-4. Since this procedure would have to be repeated many times to build up a response curve at all instants of time, the technique is usually applied when an estimate of the response at a single instant is required. However, this perspective is sometimes valuable when a system's input and impulse response are known and an estimate of the value of the system response at a single instant of time is desired.

General Solution of the Linear, Matrix State Equation

The solution of the vector state equation, Eq. (3-39), restated here

$$\frac{d}{dt}\underline{x}(t) = \underline{A}\,\underline{x}(t) + \underline{B}\,\underline{u}(t) \qquad \underline{x}(0) = \underline{x}_0 \qquad (5\text{-}36)$$

has the same form as Eq. (5-31b) except that the scalar parameters a and b are replaced by coefficient matrices $\underline{A}$ and $\underline{B}$, and is

$$\underline{x}(t) = e^{\underline{A}t}\underline{x}_0 + \int_0^t e^{\underline{A}(t - \tau)}\,\underline{B}\,\underline{u}(\tau)\,d\tau \qquad (5\text{-}37)$$

To derive this result, we note that the first term of the solution is the free response as shown in Sec. 5.1. The steps of the derivation of the righthand term in Eq. (5-37), the vector forced response, parallel those of the derivation leading to the scalar forced response of Eq. (5-31a). First we assume a forced solution in the form of

$$e^{\underline{A}t}\underline{x}_p = \underline{x}_{forced}$$

where $\underline{x}_p$ is the as yet unknown particular solution, and substitute into the differential equation, Eq. (5-36). Using the fact that $\underline{x}_{forced}$ is a solution to Eq. (5-36), we get

$$e^{\underline{A}t}\frac{d}{dt}\underline{x}_p = \underline{B}\,\underline{u}(t)$$

To solve for $\underline{x}_p$, we note that, as for the scalar exponential

$$\left(e^{\underline{A}t}\right)^{-1} = e^{-\underline{A}t} \quad \dagger$$

Therefore

$$\frac{d}{dt}\underline{x}_p = e^{-\underline{A}t}\, \underline{B}\, \underline{u}(t)$$

$$\underline{x}_p = \int_0^t e^{-\underline{A}\tau}\, \underline{B}\, \underline{u}(\tau)\, d\tau$$

and

$$\underline{x}_{forced} = \int_0^t e^{\underline{A}(t-\tau)}\, \underline{B}\, \underline{u}(\tau)\, d\tau$$

Eq. (5-37) is meaningful as the general solution of the state equation with forcing input and it offers the basis for further analytical development.

5.3 FREE TRAJECTORY AND MODES OF RESPONSE

Let us consider, as an example, the two competing species problem which was presented in Sec. 3.4. We linearize Eq. (3-23) in the vicinity of the stable equilibrium point D, Fig. 3-8, where $N_{1e} = 4$ and $N_{2e} = 6$, by defining the deviations x_1 and x_2 of N_1 and N_2 from their equilibrium state as state variables

$$x_1(t) = N_1(t) - N_{1e} \qquad x_2(t) = N_2(t) - N_{2e} \tag{5-38}$$

The general form of Eq. (3-23) is

$$DN_1 = f_1(N_1, N_2) \qquad DN_2 = f_2(N_1, N_2) \tag{5-39}$$

and the linearization, using a tangent approximation as in Fig. 3-11, is given by

$$Dx_1 = \left.\frac{\partial f_1}{\partial N_1}\right|_e \cdot x_1 + \left.\frac{\partial f_1}{\partial N_2}\right|_e \cdot x_2 \qquad Dx_2 = \left.\frac{\partial f_2}{\partial N_1}\right|_e \cdot x_1 + \left.\frac{\partial f_2}{\partial N_2}\right|_e \cdot x_2$$

$$\tag{5-40}$$

---

† This can be demonstrated by performing term by term multiplication of the series expansions for $e^{\underline{A}t}$ and $e^{-\underline{A}t}$ to show that $e^{\underline{A}t}\, e^{-\underline{A}t} = \underline{I}$.

The subscript e in Eq. (5-40) means that we are to evaluate the partial derivatives at an equilibrium point (D in Fig. 3-8 for our example). Substituting Eq. (3-23) into Eq. (5-40) (or substituting $N_1 = 4 + x_1$ and $N_2 = 6 + x_2$ into Eq. (3-23), and neglecting terms with x_1^2, $x_1 x_2$ and x_2^2 — all second order effects), we obtain

$$Dx_1 = -12x_1 - 4x_2$$
$$Dx_2 = -6x_1 - 6x_2$$

(5-41)

In the state equation form, $D\underline{x} = \underline{A}\,\underline{x}$

$$\underline{A} = \begin{bmatrix} -12 & -4 \\ -6 & -6 \end{bmatrix}$$

(5-42)

From our discussion in Sec. 5.1, we consider the pair of functions

$$x_1 = e^{\lambda t} x_{10} \qquad x_2 = e^{\lambda t} x_{20}$$

(5-43)

as candidates for a possible solution of Eq. (5-41). Substituting Eq. (5-43) into Eq. (5-41) and cancelling out $e^{\lambda t}$ ($\neq 0$) from both sides

$$\lambda x_{10} = -12x_{10} - 4x_{20} \qquad \text{or} \qquad \frac{x_{20}}{x_{10}} = \frac{\lambda + 12}{-4}$$

and

(5-44)

$$\lambda x_{20} = -6x_{10} - 6x_{20} \qquad \text{or} \qquad \frac{x_{20}}{x_{10}} = \frac{-6}{\lambda + 6}$$

Equating the righthand sides of Eq. (5-44), $(\lambda + 12)/4 = 6/(\lambda + 6)$, or

$$\lambda^2 + 18\lambda + 48 = 0$$

(5-45)

This is the same characteristic equation of the linear system in Eq. (5-41) as would be found by Eq. (5-20). Its roots, the eigenvalues, are

$$\lambda_1 = -9 + \sqrt{33} = -3.255 \qquad \lambda_2 = -9 - \sqrt{33} = -14.745$$

(5-46)

and the ratio values (slope) in Eq. (5-44) are

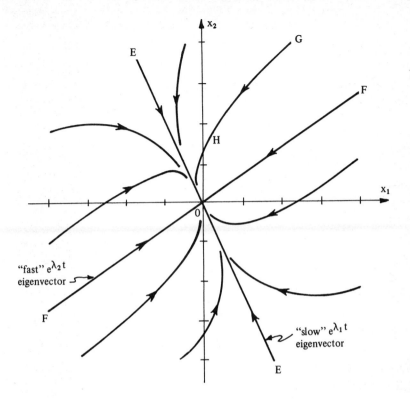

Fig. 5-5 Linear Trajectories of the Two Species System

$$\frac{x_{20}}{x_{10}} = -2.186 \text{ for } \lambda_1 \qquad \frac{x_{20}}{x_{10}} = 0.686 \text{ for } \lambda_2 \qquad (5\text{-}47)$$

The two directions are indicated by EE and FF in Fig. 5-5, respectively. A vector from the origin that has such a direction is precisely one of the eigenvectors that appeared in Section 5.1 as columns of the transformation matrix $\underline{T}$. The approach leading to Eq. (5-47) is equivalent to the technique using Eq. (5-26).

If the system starts out with initial conditions in Eq. (5-43) which lie on either EE or FF in Fig. 5-5, then the system response will stay on that straight line. This is equivalent to choosing initial values in either of the ratios of Eq. (5-47), so that only one eigenmode, $e^{\lambda_i t}$, appears in the solution given by Eq. (5-17b).

The two specific exponentials $e^{+\lambda_1 t}$ and $e^{+\lambda_2 t}$ characterize all the free motions of the system; they are the eigenmodes. In our example, $|\lambda_1| < |\lambda_2|$ so that decay $e^{+\lambda_1 t}$ is much slower than that of $e^{+\lambda_2 t}$; $e^{+\lambda_1 t}$ is the slow mode and $e^{+\lambda_2 t}$ is the fast mode. Any trajectory (other than the straight ones) in Fig. 5-5, GH for example, is characterized by contents from both modes. However, the fast mode decays out far quicker than the slow mode. Therefore, the last part of the trajectory becomes asymptotic to EE — the direction of the slow mode. The free trajectories for this example may be determined by the isocline method (Sec. 3.4) or plotted as part of the output from one of the analog or digital solutions given in Chapter 4. There is merit to indicating a time scale along a trajectory. If an analog computer is used for the trajectory plot, as explained in Sec. 4.3, the "feel" for the speed of motion can only be obtained by observing the motion of a point on an oscilloscope or x-y recorder.

The origin of the state plane, Fig. 5-5, is the only equilibrium point of the linearized system. This is true since at equilibrium

$$\frac{d}{dt}\underline{x} = \underline{0}$$

in

$$\frac{d}{dt}\underline{x} = \underline{A}\,\underline{x}$$

so that

$$\underline{A}\,\underline{x} = \underline{0}$$

or

$$\underline{x}_{eq} = \underline{0}$$

for all systems with $|\underline{A}| \neq 0$. The trajectory pattern of Fig. 5-5 is an approximation of the pattern in some vicinity of state D in Fig. 3-8. The equilibrium point is asymptotically stable (refer to Sec. 3.5). In general, free systems with linear models for which $|\underline{A}| \neq 0$ have global stability properties, since they have only a single equilibrium point.

The n roots of Eq. (5-20) are the eigenvalues of the system. An eigenvector $\underline{v}$ for each real eigenvalue can be fixed by Eq. (5-24) up to a proportionality constant, which gives the direction of the straight line trajectory for that eigenvector in the n dimensional state space. If all roots of Eq. (5-20) are real and distinct, n eigenvectors (straight line trajectories that pass through the origin) will appear. If Eq. (5-20) has some duplications in the roots, however, the number of straight line trajectories may become less than n.

Some of the roots of Eq. (5-20) may have imaginary parts or be imaginary. Since all coefficients of Eq. (5-20) are real numbers, complex roots, if there are any, must always appear as conjugate pairs. We saw this to be true in the predator-prey example at the end of Sec. 5.1 where the complex eigenvectors corresponded to the complex roots. These eigenvectors do not represent straight line trajectories anymore. For instance, there is no straight line trajectory in the oscillator's state plane, Fig. 3-9.

It has been shown that distinct eigenvalues $\lambda_1, \lambda_2, \ldots, \lambda_n$ will produce exponential modes $e^{\lambda_1 t}, e^{\lambda_2 t}, \ldots, e^{\lambda_n t}$, respectively. If some λ's are complex conjugates, the resulting modes will involve harmonic oscillation. For the predator-prey problem of Eq. (3-26), for example, we saw in Sec. 5.1 that the pure imaginary eigenvalues $(\pm j)$ lead to an undamped harmonic oscillation containing constant amplitude $\sin(t)$ and $\cos(t)$ terms. Likewise the mode for a conjugate complex pair of eigenvalues

$$\lambda_1 = \sigma + j\omega \qquad \lambda_2 = \sigma - j\omega \tag{5-48}$$

where σ and ω are both real and $0 < \omega$, is characterized by a sinusoidal motion

$$e^{\sigma t}\sin \omega t \qquad e^{\sigma t}\cos \omega t \tag{5-49}$$

This motion is a damped oscillation when σ is negative, an oscillation of increasing amplitude if the real part (σ) is positive and an oscillation of constant amplitude if $\sigma = 0$. The state plane trajectory is a spiral, converging to the origin if $\sigma < 0$, diverging from it if $0 < \sigma$ and is a closed curve if $\sigma = 0$.

The relation between eigenvalue locations and modal patterns are summarized in Table 5-1 for distinct roots. The root location is indicated by an x in the complex plane where the horizontal axis is real (λ or σ) and the vertical axis is imaginary ($j\omega$). As cautioned before, a complication arises if some (or all) eigenvalues are not distinct. We shall see in the next chapter that a triple real eigenvalue, $\lambda_1 = \lambda_2 = \lambda_3 = p$, may produce $t \cdot e^{pt}$ and $t^2 \cdot e^{pt}$ in addition to its original mode e^{pt}. Likewise if Eq. (5-48) repeats twice (i.e., $\lambda_1 = \lambda_3$ and $\lambda_2 = \lambda_4$), $t \cdot e^{\sigma t}\sin \omega t$ and $t \cdot e^{\sigma t}\cos \omega t$ may appear in addition to the sinusoidal mode, Eq. (5-49).

A general conclusion on global *asymptotic stability* of a linear system may be drawn from the discussion in this section. A linear system is asymptotically stable, that is, its free motion will converge to the zero state (i.e., the origin of

Table 5-1 Modal Response Patterns of Distinct Eigenvalues due to an Impulse Input

the state space) if and only if all eigenvalues are in the left half side of the complex root plane (excluding pure imaginary and zero eigenvalues). In other words, for a linear system to be asymptotically stable, all eigenvalues must be either negative real, complex conjugate with negative real parts or both.

SUMMARY

When dealing with simple and straighforward systems, the analytical methods of this chapter offer a convenient design tool. These methods include finding the system's time response utilizing either modal or nondiagonal coordinates, solving for the system's eigenvalues and eigenmodes, identifying the eigenvectors of the system, finding the forced response of the system by convolution, and interpreting all of this in terms of the trajectories of the system in its state space.

In order for these methods to be applicable, the system under study must be linear and stationary. In this chapter, the introductory views on linearizing a system given in Section 3.6 have been expanded to clarify the concept of linearity. The resulting conditions for system linearity indicate that linear superposition must apply to both initial conditions and forcing functions. In order for the system to exhibit these linear characteristics, all of the system parameters must be constant and all of the system variables must appear linearly (to the first power) in the system equations. In this chapter, the concept of stability at an equilibrium point has been expanded for linear systems to include global stability properties.

The analytical methods of this chapter, while limited to linear systems, do offer insight into the behavior of complex linear systems via linearization. In addition, they are a springboard for the development of further theory. The remainder of this text will utilize much of this theoretical work while blending in the computer simulation techniques of the previous chapter.

REFERENCES

1. Y. Takahashi, M. Rabins and D. Auslander, *Control*, Addison-Wesley, Reading, Mass., 1970, Section 3.3

2. R. Bellman, *Introduction to Matrix Analysis*, McGraw-Hill, New York, 1960

PROBLEMS

5-1 In Fig. 5-1(a), prove that the tangent to an exponential response at any instant of time intersects the asymptotic final value of the response T time units after the tangent point.

5-2 At the end of Sec. 5.1, it is stated that the Euler method of Chapter 4 is an approximation of the transition matrix e^{At} over a short time interval Δt, that is
$$e^{A\Delta t} \approx I + A\,\Delta t$$
Show that this equivalence is true.

5-3 Referring to Eq. (5-5), state the condition for
$$\det \underline{A} = 0$$
When this takes place, does the determinant of the system matrix $\underline{A}$ also vanish?

5-4 The $\underline{A}$ matrix of a linear, second order system is
$$\underline{A} = \begin{bmatrix} -1.6 & 0.2 \\ 1.2 & -1.4 \end{bmatrix}$$
which might apply, for instance, to the system of Fig. P-3-5. Obtain the characteristic equation, modes, eigenvectors and deduce the general trajectory pattern in the state plane. Check the validity of your deduction by the isocline method. Is this system stable?

5-5 The eigenvector (a column vector) $\underline{v}_i$ for a particular eigenvalue λ_i was defined by Eq. (5-24)

$$(\underline{A} - \lambda_i \underline{I})\underline{v}_i = \underline{0}$$

Let us define a *row* vector $\underline{w}_i$ by

$$\underline{w}_i(\underline{A} - \lambda_i \underline{I}) = \underline{0}$$

where $\underline{0}$ is also a row vector, and call $\underline{w}_i$ an adjoint eigenvector. Determine $\underline{w}_1$ and $\underline{w}_2$ for the system

$$\underline{A} = \begin{bmatrix} -1 & 0 \\ 1 & -2 \end{bmatrix}$$

for which $\underline{v}_1$ and $\underline{v}_2$ were computed in Section 5.1. Is it possible to use a transformation matrix $\underline{T}_a$, defined by

$$\underline{T}_a = \begin{bmatrix} \underline{w}_1 \\ \underline{w}_2 \end{bmatrix}$$

to relate $\underline{x}$ and $\underline{x}^*$? Recall that previously, $\underline{x} = \underline{T}\underline{x}^*$ where $\underline{T} = [\underline{v}_1 \; \underline{v}_2]$.

5-6 Prove that the (column) eigenvectors $\underline{v}_i$, $i = 1, 2, \ldots, n$, for which

$$(\underline{A} - \lambda_i \underline{I})\underline{v}_i = \underline{0}$$

will hold, are orthogonal to the adjoint (row) eigenvectors $\underline{w}_i$ such that

$$\underline{w}_i(\underline{A} - \lambda_i \underline{I}) = \underline{0}$$

where all eigenvalues λ_i, $i = 1, 2, \ldots, n$, are assumed to be distinct. Orthogonality means that the following conditions hold:

$$w_i v_j = 0 \quad \text{for all } i \neq j \qquad \underline{w}_i \underline{v}_j \neq 0 \quad \text{if } i = j$$

5-7 Consider two nxn matrices $\underline{A}_1$ and $\underline{A}_2$ such that $\underline{A}_1\underline{A}_2 \neq \underline{A}_2\underline{A}_1$ (which is normally true) and, using Eq. (5-28), show that

$$e^{\underline{A}_1 t} e^{\underline{A}_2 t} \neq e^{(\underline{A}_1 + \underline{A}_2)t}$$

(See Ref. [1] for other properties of the exponential matrix.)

5-8 According to Eqs. (5-11), (5-14) and (5-27), the following relation is true

$$e^{\underline{A}t} = \underline{T} e^{\underline{\Delta}t} \underline{T}^{-1}$$

Using Eqs. (5-15b) and (5-28), prove that this is so. (Since an analytical form like Eq. (5-8) applies to $e^{\underline{A}t}$, this result implies one way to obtain an analytical expression for $e^{\underline{A}t}$; but, in general, such an approach is too complicated to be practical.)

5-9 In a first order system described by

$$\frac{dx(t)}{dt} = ax(t) + bu(t) \quad \text{where } b = 1$$

eigenvalue, a, can be positive, zero or negative. The initial state is zero, $x(0) = 0$, and the input is exponential, $u(t) = e^{pt}$, for $0 \leqslant t$, where p is real, either positive, zero or negative. Obtain the solution $x(t)$ for $0 \leqslant t$ and sketch all possible $x(t)$ patterns.

5-10 A second order system, given by the state equation

$$\frac{d}{dt}\begin{bmatrix} x_1 \\ x_2 \end{bmatrix} = \begin{bmatrix} p & 1 \\ 0 & p \end{bmatrix}\begin{bmatrix} x_1 \\ x_2 \end{bmatrix}$$

consists of a first order free system

$$\frac{dx_2}{dt} = px_2$$

and another first order system for which x_2 acts as an input

$$\frac{dx_1}{dt} = px_1 + bu(t) \qquad u(t) = x_2(t) \qquad b = 1$$

The original second order system is characterized by a double eigenvalue p. Applying Eq. (5-31b) to the latter equation for x_1, obtain the solution matrix $e^{\mathbf{A}t}$ of the second order system. Apply a similar technique to obtain the solution matrix for a third order system described by

$$\frac{d}{dt}\begin{bmatrix} x_1 \\ x_2 \\ x_3 \end{bmatrix} = \begin{bmatrix} p & 1 & 0 \\ 0 & p & 1 \\ 0 & 0 & p \end{bmatrix}\begin{bmatrix} x_1 \\ x_2 \\ x_3 \end{bmatrix}$$

5-11 A thermal or concentration system, as shown in Fig. P-3-4 is characterized by a pair of dominant storage components C_1 and C_2. The system causality is determined by the carrier flow w so that it is unilateral from C_1 to C_2. Suppose the state equation is

$$T_1\frac{dx_1}{dt} = u - x_1 \qquad T_2\frac{dx_2}{dt} = x_1 - x_2$$

where $T_1 = C_1/w$ and $T_2 = C_2/w$ are time constants. Compute the unit step input response of $x_1(t)$ and $x_2(t)$ for zero initial state and sketch them. Also sketch the trajectory pattern in the state plane when the system is free, that is, for u = 0.

5-12 The predator-prey example at the end of Sec. 5.1 led to a pair of imaginary eigenvalues, $\pm j$. This is an undamped oscillator. Generalize the treatment to a system with eigenvalues given by Eq. (5-48), that is

$$\lambda_1 = \sigma + j\omega \qquad \lambda_2 = \sigma - j\omega$$

and show that

$$\mathbf{A} = \begin{bmatrix} \sigma & \omega \\ -\omega & \sigma \end{bmatrix} \qquad e^{\mathbf{A}t} = e^{+\sigma t}\begin{bmatrix} \cos\omega t & \sin\omega t \\ -\sin\omega t & \cos\omega t \end{bmatrix}$$

Construct a signal flow graph for this system and convert it into an analog computer program for which σ will be negative.

CHAPTER 6
LINEAR INPUT-OUTPUT SYSTEMS

Although the matrix, state-space notation we have been using thus far can handle systems with many inputs and outputs in a compact manner, even greater simplifications can be obtained for the important special case of linear systems with a single input and single output. In a home heating system, for example, there is one important output, the room temperature, and one system input, the heat supply by the furnace. Such systems are very common; in fact, they were the first to which automatic control theory was applied. We can realize significant simplification in analyzing and manipulating system equations by describing single-input–single-output systems with transfer functions, which are based on a Laplace transformation of the system variables. The Laplace transformation converts linear relations described by differential equations into algebraic relations from which the transfer function is derived.

A system is not restricted to having only a single state variable just because it may have only a single input and single output. In using the state-space notation we concentrated on choosing state variables that described the internal memory or energy storage of a system. In this chapter we will concentrate on transfer function notations that describe the input-output relation in a concise form but do not assign explicit variables to the internal energy storage modes.

There is considerable overlap between the state-space and input-output notations and, since they can both be applied to the same problem to get the same final answer, we know that they must be mathematically equivalent. In some cases, it is even convenient to combine the input-output notation with a matrix formulation. In the final analysis, it is up to the individual engineer to decide which notation is likely to be more effective in solving a given problem.

140

6.1 OPERATOR NOTATION AND
THE LAPLACE TRANSFORMATION

We have already made some use of operator notation by adopting the habit of writing the symbol for differentiation as D instead of d/dt. D is called an *operator* because it does not stand for an algebraic variable or function but, rather, represents a calculus operation. From our knowledge of calculus, we learn that in some ways the D can be treated algebraically and this is one of the conveniences of using it. For example, the first order differential equation

$$\frac{dx}{dt} + ax = u$$

can be written as $Dx + ax = u$ by substituting D for d/dt. Factoring the x out, we get $(D + a)x = u$. For second derivatives, d^2/dt^2, we write D^2 for convenience, but we can also use it as the operator D, squared. For example, starting with the second order differential equation

$$D^2 x + 3Dx + 2x = u$$

(which could apply to the mass-spring-dashpot system of Eq. (3-11) with $m = 1$, $k = 2$ and $b = 3$), we can remove the x, $(D^2 + 3D + 2)x = u$, and then factor the polynomial to get $(D + 1)(D + 2)x = u$. Applying this literally, in order for these algebraic operations to be valid, the differential equation

$$\frac{d}{dt}\left(\frac{dx}{dt} + 2x\right) + \left(\frac{dx}{dt} + 2x\right) = u$$

which comes from the final factored form, must be equivalent to the original second order differential equation. Using the rules of calculus, we see that it is indeed the same. This notation can be further extended by using $1/D$ to represent integration.

These convenient representations for differential equations form the basis for transfer function and block diagram notations that are central to classical automatic control theory. As long as our only validation for these operations is the type of heuristic argument given above, we have no clues about how to proceed directly from an equation in operator form to a solution. For this reason we introduce the Laplace transform. Laplace transforms have nothing to do with operator notation itself, but use of the transform not only leads to a formulation for linear differential equations that looks like the operator notation, it also gives the solution.

The Laplace transform of a signal f(t) is defined by

$$F(s) = \int_0^\infty f(t)e^{-st}dt \tag{6-1}$$

where the signal f(t) is assumed to exist only for positive time, $t \geqslant 0$, f(t) = 0 for all of the negative time range and s is a complex-valued variable. We write Eq. (6-1) as $\mathcal{L}[f(t)] = F(s)$. For example, the transform of $f(t) = e^{-\lambda t}$ is

$$\mathcal{L}[e^{-\lambda t}] = \int_0^\infty e^{(-\lambda - s)t}\,dt = \left.\frac{e^{(-\lambda - s)t}}{-\lambda - s}\right|_0^\infty = \frac{1}{s + \lambda} = F(s) \tag{6-2}$$

Here it is assumed that

$$\lim_{t \to \infty} \frac{e^{(-\lambda - s)t}}{-\lambda - s} = 0$$

This condition is satisfied as long as $\lambda > 0$ (i.e., we are dealing with a stable linear system) and the real part of the complex variable s is greater than zero, $Re(s) > 0$. These kinds of limiting conditions apply to most situations of practical importance. Caution in viewing these convergence conditions is required when considering unstable linear systems using Laplace transformation.†

Because the definition of the Laplace transformation, Eq. (6-1), involves a definite integral, a *time domain* function f(t) is converted by the transformation into a function of s, F(s). This function is referred to as being in the s domain (or the Laplace domain). Lower case symbols will be used for variables in the t domain and corresponding upper case symbols for their s domain equivalents.

Let us transform the derivative operation (D = d/dt) into the Laplace domain. Let f(t) be an arbitrary but differentiable function of time for which $\mathcal{L}[f(t)] = F(s)$ will exist. Applying integration by parts, the Laplace transform of df(t)/dt can be calculated in the following way:

$$\mathcal{L}[\frac{d}{dt}f(t)] = \int_0^\infty \frac{df(t)}{dt}e^{-st}dt$$

$$= \left. f(t)e^{-st}\right|_0^\infty + s\int_0^\infty f(t)e^{-st}dt$$

$$= -f(0) + sF(s) \tag{6-3}$$

---

† Further theoretical consideration of the region of convergence of the Laplace transformation is not required for the material presented here. For a more mathematical treatment, consult Ref. [1].

As we shall see, this is the most important relation in the Laplace transforma-tion method.

Example 6-1: Laplace Transforming a Differential Equation
    Let's start with the same second order differential equation we used earlier

$$D^2x + 3Dx + 2x = u(t) \qquad\qquad (6\text{-}4)$$

and apply the result we just obtained for taking Laplace transforms of deriva-tives. Taking the transform of both sides of the equation

$$\mathcal{L}[D^2x + 3Dx + 2x] = \mathcal{L}[u(t)] = U(s) \qquad\qquad (6\text{-}5)$$

where U(s) is the Laplace transform of u(t). Since we have no further informa-tion about the nature of u, all we can do at this point is leave U(s) in the equation. On the lefthand side, however, we first note that by using linearity in Eq. (6-1) that the transform of a sum of terms is equal to the sum of the trans-forms. Eq. (6-5) thus becomes

$$\mathcal{L}[D^2x] + \mathcal{L}[3Dx] + \mathcal{L}[2x] = U(s) \qquad\qquad (6\text{-}6)$$

Working on this term by term, we see that $\mathcal{L}[2x] = 2X(s)$ and, applying the formula for the transform of a derivative, $\mathcal{L}[3Dx] = 3sX(s) - 3x(0)$. We have to apply the derivative transform formula twice to get the Laplace transform of D^2x. Using the notation $x' = Dx$ and $x'(0)$ equals the initial value of the deriva-tive, after applying the transform once we have

$$\mathcal{L}[D^2x] = \mathcal{L}[Dx'] = s\mathcal{L}[x'] - x'(0)$$

Substituting the transform of x' yields

$$\mathcal{L}[D^2x] = s[sX(s) - x(0)] - x'(0)$$

Combining all of these results, the Laplace transform of the differential equa-tion is

$$s^2X(s) + 3sX(s) + 2X(s) - x'(0) - sx(0) - 3x(0) = U(s) \qquad\qquad (6\text{-}7)$$

Note that the initial conditions appear in the transformed differential equation even though they did not appear explicitly in the original equation. Also note that the first three terms of the transformed equation look very much like the operator form of the equation, Eq. (6-4), with D replaced by s and x(t) replaced by X(s).

After transformation, the differential equation becomes an algebraic equation, such as Eq. (6-7). The transformed equation can be solved algebraically for X(s) as an explicit function of s. Let's continue from where we left off in Example 6-1 to see how this works.

Example 6-2: Laplace Domain Solution
Solving Eq. (6-7) for X(s) yields

$$X(s) = \frac{sx(0) + 3x(0) + x'(0) + U(s)}{s^2 + 3s + 2} \tag{6-8}$$

We cannot go much further until the nature of the input function u(t) is specified. In deriving Eq. (6-7), we just wrote its Laplace transform in symbolic form U(s). Let's solve this differential equation for u(t) equal to a step input, that is, u(t) = 0 for t < 0 and u(t) = h for t ⩾ 0. We can obtain the Laplace transform of this function by direct substitution in the defining integral, Eq. (6-1). We get $\mathcal{L}[u(t)] = U(s) = h/s$. Substituting this result into Eq. (6-8) and noting that the denominator can be factored into $(s + 2)(s + 1)$, we can rearrange Eq. (6-8) into the following form:

$$X(s) = (\frac{-1}{s+2} + \frac{2}{s+1})x(0) + (\frac{-1}{s+2} + \frac{1}{s+1})x'(0)$$

$$+ (\frac{0.5}{s} + \frac{0.5}{s+2} - \frac{1}{s+1})h \tag{6-9}$$

Why this particular form? We already know from Chapter 5 that solutions to ordinary differential equations will most likely be sums of exponential functions and that, by transforming X(s) into the form given by Eq. (6-9), we are in a position to utilize the result of Eq. (6-2) directly. The *inverse Laplace transform*, written as $\mathcal{L}^{-1}$, takes a function in the s domain into the time domain, for example, $\mathcal{L}^{-1}[X(s)] = x(t)$. Applying this to Eq. (6-2)

$$\mathcal{L}^{-1}[\frac{1}{s+\lambda}] = e^{-\lambda t} \tag{6-10}$$

The logic implied here is that, since $1/(s + \lambda)$ is the Laplace transformation of $e^{-\lambda t}$, an inverse process must transform $1/(s + \lambda)$ back into $e^{-\lambda t}$.† We have arranged Eq. (6-9) so that each of its terms is in the form $k/(s + \lambda)$. We can thus take the inverse transform term by term to find the solution to the differential equation, $x(t)$.

$$x(t) = (-e^{-2t} + 2e^{-t})x(0) + (-e^{-2t} + e^{-t})x'(0)$$
$$+ (0.5 + 0.5e^{-2t} - e^{-t})h \qquad (6\text{-}11)$$

An important property of the Laplace transform method of solving differential equations is that it explicitly keeps track of initial conditions. The method gives the complete solution, with terms for all possible initial conditions and for all forcing inputs.

Initial and Final Value Theorems

One feature of the Laplace transform method is that we can use it to obtain important information about a system's behavior without having to solve the differential equation. The initial and final value theorems can give us such information about the system's behavior at the start and end of a transient by examining the limits of $X(s)$ as $s \to \infty$ and $s \to 0$. The final value theorem is

$$\lim_{t \to \infty} f(t) = \lim_{s \to 0} sF(s) \qquad (6\text{-}12)$$

and the initial value theorem is

$$\lim_{t \to 0^+} f(t) = \lim_{s \to \infty} sF(s) \qquad (6\text{-}13)$$

Both of these theorems stem from Eq. (6-3). To derive the final value theorem, we consider a limiting process in which s approaches 0. Then we see in the second line of Eq. (6-3) that

$$\lim_{s \to 0} [f(t)e^{-st}\big|_0^\infty] \to f(t)\big|_0^\infty \to \lim_{t \to \infty} f(t) - f(0)$$

---

† This is a table look-up procedure for which formal application of inverse transformation theory involving contour integration (Ref. [1]) is not necessary.

and

$$\lim_{s \to 0} [s \int_0^\infty f(t)e^{-st}dt] \to 0$$

so that

$$\lim_{t \to \infty} f(t) - f(0) = -f(0) + \lim_{s \to 0} sF(s)$$

Cancelling the $-f(0)$ from both sides of this last result, we obtain Eq. (6-12). Next, letting $s \to \infty$ in the second line of Eq. (6-3), we have

$$\lim_{s \to \infty} [f(t)e^{-st} \big|_0^\infty] \to 0$$

and

$$\lim_{s \to \infty} [s \int_0^\infty f(t)e^{-st}dt] = \lim_{s \to \infty} [\int_0^\infty f(t)(se^{-st})dt] \to 0$$

since

$$\lim_{s \to \infty} (se^{-st}) = \lim_{s \to \infty} (\frac{s}{e^{st}}) = \lim_{s \to \infty} \frac{s}{1 + st + \frac{1}{2}s^2t^2 + \cdots} \to 0$$

This leads to the initial value theorem, Eq. (6-13). Note the interesting pattern: as $s \to \infty$, $t \to 0$ and vice versa.

It is important to note that in the initial value theorem the limit is taken as t approaches zero from the positive side, as indicated by the 0^+ notation in Eq. (6-13). Because we are using one-sided Laplace transforms, that is, we assume that $f(t)$, $u(t)$, etc. are zero for t less than zero, there can be discontinuous behavior of the time function at $t = 0$. The best illustration of this is the step function we used for $u(t)$ in Example 6-2, which is zero until $t = 0$ and then takes on the value h for t greater than zero. Applying the initial value theorem to the step, $U(s) = h/s$, we get

$$\lim_{t \to 0^+} [u(t)] = \lim_{s \to \infty} [sU(s)] = \lim_{s \to \infty} [h] = h$$

which is the value of the step after it has made its change in value at $t = 0$. The use of these theorems is best illustrated with an example.

Example 6-3: Initial and Final Value Theorems Applied to a Differential Equation

It is often useful to know not only the value of a variable at the start and end of a transient but also the values of some of its derivatives. For example, recalling that Eq. (6-4) describes the mass-spring-dashpot system of Eq. (3-11), the initial and final value theorems can be used to find the position, velocity and acceleration at the beginning and end of a transient without solving the differential equation. We will utilize the initial and final value theorems to find x, x′ and x″ as t→0⁺ and as t→∞. If we substitute $U(s) = h/s$ for a step input into Eq. (6-8), we will have as the Laplace transform of x(t)

$$X(s) = \frac{sx(0) + 3x(0) + x'(0) + h/s}{s^2 + 3s + 2} \tag{6-14}$$

Applying the final value theorem to this

$$\lim_{s \to 0} [sX(s)] = \lim_{s \to 0} [\frac{s^2x(0) + 3sx(0) + sx'(0) + h}{s^2 + 3s + 2}] \tag{6-15}$$

As s→0, all terms on the righthand side involving s will disappear, so

$$\lim_{t \to \infty} x(t) = \lim_{s \to 0} sX(s) = \frac{h}{2}$$

To apply the initial value theorem, it is easiest to divide the numerator and denominator by s^2. Then, as s→∞, all terms involving $1/s$ or $1/s^2$ will disappear, leaving

$$\lim_{t \to 0^+} x(t) = \lim_{s \to \infty} sX(s) = x(0)$$

Thus, without having even to factor or to rearrange the transform, we can find initial and final values in the time domain (when they exist) from purely algebraic manipulations in the s domain.

Using Eq. (6-3), we find transforms of $dx(t)/dt$ and $d^2x(t)/dt^2$ and multiply them by s to get the form we need for application of the initial or final value theorems

$$s\mathcal{L}[\frac{dx(t)}{dt}] = s[sX(s) - x(0)] = \frac{s^2x'(0) - 2sx(0) + sh}{s^2 + 3s + 2}$$

and

$$s\mathcal{L}[\frac{d^2x(t)}{dt^2}] = s[\![s\mathcal{L}[\frac{dx(t)}{dt}] - x'(0)]\!] = s[\![s^2X(s) - sx(0) - x'(0)]\!]$$

$$= \frac{-2s^2x(0) - 3s^2x'(0) - 2sx'(0) + s^2h}{s^2 + 3s + 2}$$

From the final value theorem we find that both the mass velocity $dx(t)/dt$ and acceleration $d^2x(t)/dt^2$ approach zero as t approaches infinity. This is what we anticipate for a stable system with a step input.

Applying the initial value theorem to $dx(t)/dt$, we see that

$$\lim_{t \to 0^+} \left[\frac{dx(t)}{dt} \right] = x'(0)$$

This implies that when $x(t)$ from Eq. (6-11) is plotted against time with $x'(0) = 0$, the curve is flat (the slope = 0) at the start. However, the initial value theorem applied to $d^2x(t)/dt^2$ yields

$$\lim_{t \to 0^+} \left[\frac{d^2x(t)}{dt^2} \right] = \lim_{s \to \infty} \mathcal{L}\left[\frac{d^2x(t)}{dt^2} \right] = -2x(0) - 3x'(0) + h$$

Since $x'(0) = 0$, as we just saw, we note that $d^2x(t)/dt^2$ is discontinuous at $t = 0$ when $h \neq 2x(0)$.

These results can all be checked by using the solution to the differential equation given in Eq. (6-11).

6.2 VECTOR STATE EQUATION IN THE LAPLACE DOMAIN

The basic relations presented in the preceding section for scalar variables, Eqs. (6-1) and (6-3), apply to vector variables as well. The Laplace transformation applied to the vector state equation

$$D\underline{x}(t) = \underline{A}\,\underline{x}(t) + \underline{B}\,\underline{u}(t) \qquad \underline{x}(0) = \underline{x}_0 \tag{6-16}$$

yields the same form as in the scalar case, i.e.,

$$s\underline{X}(s) - \underline{x}_0 = \underline{A}\,\underline{X}(s) + \underline{B}\,\underline{U}(s) \tag{6-17}$$

However, the s domain solution for the n dimensional vector $\underline{X}(s)$ proceeds differently because we must follow the rules of matrix algebra. The solution is

$$\underline{X}(s) = (s\underline{I} - \underline{A})^{-1}\underline{x}_0 + (s\underline{I} - \underline{A})^{-1}\underline{B}\,\underline{U}(s) \tag{6-18}$$

Comparing Eq. (6-18) with the time domain solution, Eq. (5-37), term by term, we see the following general relations:

$$\mathcal{L}^{-1}\left[(s\underline{I} - \underline{A})^{-1} \right] = e^{\underline{A}t} \tag{6-19}$$

and

$$\mathcal{L}^{-1}\left[(s\underline{I} - \underline{A})^{-1}\underline{B}\,\underline{U}(s) \right] = \int_0^t e^{\underline{A}(t - \tau)}\underline{B}\,\underline{u}(\tau)d\tau$$

The first relation, for the solution matrix $e^{\underline{A}t}$, closely parallels the scalar exponential of Eq. (6-10). The second equation demonstrates an interesting relationship: the inverse Laplace transform of the product of two functions of s in the s domain, $(s\underline{I} - \underline{A})^{-1}$ and $\underline{B}\,\underline{U}(s)$ in our case, yields a convolution integral (of two functions of time) in the t domain.

Taking an undamped oscillator as an example, we obtained the solution matrix in analytical form, Eq. (5-28a) in Sec. 5.1. How do we solve the same problem using Laplace transforms? The $\underline{A}$ matrix for the normalized oscillator is

$$\underline{A} = \begin{bmatrix} 0 & 1 \\ -1 & 0 \end{bmatrix}$$

Thus

$$(s\underline{I} - \underline{A})^{-1} = \begin{bmatrix} s & -1 \\ 1 & s \end{bmatrix}^{-1} = \frac{1}{\Delta}\begin{bmatrix} s & 1 \\ -1 & s \end{bmatrix} = \begin{bmatrix} s/\Delta & 1/\Delta \\ -1/\Delta & s/\Delta \end{bmatrix} \tag{6-20}$$

where

$$\Delta = \begin{vmatrix} s & -1 \\ 1 & s \end{vmatrix} = s^2 + 1 \tag{6-21}$$

Using Eq. (6-19), the solution matrix is expressed by the inverse Laplace transform

$$e^{\underline{A}t} = \mathcal{L}^{-1}[(s\underline{I} - \underline{A})^{-1}] = \mathcal{L}^{-1}\left\{\begin{bmatrix} s/\Delta & 1/\Delta \\ -1/\Delta & s/\Delta \end{bmatrix}\right\} \tag{6-22}$$

We now find the inverse Laplace transformation for each element of the matrix in Eq. (6-22). For example

$$\mathcal{L}^{-1}[\tfrac{s}{\Delta}] = \mathcal{L}^{-1}[\frac{s}{s^2 + 1}] = \mathcal{L}^{-1}[\tfrac{1}{2}(\frac{1}{s - j} + \frac{1}{s + j})]$$

$$= \tfrac{1}{2}[\mathcal{L}^{-1}[\frac{1}{s - j}] + \mathcal{L}^{-1}[\frac{1}{s + j}]]$$

where, using Eq. (6-10)

$$\mathcal{L}^{-1}[\tfrac{s}{\Delta}] = \tfrac{1}{2}(e^{jt} + e^{-jt})$$

which becomes cos(t) by using the Euler relations of Eq. (5-25). Likewise

$$\mathcal{L}^{-1}[\tfrac{1}{\Delta}] = \sin t$$

Table 6-1: Laplace Transform Pairs

		$F(s)$	$\mathcal{L}^{-1}[F(s)] = f(t)$
1	$a > 0$	$\dfrac{1}{s+a}$	e^{-at}
	$a = 0$	$\dfrac{1}{s}$	1
2	$b > a > 0$	$\dfrac{b-a}{(s+a)(s+b)}$	$e^{-at} - e^{-bt}$
	$b > 0$ $a = 0$	$\dfrac{b}{s(s+b)}$	$1 - e^{-bt}$
3	$a > 0$	$\dfrac{1}{(s+a)^2}$	te^{-at}
	$a = 0$	$\dfrac{1}{s^2}$	t
4	$\alpha > 0$	$\dfrac{\beta}{(s+\alpha)^2 + \beta^2}$	$e^{-\alpha t}\sin(\beta t)$
	$\alpha = 0$	$\dfrac{\beta}{s^2 + \beta^2}$	$\sin(\beta t)$
5	$\alpha > 0$	$\dfrac{s+\alpha}{(s+\alpha)^2 + \beta^2}$	$e^{-\alpha t}\cos(\beta t)$
	$\alpha = 0$	$\dfrac{s}{s^2 + \beta^2}$	$\cos(\beta t)$
6		1	$\delta(t)$
7		e^{-sT}	$\delta(t - T)$

The solution matrix is therefore

$$e^{\underline{A}t} = \begin{bmatrix} \cos t & \sin t \\ -\sin t & \cos t \end{bmatrix} \tag{6-23}$$

which is the same as the previous result, Eq. (5-28a).

Basic $F(s) \Leftrightarrow f(t)$ *transform pairs* are listed in Table 6-1, where some pairs, like both items of 1, the second item of 4 and the second item of 5, are already familiar to us. The pairs in the table serve as building blocks for the transformation and inverse transformation of more complicated functions. *Partial fraction expansion* is a particularly useful technique for reduction of Laplace domain functions to forms found in the table.

We introduce the partial fraction expansion method by considering the following algebra:

$$\frac{c}{s+a} + \frac{d}{s+b} = \frac{(c+d)s + (ad+bc)}{(s+a)(s+b)} \tag{6-24}$$

Reversing the process, it is possible to expand, for example, a second order form into two first order partial fractions

$$\frac{b-a}{(s+a)(s+b)} = \frac{1}{s+a} - \frac{1}{s+b} \tag{6-25}$$

which is a special case of Eq. (6-24) for $c = -d = 1$. Pair No. 2 in the Laplace transformation table is obtained by applying pair No. 1 to the righthand side of Eq. (6-25).

To illustrate the process of finding the numerator coefficients of the partial fraction terms, let us consider a third order case:

$$F(s) = \frac{B(s)}{(s-\lambda_1)(s-\lambda_2)(s-\lambda_3)} = \frac{K_1}{s-\lambda_1} + \frac{K_2}{s-\lambda_2} + \frac{K_3}{s-\lambda_3} \tag{6-26}$$

where $B(s)$ is a polynomial in s of order 3 or less. Multiplying through by the denominator of the lefthand side

$$B(s) = K_1(s-\lambda_2)(s-\lambda_3) + K_2(s-\lambda_1)(s-\lambda_3) + K_3(s-\lambda_1)(s-\lambda_2)$$

To determine K_2, for instance, let $s = \lambda_2$ so that the first and the last terms of the righthand side will vanish; thus

$$K_2 = \frac{B(s)|_{s=\lambda_2}}{(\lambda_2 - \lambda_1)(\lambda_2 - \lambda_3)} \tag{6-27}$$

Letting $A(s)$ stand for the denominator polynomial of $F(s)$

$$A(s) = (s-\lambda_1)(s-\lambda_2)(s-\lambda_3) \tag{6-28}$$

so that

$$\frac{dA(s)}{ds} = (s-\lambda_2)(s-\lambda_3) + (s-\lambda_1)(s-\lambda_3) + (s-\lambda_1)(s-\lambda_2)$$

we see that the denominator for K_2 in Eq. (6-27) is obtained by letting $s = \lambda_2$ in $dA(s)/ds$.

Generally, for F(s) written as the ratio of two polynomials in s, B(s) and A(s),

$$F(s) = \frac{B(s)}{A(s)} \qquad (6\text{-}29)$$

where A(s) is n-th order while the order of B(s) is n or less, the expanded form is

$$\frac{B(s)}{A(s)} = \sum_{j=1}^{n} \frac{K_j}{s - \lambda_j} \qquad (6\text{-}30)$$

where

$$K_j = \frac{B(s)}{d\,A(s)/ds}\bigg|_{s=\lambda_j} \qquad (6\text{-}31)$$

and λ_j, j = 1, 2, . . ., n, are the *distinct* roots of

$$A(s) = 0 \qquad (6\text{-}32)$$

The roots of the denominator of Eq. (6-29), the λ_j's, are referred to as the system *poles*. Pairs No. 4 and No. 5 of Table 6-1, for example, are calculated using this principle. Looking back to Eq. (6-20), the roots of the denominator polynomial — the system poles — are the roots of $\Delta(s) = \det (s\underline{I} - \underline{A})$, which we recognize as the same as the eigenvalues determined from Eq. (5-20).

The general principle of partial fraction expansion must be modified, however, if A(s) involves any pole(s) having multiplicity greater than one. For instance, No. 3 in Table 6-1 has a *double pole*. It is impossible to expand the F(s) of No. 3 into first order partial fractions. To evaluate $\mathcal{L}^{-1}[1/(s+a)^2]$, for example, let us apply pair No. 2 of Table 6-1 and use a limiting process to get the inverse transform. Letting

$$b = a + \epsilon \qquad \text{where } \epsilon \to 0$$

we have

$$\mathcal{L}^{-1}\left[\frac{1}{(s+a)^2}\right] = \lim_{b \to a}\left[\frac{e^{-at} - e^{-bt}}{b - a}\right] = \lim_{\epsilon \to 0}\left[\frac{e^{-at} - e^{-\epsilon t}e^{-at}}{\epsilon}\right]$$

$$= \left[\lim_{\epsilon \to 0}\frac{1 - e^{-\epsilon t}}{\epsilon}\right] e^{-at}$$

Using Taylor's series expansion for $e^{-\epsilon t}$

$$1 - e^{-\epsilon t} = 1 - (1 - \epsilon t + \frac{1}{2!}\epsilon^2 t^2 - \cdots) = \epsilon t - \frac{1}{2!}\epsilon^2 t^2 + \cdots$$

hence

$$\lim_{\epsilon \to 0} \left[\frac{1 - e^{-\epsilon t}}{\epsilon} \right] = t$$

and we get

$$\mathcal{L}^{-1}\left[\frac{1}{(s+a)^2}\right] = te^{-at} \tag{6-33}$$

Likewise

$$\mathcal{L}^{-1}\left[\frac{1}{(s+a)^3}\right] = \frac{1}{2!}t^2 e^{-at} \quad \text{and so on} \tag{6-34}$$

To summarize, we use Table 6-1 to find inverse Laplace transformations by manipulating a function F(s) algebraically until it is composed of a sum of terms that look like entries in the table. Then, the inverse transform is given by the corresponding f(t) in the table.†

6.3 INPUT-OUTPUT RELATIONS

In the previous chapters, we have concentrated on the state equation for linear dynamic objects. However, as we have noted earlier, both state and output relations are necessary to deal with real dynamic systems. It is therefore necessary to write two vector equations for a linear dynamic system: a differential equation to describe the time course of the system state and an algebraic equation to relate the output to the state and the input. These equations are

$$D\underline{x}(t) = \underline{A}\,\underline{x}(t) + \underline{B}\,\underline{u}(t) \quad \underline{x}(t) = \underline{x}_0 \text{ at } t = 0 \quad \text{(the state equation)} \tag{6-35}$$
$$\underline{y}(t) = \underline{C}\,\underline{x}(t) + \underline{D}\,\underline{u}(t) \qquad \text{(the output equation)} \tag{6-36}$$

where the input vector $\underline{u}(t)$ is r dimensional, the state vector $\underline{x}(t)$ is n dimensional and the output vector $\underline{y}(t)$ is m dimensional. The four coefficient matrices $\underline{A}$, $\underline{B}$, $\underline{C}$ and $\underline{D}$ are thus nxn, nxr (n rows, r columns), mxn and mxr, respectively.

---

† For more extensive tables of Laplace transform pairs, see, for example, Ref. [2].

It has been emphasized in earlier chapters that the number of state variables, n, is closely tied to the system's structure; for instance, it can be equal to the number of (lumped) energy storage elements (total number of C's and I's in a system) in energetic systems. The number m of the outputs, on the other hand, is a design decision because the outputs are either the response variables of interest to us or those that are needed for monitoring or controlling purposes.

In some cases, we are interested primarily in the internal details of the input-to-output relations. In others, we lack enough information about the internal structure to build a state model, so we are obliged to limit our interest to input and output only. To establish a theoretical basis for these latter cases, we take a *black box approach*; that is, we sacrifice information about the internal state of the system by eliminating $\underline{x}(t)$ from Eqs. (6-35) and (6-36) and imagining that the internal structure is covered by a black box. It is easiest to eliminate the state vector in the Laplace domain where the relation is algebraic. Since there is no knowledge available about (or no interest in) the internal state in this approach, it is logical to assume a zero initial state $(\underline{x}_0 = \underline{0})$ in Eq. (6-35), so that by Eq. (6-18)

$$\underline{X}(s) = (s\underline{I} - \underline{A})^{-1} \underline{B}\, \underline{U}(s) \qquad (6\text{-}37)$$

Substituting for $\underline{X}(s)$ in the output equation which, in the s domain, is

$$\underline{Y}(s) = \underline{C}\, \underline{X}(s) + \underline{D}\, \underline{U}(s) \qquad (6\text{-}38)$$

we obtain the following direct input-output relation:

$$\underline{Y}(s) = \underline{G}(s)\underline{U}(s) \qquad (6\text{-}39)$$

where

$$\underline{G}(s) = \underline{C}(s\underline{I} - \underline{A})^{-1}\underline{B} + \underline{D} \qquad (6\text{-}40)$$

For the important special case of a single input and a single output, $\underline{C}$ is a 1xn matrix (i.e., a row vector), $\underline{B}$ is an nx1 matrix (i.e., a column vector) and $\underline{D}$, if it is nonzero, is a scalar. Performing the indicated matrix multiplications in Eq. (6-40), the first term on the righthand side also reduces to a scalar, so that $G(s)$ is thus a scalar function of s. This scalar function is called the *transfer function* because of the property shown in Eq. (6-39): when it premultiplies the Laplace transform of the input, it yields the Laplace transform of the output. When there is more than one input and/or more than one output, $\underline{G}(s)$ will be an m×r matrix called the *matrix transfer function*; each of the m·r elements of $\underline{G}$ is a scalar transfer function that relates one of the r inputs to one of the m outputs.

Consider, as an example, a two-input—three-output system for which Eq. (6-39) is

$$
\begin{bmatrix} Y_1(s) \\ Y_2(s) \\ Y_3(s) \end{bmatrix} = \begin{bmatrix} G_{11}(s) & G_{12}(s) \\ G_{21}(s) & G_{22}(s) \\ G_{31}(s) & G_{32}(s) \end{bmatrix} \begin{bmatrix} U_1(s) \\ U_2(s) \end{bmatrix}
\tag{6-41}
$$

The second output $Y_2(s)$, for example, is

$$
Y_2(s) = G_{21}(s)U_1(s) + G_{22}(s)U_2(s)
\tag{6-42}
$$

Eq. (6-42) is a linear superposition of two response components: one component due to input u_1, $Y_{21}(s) = G_{21}(s)U_1(s)$, and the other due to input u_2, $Y_{22}(s) = G_{22}(s)U_2(s)$. $Y_2(s)$ is the total output, $Y_2(s) = Y_{21}(s) + Y_{22}(s)$.

6.4   THE IMPULSE FUNCTION

One input function we have not yet considered in the Laplace domain is the impulse, which was first introduced in the discussion associated with Fig. 5-2 and thereafter. In addition to its mathematical importance, the impulse is a good representation for many physical phenomena. For example, in studying the use of predators as a control agent for an insect pest, where the rate of release of the predators is the system input variable, the impulse function models the case in which we release a batch of predators all at once, thus causing a sudden jump in the predator population. Or, in modeling a leaking tank problem, where the flow rate into the tank is the input variable, if an amount of liquid is dumped into the tank suddenly, that input function is most easily modeled by an impulse.

In the real world, nothing happens instantaneously. However, since the impulse function provides a convenient and powerful mathematical tool for dealing with rapidly occurring events, we shall derive its Laplace transform, which is

$\mathcal{L}[\text{unit impulse}] = 1$ †

To obtain an intuitive feeling for the impulse function as well as to derive its Laplace transform, we start by considering a pulse of finite width. The square pulse of Fig. 6-1(a) can be decomposed into two steps of height h: a

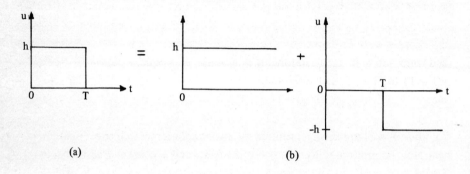

(a)   (b)

Fig. 6-1 A Square Pulse

---

† As a heuristic demonstration of this result, recall that Eq. (5-35), restated
$$x(t) = be^{at}$$
is a unit impulse input response of a first order system described by

$$\frac{dx(t)}{dt} = ax(t) + bu(t)$$

Noting that u(t) is the unit impulse function $\delta(t)$ and the transfer function of this system is (from Laplace transforming its differential equation)

$$G(s) = \frac{b}{s - a}$$

we then have the following relations:

$$\mathcal{L}[x(t)] = \mathcal{L}[be^{at}] = G(s)U(s) = [\frac{b}{s - a}] \, \mathcal{L}[\delta(t)]$$

where

$$\mathcal{L}[be^{at}] = \frac{b}{s - a}$$

Hence

$$\mathcal{L}[\delta(t)] = 1 \ !$$

positive step at time t = 0 and a negative step at time t = T, as shown in Fig.
6-1(b). We can use the techniques discussed earlier in this chapter to compute a
system's response to the square pulse input because of the decomposition of the
input into two steps. The first step input is normal and the response to it can
be computed by using its Laplace transform, h/s (the second item of pair No. 1
in Table 6-1). The response to the negative step at time t = T is zero (assuming
zero initial state) until t = T. For any time greater than T, the response is the
same as a normal step response but shifted in time by an amount T. If y(t) is
the response of a linear system with zero initial state to a step input of height h
at time t = 0, the response to a step of −h at time t = T is −y(t − T) for t ⩾ T
and zero for t < T. Therefore, the response to a square pulse will be y(t) −
y(t − T) for t ⩾ T. Let us examine these statements more closely in an example.

Example 6-4: Response of a System of Leaking Tanks to a Square Pulse
        Two liquid-filled tanks, joined by a short pipe with a valve, are shown in
Fig. 6-2. Assume that we have chosen the flow out of the second tank, q_2, as
the output variable. Logical state variables to describe the two energy storages,
one for each tank, are the liquid heights in each tank, h_1 and h_2. Assuming that
the tanks have straight sides with cross-sectional areas A_1 and A_2, the rate of
change of height in each tank can be written in terms of the flows as

$$A_1 \, Dh_1 = q_1 - q_{12} \qquad\qquad (6\text{-}43a)$$
$$A_2 \, Dh_2 = q_{12} - q_2 \qquad\qquad (6\text{-}43b)$$

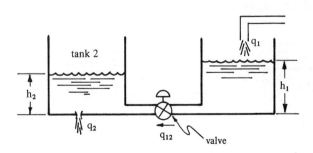

Fig. 6-2 Liquid-Filled Tank System

where $D = d/dt$. If the fluid resistors have linear constitutive relations, the flows can be related to the state variables h_1 and h_2 by

$$q_{12} = \frac{1}{R_{12}}(h_1 - h_2) \tag{6-44a}$$

and

$$q_2 = \frac{1}{R_2}h_2 \tag{6-44b}$$

We can substitute from Eqs. (6-44) into Eqs. (6-43) to get the system equations, which have been rearranged into matrix form below

$$\frac{d}{dt}\begin{bmatrix} h_1 \\ h_2 \end{bmatrix} = \begin{bmatrix} \dfrac{-1}{A_1 R_{12}} & \dfrac{1}{A_1 R_{12}} \\ \dfrac{1}{A_2 R_{12}} & \dfrac{-(R_{12} + R_2)}{A_2 R_{12} R_2} \end{bmatrix}\begin{bmatrix} h_1 \\ h_2 \end{bmatrix} + \begin{bmatrix} \dfrac{1}{A_1} \\ 0 \end{bmatrix}q_1 \tag{6-45}$$

The output equation can be written directly from Eq. (6-44b)

$$y = q_2 = \begin{bmatrix} 0 & \dfrac{1}{R_2} \end{bmatrix}\begin{bmatrix} h_1 \\ h_2 \end{bmatrix} \tag{6-46}$$

This system thus has one input q_1 and one output q_2, so we are interested in finding the scalar transfer function $G(s)$ such that

$$Q_2(s) = G(s)Q_1(s) \tag{6-47}$$

where $Q_2(s)$ and $Q_1(s)$ are the Laplace transforms of $q_2(t)$ and $q_1(t)$, respectively. $G(s)$ can be found by direct substitution into Eq. (6-40), where, for this two-by-two case, the matrix inversion is not too difficult to perform (though it does require quite a bit of algebraic manipulation), or by taking the Laplace transform of Eqs. (6-45) and (6-46), taking all initial conditions to be zero, and solving algebraically for Q_2 as a function of Q_1. Either way, we obtain

$$\frac{Q_2(s)}{Q_1(s)} = G(s) = \frac{\dfrac{1}{A_1 A_2 R_{12} R_2}}{s^2 + \left(\dfrac{1}{A_1 R_{12}} + \dfrac{1}{A_2 R_2} + \dfrac{1}{A_2 R_{12}}\right)s + \dfrac{1}{A_1 A_2 R_{12} R_2}} \tag{6-48}$$

Putting in numbers, $A_1 = 0.5$, $A_2 = 2$, $R_{12} = 2.5$ and $R_2 = 0.5$, the transfer function becomes

$$G(s) = \frac{0.8}{s^2 + 2s + 0.8} \tag{6-49}$$

or, with the denominator factored

$$G(s) = \frac{0.8}{(s + 1.4472)(s + 0.5528)} \tag{6-50}$$

For a step input in flow, $Q_1(s) = h/s$ (Table 6-1, the second item in pair No. 1) where h can take on positive or negative values. $q_2(t)$ is thus the inverse transform

$$q_2(t) = \mathcal{L}^{-1}[G(s) \cdot \tfrac{h}{s}] = \mathcal{L}^{-1}[\frac{0.8h}{s(s + 1.4472)(s + 0.5528)}] \tag{6-51}$$

The inverse transform can be evaluated by using the partial fraction method and the table of transform pairs, Table 6-1. Eq. (6-31) can be used to get the partial fraction coefficients in the following expansion of Eq. (6-51):

$$q_2(t) = \mathcal{L}^{-1}[h(\frac{1}{s} + \frac{0.618}{s + 1.4472} + \frac{-1.618}{s + 0.5528})] \tag{6-52}$$

Using both lines of pair No. 1 in Table 6-1, the solution is

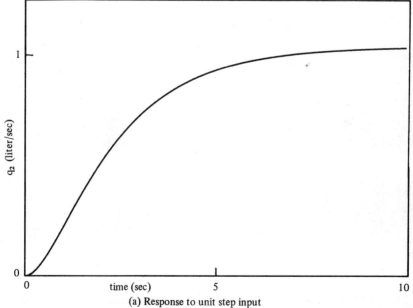

(a) Response to unit step input
Fig. 6-3 Pulse Response of Two Tank System (continued on next page)

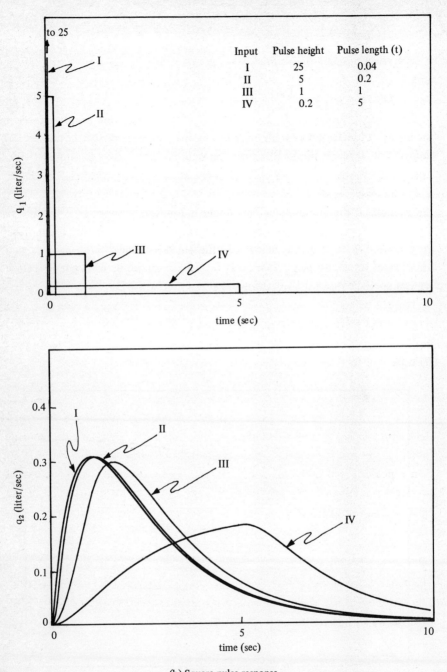

(b) Square pulse response
Fig. 6-3 Pulse Response of Two Tank System

$$q_2(t) = h[0.618e^{-1.4472t} - 1.618e^{-0.5528t} + 1] \qquad (6\text{-}53)$$

The solution for the negative step at time $t = T$ is the same as Eq. (6-53) with t replaced by $t - T$. The solution for the square pulse is therefore equal to Eq. (6-53) for t less than T and equal to the sum of Eq. (6-53) and the delayed negative step solution for t greater than T. The solution for a positive step is shown in Fig. 6-3(a). The solutions for a series of square pulses is shown in Fig. 6-3(b). For each of these solutions, the amount of liquid represented by the square pulse, that is, $V = hT$, is held constant at $V = 1$, so that as T decreases, h will increase. As discussed in Section 5.2, this is akin to maintaining constant the strength of the impulse (the area under the pulse).

We note from the output the very interesting property of the solution that as T continues to decrease below 0.2 the solution appears to stop changing. Thus, although we have not proved it for any shape other than a square pulse, we can surmise that for very short pulses the system output is nearly independent of the shape of the pulse and depends only on its area. For the tank system, this means that the output depends only on liquid volume for very short pulses. The limiting case, for T→0 with hT = constant, is the *impulse response*.

Since we now know that the pulse input response loses its dependence on pulse shape as the limiting case of pulse width T→0 is approached, let's again start with the square pulse as shown in Fig. 6-1 and derive the Laplace transform for an impulse input. If we designate a unit step at time τ by $u(t - \tau)$, then a positive step of height h occurring at $\tau = 0$ is written $hu(t)$ and a negative step of height $-h$ at $\tau = T$ is written $-hu(t - T)$. The square pulse of Fig. 6-1(a) is the sum of two steps

square pulse of height h and width T $= hu(t) - hu(t - T)$

The Laplace transform of the first term on the right is h/s (second item of No. 1 in Table 6-1), but there is no entry in our table for the second term on the right, so we will derive it directly from Eq. (6-1)

$$\mathcal{L}[hu(t - T)] = h \int_0^\infty u(t - T)e^{-st}dt \qquad (6\text{-}54)$$

For $0 < t < T$, $u(t - T)$ is zero and so is the integral of Eq. (6-54). For $t > T$, $u(t - T) = 1$, leaving the following integral to be evaluated:

$$\mathcal{L}[hu(t - T)] = h \int_T^\infty e^{-st} dt = -\frac{h}{s} e^{-st} \Big|_{t=T}^{t=\infty} = \frac{h}{s} e^{-sT} \qquad (6\text{-}55)\dagger$$

The transform of the complete square pulse is therefore

$$h(\frac{1}{s} - \frac{e^{-sT}}{s}) = \frac{h}{s}(1 - e^{-sT})$$

As the pulse gets very short, T becomes smaller and the exponential term can be approximated from its Taylor series

$$e^{-sT} = 1 - sT + \frac{1}{2!}(sT)^2 - \frac{1}{3!}(sT)^3 + \cdots$$

For very small T's, we can neglect all but the first two terms which, when substituted into the transform for the square pulse, yield

$$\mathcal{L}[\text{short square pulse}] = \frac{h}{s}[1 - (1 - sT)] = hT \qquad (6\text{-}56)$$

Thus the Laplace transform of an impulse, which is the limiting case of a short pulse as T→0 with pulse area equal to a constant, is just the area of the pulse. Writing $\delta(t)$ (the Dirac delta function) for a unit impulse (i.e., area equal to one) at time zero, the Laplace transform for an impulse of the sort we have been studying, occurring at the origin, is

$$\mathcal{L}[\delta(t)] = 1 \qquad (6\text{-}57)$$

Example 6-5: Impulse Response of the Two Tank System

We can now use the Laplace transform of the impulse to obtain the impulse response of the two tank system of Example 6-4. For a unit impulse, the case studied in that example, $Q_1(s) = \mathcal{L}[\delta(t)] = 1$ and $Q_2(s) = G(s)$. Using G(s) from Eq. (6-50), $Q_2(s)$ is

$$Q_2(s) = \frac{0.8}{(s + 1.4472)(s + 0.5528)} \qquad (6\text{-}58)$$

Again using the partial fraction expansion

---

† This result is more widely applicable than this derivation implies. We will show later in this chapter that the Laplace transform of any time delayed function can be represented in terms of the transform of the original function by

$$\mathcal{L}[f(t - T)] = e^{-st}\mathcal{L}[f(t)] = e^{-st}F(s)$$

$$Q_2(s) = \frac{-0.8945}{s + 1.4472} + \frac{0.8945}{s + 0.5528}$$

and finding the inverse transformation

$$q_2(t) = 0.8945(- e^{-1.4472t} + e^{-0.5528t}) \tag{6-59}$$

This result is plotted in Fig. 6-4. The response can be compared to the response to the shortest pulses in Fig. 6-3 to verify the impulse response formulation.

   We recognize the importance of the impulse input by comparing the ease with which an impulse response was calculated in the above example to the much more difficult calculation used in Example 6-4 to get the response to the simplest of pulse shapes, the square pulse. Thus, even though true impulse functions do not occur in physical systems, we often use the impulse as an approximation for a short, pulse-type input applied to a system. It should be noted that the above arguments concerning the insensitivity of the output to

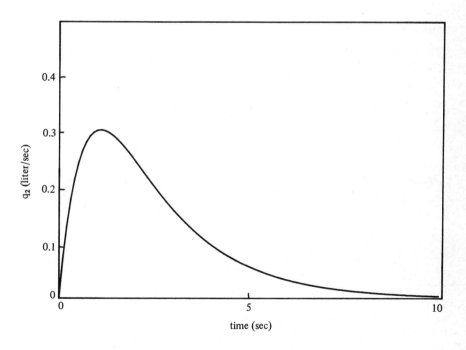

Fig. 6-4 Impulse Response of Two Tank System

pulse shape are valid for those cases for which $\underline{D} = \underline{0}$ in Eq. (6-38), that is, those systems in which the output does not have a direct connection with the input. If $\underline{D}$ is not zero, the output will be the sum of a part for which the impulse response is a good approximation and an additional part retaining the shape of the input pulse.

6.5 GRAPHICAL REPRESENTATIONS

An input-output relation represented by a transfer function can be conveniently shown by a block (Fig. 6-5(a)). Any linear operation in the s domain can be represented by a *block diagram* using the three elements shown in Fig. 6-5. Such a representation has already been used in Fig. 3-7. The derivative operator D in that figure may be replaced by s because, as noted in Sec. 6.3, zero initial state is implied in transfer functions so that $d/dt = D \to s$ by Eq. (6-3).

Although block diagrams can be used to show internal relations between state variables, the *signal flow graph* is generally more practical for dealing with internal states. In a signal flow graph, a small circle is assigned for a variable and lines joining the circles indicate linear operations with summation at the junction. Arrows for causality and symbols for each operation are written along the lines. The basic elements for the graph are shown in Fig. 6-6. Operations can be indicated either in the time domain or in the s domain. If desired, nonzero initial states may be indicated on an integrator.

A normal sequence to follow in constructing a signal flow graph is illus-

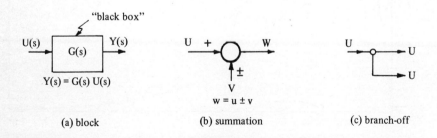

Fig. 6-5 Block Diagram Elements

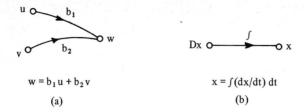

$$w = b_1 u + b_2 v$$

(a)

$$x = \int (dx/dt)\, dt$$

(b)

Fig. 6-6 Elements for Signal Flow Graphs

trated in Fig. 6-7 for a first order system given by the pair of general equations

$$Dx = ax + bu \qquad y = cx + du \tag{6-60}$$

We begin with an integrator, using straight lines to distinguish dynamic from static operations. For the latter, curved lines will be used. Next, we build the right side of the state equation by bringing bu and ax into the junction representing Dx. The last step in this example is the representation of the output equation, $y = cx + du$. Unity coefficients should be included with the appropriate sign to indicate addition or subtraction.

Signal flow graphs are closely related to the computing diagrams used for analog computer programming. Let us consider the linearized leaking tank (Fig. 3-12, Sec. 3.6) to demonstrate the similarity. The system's equation is

$$TDx = -x + ku \tag{6-61}$$

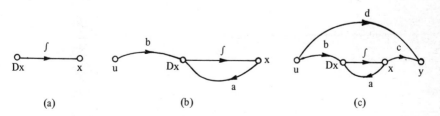

(a)   (b)   (c)

Fig. 6-7 Construction Sequence of a Signal Flow Graph

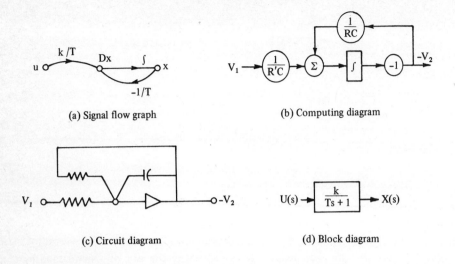

(a) Signal flow graph   (b) Computing diagram

(c) Circuit diagram   (d) Block diagram

Fig. 6-8 Graphical Representations for the Leaking Tank Problem

where T is the time constant (see Fig. 5-1), x is a deviation in level (Fig. 3-12) and u is a deviation in inflow rate, k being a conversion factor from the flow-rate to the level variable. As shown in Fig. 6-8(a) and (b), the two are almost identical. If T = RC is satisfied by a pair of available R and C components, the pot (Fig. 4-9(f)) for fine trimming may be omitted and the resistor R can be inserted parallel to the capacitor C (Fig. 6-8(c)). The transfer function for this system is

$$G(s) = \frac{X(s)}{U(s)} = \frac{k}{Ts + 1} \qquad\qquad (6\text{-}62)$$

6.6 TRANSFER FUNCTIONS

The transfer function shown in Fig. 6-8 for a leaking tank

$$G(s) = \frac{k}{Ts + 1} \qquad k = \text{gain}, \ T = \text{time constant} \qquad (6\text{-}63)$$

is a typical form that applies to a variety of simple dynamic systems that are characterized by one lumped storage element. A higher order example might be

$$G(s) = \frac{1}{ms^2 + bs + k} \tag{6-64}$$

which applies to the mechanical oscillator (Fig. 3-5(a)) for force-input (u) and displacement-output (x). This is obtained by replacing the D of Eq. (3-11) with an s. Such direct substitution of s for D is generally allowed in constructing transfer functions, where all initial states are considered to be zero.

The two examples of Eqs. (6-63) and (6-64) are included in the following general form:

$$G(s) = \frac{B(s)}{A(s)} = \frac{b_0 s^m + b_1 s^{m-1} + \cdots + b_{m-1}s + b_m}{s^n + a_1 s^{n-1} + \cdots + a_{n-1}s + a_n} \tag{6-65}$$

where A(s) and B(s) are denominator and numerator polynomials in s, respectively.[†] The first coefficient, a_0, for the highest order term (s^n) in the denominator is considered 1 to make it clear that the system's order is n. There is no loss of generality in doing this since, for instance, this can be done in Eq. (6-64) by dividing top and bottom by mass m. Some of the coefficients in Eq. (6-65) may be zero. For instance, n = 2 and m = 0 in Eq. (6-64).

Referring back to Eq. (6-37), we see that the denominator polynomial A(s) of Eq. (6-65) stems from $\Delta(s) = |(s\underline{I} - \underline{A})|$. In Eq. (6-32) we saw that the characteristic equation of the system is

$$A(s) = 0 \tag{6-66}$$

the roots of which are the system eigenvalues. Because the eigenvalues are points at which $G(s) \rightarrow \infty$, they are also called the *poles* of G(s). Likewise, the roots of B(s) are called the *zeros* of G(s). Note that in a typical forced response, $Y(s) = G(s) \cdot U(s)$, there can be poles and zeroes contributed by U(s) also. Thus, the poles of Y(s) are equal to the sum of the poles of G(s) (the system eigenvalues) and the poles of U(s). In Eq. (6-64), for instance, the quadratic factor $(ms^2 + bs + k)$ is given by the characteristic polynomial of the oscillator system described by Eq. (3-10) for which

$$\underline{A} = \begin{bmatrix} 0 & -1 \\ \dfrac{k}{m} & \dfrac{-b}{m} \end{bmatrix}$$

---

† Note that the symbols A and B are not the same as the symbols $\underline{A}$ and $\underline{B}$ used for the coefficient matrices of the matrix state equation.

so that

$$\left| (s\underline{I} - \underline{A}) \right| = \begin{vmatrix} s & 1 \\ \dfrac{-k}{m} & s + \dfrac{b}{m} \end{vmatrix} = s^2 + \frac{b}{m} s + \frac{k}{m}$$

Our earlier discussions of causality, in which we noted that integration is a physically realizable operation whereas differentiation is not, have a direct corollary in transfer function considerations. The transfer function of a pure differentiator is just $G(s) = s$. Any transfer function of the form of Eq. (6-65) which has a numerator polynomial $B(s)$ of higher order in s than the denominator polynomial $A(s)$ can be expanded into a form containing positive powers of s and thus differentiators. We can therefore conclude that the *realizability condition* for a transfer function $G(s) = B(s)/A(s)$ is that

$$\text{Order of } B(s) \leqslant \text{Order of } A(s) \tag{6-67}$$

or $m \leqslant n$ in Eq. (6-65). Because the matrix state equation is based on integral causality, we would expect that transfer functions derived from state equations satisfy the realizability condition. In fact, because the inverse matrix $(s\underline{I} - \underline{A})^{-1}$ in Eq. (6-37) will generate numerator polynomials in s of order $(n-1)$ or lower, the highest possible order of the transfer function numerator polynomial $B(s)$ will be $(n-1)$ in the absence of the "d" term. When d (or $\underline{D}$ in Eq. (6-40)) exists in the output equation, Eq. (6-36), it will form a direct path from input u to output y (Fig. 6-7(c)) and the order of $B(s)$ becomes equal to the order n of the numerator. This rarely happens in practice.

Reversing the step that was taken to obtain Eq. (6-64) from Eq. (3-11) where D was replaced by s, the general form, Eq. (6-65), will give a time domain relation between input u(t) and output y(t) in the operational form

$$\frac{y(t)}{u(t)} = \frac{B(D)}{A(D)} \tag{6-68}$$

Cross-multiplying leads us to an n-th order ordinary differential equation

$$\frac{d^n}{dt^n} y(t) + a_1 \frac{d^{n-1}}{dt^{n-1}} y(t) + \cdots + a_n y(t) = b_0 \frac{d^m}{dt^m} u(t) + \cdots + b_m u(t) \tag{6-69}$$

where y(t) is an unknown function of time to be determined by solving the equation and the right side consists of a set of given functions of time. Here, n initial conditions must be given not only for y(t) at time zero but also for the $(n-1)$ time derivatives, $dy(t)/dt$, $d^2y(t)/dt^2$, etc. To convert Eq. (6-69) into the Laplace domain requires not only Eq. (6-3) for the first derivative, but also the general form for higher order derivatives. In addition, u(t) and its $(m-1)$ derivatives on the right side must be defined for positive time, i.e., for $t > 0^+$, excluding the time origin. If a problem is stated in terms of an ordinary differential equation, like Eq. (6-69), we usually convert it into the state space form (see Ref. [3], p. 44) or the transfer function form. Note that the state space form is also convenient for either digital computer programming or analog computer wiring (Chapter 4).

6.7 RESPONSE PATTERNS

Let us begin with an example, the thermal system shown in Fig. 6-9(a) where a solid object is immersed in a tank of liquid. A liquid at constant temperature flows into the tank and is assumed to mix instantly with the liquid already in the tank. Mixed liquid flows out of the tank at the same rate fresh liquid flows in. The temperature of the incoming fluid is zero (i.e., an arbitrary reference), the temperature of the mixed liquid† is x_1 and the temperature of

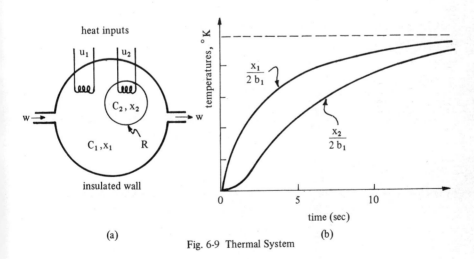

(a)

(b)

Fig. 6-9 Thermal System

---

† The idealized assumption of complete mixing permits us to treat the tank as a lumped thermal mass with a single temperature.

the solid object is x_2. The tank is completely heat insulated and has a heat supply $u_1(t)$ and a thermal capacitance C_1 which relates net heat input to a mass to its temperature change. The solid object, which we also approximate as a lumped thermal mass, has a thermal capacitance C_2 and a heat supply $u_2(t)$ applied to it. Heat exchange between C_1 and C_2 will take place when the main tank temperature x_1 is different from x_2. Assuming that the heat transfer rate between the two objects is linearly proportional to their temperature difference (Newton's law), we consider the heat flow rate from C_1 to C_2 to be $(x_1 - x_2)/R$, where the linear "resistance" R is the proportionality constant. Letting w = (fluid mass flow rate)·(fluid specific heat), we can write the following heat balance equations:

$$C_1 Dx_1 = \frac{x_2 - x_1}{R} - wx_1 + u_1 \qquad C_2 Dx_2 = \frac{x_1 - x_2}{R} + u_2 \qquad (6\text{-}70)$$

Assuming numerical values for the system parameters

$$C_1 = 0.6 \quad \frac{joule}{°K}$$

$$C_2 = 0.6 \quad \frac{joule}{°K}$$

$$R = 5.0 \quad \frac{°K}{joule/sec}$$

$$w = \frac{1}{3} \quad \frac{kg}{sec} \cdot \frac{joule}{°K \cdot kg}$$

Eq. (6-70) reduces to

$$Dx_1 = \frac{-1}{1.5} x_1 + \frac{1}{3} x_2 + b_1 u_1$$

$$Dx_2 = \frac{1}{3} x_1 - \frac{1}{3} x_2 + b_2 u_2 \qquad (6\text{-}71)$$

where b_1 and b_2 may also include unit conversion factors from, say, kW to heat rate (joules/sec) if the u's are electric heaters rated in kilowatts. The second order system, Eq. (6-71), can be programmed on an analog or digital computer to obtain responses to inputs u_1 and u_2. For instance, a unit step change of u_1 at time zero will result in the responses shown in Fig. 6-9(b), where the initial states are set at zero ($x_1 = 0$, $x_2 = 0$ at t = 0). Intuitively, it is obvious that the temperature x_1, which is directly exposed to the step input u_1, will start rising immediately. This rise in x_1 will generate a temperature difference $(x_1 - x_2)$, thus a heat flow from C_1 to C_2 (note that we have not turned u_2 on) and thus x_2 will start rising. The initial rise in x_2 is very slow; its slope is zero at the beginning.

To see how these differences in behavior will appear in the system transfer functions, we apply Eq. (6-40) to the system equation, Eq. (6-71), with $\underline{C} = \underline{I}$, $\underline{D} = \underline{0}$ and $\underline{B} = \begin{bmatrix} b_1 & 0 \\ 0 & b_2 \end{bmatrix}$ to get for the first column of $\underline{G}$

$$G_{11}(s) = \frac{X_1(s)}{U_1(s)} = \frac{b_1 \left(s + \frac{1}{3}\right)}{(s + 1)\left(s + \frac{1}{6}\right)}$$

$$(6\text{-}72)$$

$$G_{21}(s) = \frac{X_2(s)}{U_1(s)} = \frac{\dfrac{b_1}{3}}{(s + 1)\left(s + \frac{1}{6}\right)}$$

The two have a common denominator (which is $\Delta(s) = \left| (s\underline{I} - \underline{A}) \right|$ as we saw in Sec. 6.2), so that the two responses in Fig. 6-9(b) both have the two modes $e^{-t/6}$ (slow mode) and e^{-t} (fast mode). The way the two modes are combined, which is affected by the presence of a zero at $s = -1/3$ in G_{11} whereas G_{21} has no zero, makes the difference in the x_1 and x_2 response patterns. We see that x_1 in the figure (which, at first glance, looks almost like the single exponential rise of the curve in Fig. 1-6) starts rising immediately while x_2 has a slow initial rise. Thus, in this case, the zero at $-1/3$ causes the fast-rise response pattern. The nature of the response for short periods following the application of a step input can be easily studied by using the initial value theorem, as in the following example.

Example 6-6: Behavior of a Thermal System Immediately Following a Step Input

The most telling characteristic of the early part of a step response is its slope just after the application of the step. Eq. (6-72), for a unit step input, $U_1(s) = 1/s$, with all zero initial conditions

$$X_1(s) = G_{11}(s)U_1(s) = \frac{b_1 \left(s + \frac{1}{3}\right)}{s(s + 1)\left(s + \frac{1}{6}\right)}$$

and

$$X_2(s) = G_{21}(s)U_1(s) = \frac{\frac{b_1}{3}}{s(s+1)(s+\frac{1}{6})}$$

The Laplace transforms of the slopes, dx_1/dt and dx_2/dt, are these functions multiplied by s

$$\mathcal{L}[\frac{dx_1}{dt}] = \frac{b_1(s+\frac{1}{3})}{(s+1)(s+\frac{1}{6})} \tag{6-73a}$$

$$\mathcal{L}[\frac{dx_2}{dt}] = \frac{\frac{b_1}{3}}{(s+1)(s+\frac{1}{6})} \tag{6-73b}$$

Restating the initial value theorem, Eq. (6-13), for this case

$$\lim_{t \to 0^+}(\frac{dx_i}{dt}) = \lim_{s \to \infty}(s\mathcal{L}[\frac{dx_i}{dt}])$$

Applying this to Eqs. (6-73)

$$\lim_{t \to 0^+}(\frac{dx_1}{dt}) = \lim_{s \to \infty} s\frac{b_1(s+\frac{1}{3})}{(s+1)(s+\frac{1}{6})} = b_1$$

and

$$\lim_{t \to 0^+}(\frac{dx_2}{dt}) = \lim_{s \to \infty} s\frac{\frac{b_1}{3}}{(s+1)(s+\frac{1}{6})} = 0$$

Therefore, because of the zero of $G_{11}(s)$, $x_1(t)$ has a finite slope just after the imposition of the step and, because there are no zeroes in $G_{21}(s)$, $x_2(t)$ then has a zero slope.

In the general case, we can deduce from the above results that if the number of zeroes of a transfer function is at least two less than the number of poles, the initial slope of the step response will be zero. If the number of zeroes is one less than the number of poles, the slope will be finite. If the number of zeroes equals the number of poles, application of the initial value theorem to the slope yields an indeterminate form (the impulse) because the output is discontinuous at the start.

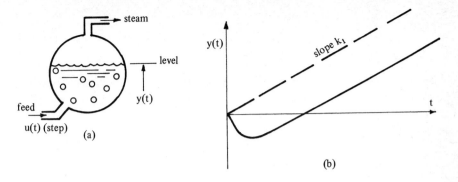

Fig. 6-10 A Reverse Reaction Process

An interesting step input response pattern is shown in Fig. 6-10(b). Because of its negative initial slope for a positive step input, it is called a *reverse reaction*. The boiler drum level system, Fig. 6-10(a), where the input is cold water feed, is an example of such a system. In normal operation, the level gets higher than the real water accumulation due to steam bubbles suspended in the boiling water. The bubbles will collapse when cold water is fed, thus lowering the level momentarily. To take a semi black box approach to this problem, where a thermodynamical system is coupled to a liquid level system, assume that the level output for flow rate input (without the bubble effect) can be described by a pure integrating process, k_1/s. Also assume a first order transfer function, $k_2/(Ts + 1)$, for the thermal effect on level of cold water feed input reducing drum water temperature. The total effect of the feed input will be approximated by a sum of the two

$$G(s) = \frac{k_1}{s} - \frac{k_2}{Ts + 1} = \frac{(k_1 T - k_2)s + k_1}{s(Ts + 1)} \qquad (6\text{-}74)$$

The time rate of the water level change right after a step input application is then computed using the initial value theorem, Eq. (6-13), as

$$\lim_{t \to 0^+} \left[\frac{dy(t)}{dt} \right] = \lim_{s \to \infty} \left(s\mathcal{L}\left[\frac{dy(t)}{dt} \right] \right)$$

where

$$\mathcal{L}\left[\frac{dy(t)}{dt} \right] = sY(s) = sG(s)U(s) = sG(s)\left(\frac{1}{s}\right) = G(s)$$

so that

$$\lim_{t \to 0^+} \left[\frac{dy(t)}{dt} \right] = \lim_{s \to \infty} [sG(s)] = \frac{k_1 T - k_2}{T} \tag{6-75}$$

The reverse reaction will occur when the righthand side of Eq. (6-75) is negative, that is, $k_1 T < k_2$. The transfer function, Eq. (6-74), is then characterized by a positive zero, $s = k_1/(k_2 - k_1 T)$.

Dead Time

Step response patterns characterized by delayed action are a common occurrence. That is, after a step input is applied to a system in an equilibrium state, nothing happens for a while. After a delay period (or *dead time*), the output variable begins to change. For example, if u(t) is the temperature of a flowing fluid entering a section of pipe (Fig. 6-11) and y(t) is the temperature of the fluid leaving the pipe, a step increase in u(t), the entrance temperature, will not cause any change in y(t) until the first slug of high temperature fluid has traveled all the way to the exit. There is thus a dead time of $T = l/v$ time units, where l is the length of the pipe section and v is the velocity of fluid flow (we assume that there is no heat loss or dispersion in the pipe).

We can derive a transfer function for this input-output relation by following the same procedure we used in Eqs. (6-54) and (6-55). The input-output relation can be written as

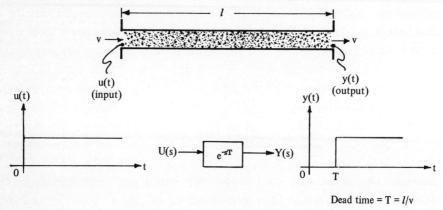

Dead time = $T = l/v$

Fig. 6-11 An Idealized Delay Line

$$y(t) = u(t - T) \tag{6-76}$$

that is, the output at time t depends on the input T units of time earlier. Using Eq. (6-1)

$$\mathcal{L}[y(t)] = \int_0^\infty y(t)e^{-st}dt \tag{6-77}$$

Substituting from Eq. (6-76)

$$\mathcal{L}[y(t)] = Y(s) = \int_0^\infty u(t - T)e^{-st}dt$$

The integrand is zero for $0 < t < T$ so

$$Y(s) = \int_T^\infty u(t - T)e^{-st}dt$$

Letting $\tau = t - T$

$$Y(s) = \int_0^\infty u(\tau)e^{-s(\tau + T)}d\tau$$

Since e^{-sT} is not a function of τ, it can come outside the integral

$$Y(s) = e^{-sT}\int_0^\infty u(\tau)e^{-s\tau}d\tau \tag{6-78}$$

The integral, however, is exactly U(s) (since the dummy variable τ used in a definite integral does not affect the outcome), so

$$Y(s) = e^{-sT}U(s) \qquad G(s) = e^{-sT} \tag{6-79}$$

which is pair No. 7 in Table 6-1.

Although the transfer function for a pure time delay has this very simple form, it is interesting to note that there is no finite order, lumped system that models a time delay. Any finite order, linear system can be represented by a transfer function that is a finite polynomial in s. Since e^{-st} can be exactly represented only by an infinite order transfer function, it corresponds to a lumped system for which n→∞.

6.8 OBSERVABILITY AND CONTROLLABILITY

We have already noted that many systems have only one output variable even though many state variables are necessary to describe their internal state. Likewise, there may be only one or a few inputs to the system. Two fundamental questions must always be asked when designing or analyzing such systems:

1) Is there any component of the system's internal behavior that is not having any effect on the output variable? In other words, are any aspects of the system response *unobservable*?

2) Is there any component of the system's internal state that is not affected by the input? Or, is any aspect of the system's response *uncontrollable*?

In addition to the mathematical interpretation of these concepts, the questions of observability and controllability can be extended to wide varieties of systems and problems. For example, in polling by political parties, companies or any other group attempting to measure attitudes of a large population, the person designing the poll generally has very specific goals for the information he would like to obtain from it. But a poll is a measuring instrument, in theory like any instrument in an engineering system, and the user of the instrument must attempt to determine to what degree the aspects of the system on which he would like information are *observable* by the instrument he has in mind.

Actions by a government are control inputs to the national political system. To what extent do particular actions have the desired effect? That is, is the aspect of the system that a governmental action is aimed at *controllable* by that input? In both the control design problem and the measurement design problem, the decision about which measuring instruments and actuators to choose and where to place them can be guided by observability and controllability analyses.

In complex, poorly defined systems such as the ones above, the concepts of observability and controllability are clear, but no methods exist for determining these properties objectively in a particular case. We have seen in Chapter 5 that linear systems can be described by state equations and that the system's response can be decomposed into independent components called eigenmodes. Because these modes are decoupled, they offer the ideal starting point for examining questions of observability or controllability. For an output y to fully observe a system, it must contain components of all the eigenmodes. Likewise, for an input u to fully control a system, it must have some effect on each of the eigenmodes.

For a system to be observable, its output must not exclude any of the eigenmodes. Each mode has a characteristic direction in the state space; this direction is described by its corresponding eigenvector $\underline{v}_i$. Thus for a single output system to be observable, the state space direction associated with the output, the n element row vector $\underline{C}$ for this case, must be such that

$$\underline{C} \cdot \underline{v}_i \neq 0 \quad \text{for any i}$$

A geometric interpretation[†] of this result is that $\underline{C}$ must not be orthogonal to any real eigenvector. To see this demonstrated, let's look at the example following Eq. (5-24).

The system $\underline{A}$ matrix in that example is

$$\underline{A} = \begin{bmatrix} -1 & 0 \\ 1 & -2 \end{bmatrix}$$

the eigenvalues are -1 and -2, and the associated eigenvectors are

$$\underline{v}_1 = \begin{bmatrix} 1 \\ 1 \end{bmatrix} \quad \underline{v}_2 = \begin{bmatrix} 0 \\ 1 \end{bmatrix}$$

A single output can be described by the output equation

$$y = \underline{C}\,\underline{x} = [k_1 \quad k_2] \begin{bmatrix} x_1 \\ x_2 \end{bmatrix}$$

We should expect an unobservable mode if $\underline{C}$ has a direction that is orthogonal to either $\underline{v}_1$ or $\underline{v}_2$, for example, $\underline{C} = [1 \quad -1]$.

Fig. 6-12 shows the results of an analog simulation of this system. The top row shows the free response from an initial state $x_1(0) = -30$ volts and $x_2(0) = 50$ volts. The first two curves are the responses of the two state variables. The third curve shows y for the case in which $\underline{C} = [1 \quad 1]$. Since $\underline{C}$ is not orthogonal to either of the eigenvectors, we expect a "normal," completely observable output. The second row has the same initial state but $\underline{C}$ is $[1 \quad -1]$ and thus orthogonal to $\underline{v}_1$. It would take a sharp eye in this case to detect that only the

---

† See Ref. [3], Section 3.4 for a geometric interpretation of the observability and controllability conditions for systems with complex eigenvectors.

second eigenmode is represented in the y shown, but in the third case we can demonstrate that this is so. For the third row, $\underline{C}$ is still the same but now the initial condition is taken along the first eigenvector, $x_1(0) = 50$ volts, $x_2(0) = 50$ volts. As we know from the material in Chapter 5, this choice of initial condition will guarantee that *only* the first eigenmode will be excited; since $\underline{C}$ is orthogonal to the eigenvector corresponding to the first mode, we should expect y to have no response at all in this case. As we see in the third row of Fig. 6-12, this is indeed what happens. Even though both state variables have responses, y remains at zero for the whole time.

An interesting thing happens to the transfer function in cases of unobservability or uncontrollability. Let's continue the above example and assume a scalar input u with $\underline{B} = \begin{bmatrix} 1 \\ 0 \end{bmatrix}$ and $\underline{C} = [k_1 \quad k_2]$. Using Eq. (6-40), the transfer function is

$$G(s) = \underline{C}\,(s\underline{I} - \underline{A})^{-1}\,\underline{B} = [k_1 \quad k_2] \begin{bmatrix} \dfrac{1}{s+1} & 0 \\ \dfrac{1}{(s+1)\,(s+2)} & \dfrac{1}{s+2} \end{bmatrix} \begin{bmatrix} 1 \\ 0 \end{bmatrix}$$

$$= \frac{k_1\,(s+2) + k_2}{(s+1)\,(s+2)} \tag{6-80}$$

For the case we just studied with one unobservable mode, we had $k_1 = 1$ and $k_2 = -1$. Note what happens when we substitute this into Eq. (6-80)

$$G(s) = \frac{1}{s+2}$$

One of the system poles seems to have disappeared! This is called *pole-zero cancellation*, that is, a numerator factor of the transfer function exactly cancels a denominator factor. The occurrence of pole-zero cancellation indicates uncontrollability or unobservability.

The determination of the controllability of an input is also related to the system's eigenmodes. The geometric interpretation is that an input aligned with a real eigenvector will excite only that eigenmode of the system. Therefore, for a controllable, single input system, the input coefficient matrix $\underline{B}$, which is a column vector, must not be in the direction of any of the system's eigenvectors. For example, taking the transfer function of Eq. (6-80) but with $\underline{C} = [0 \quad 1]$ and $\underline{B} = \begin{bmatrix} k_3 \\ k_4 \end{bmatrix}$, the system transfer function becomes

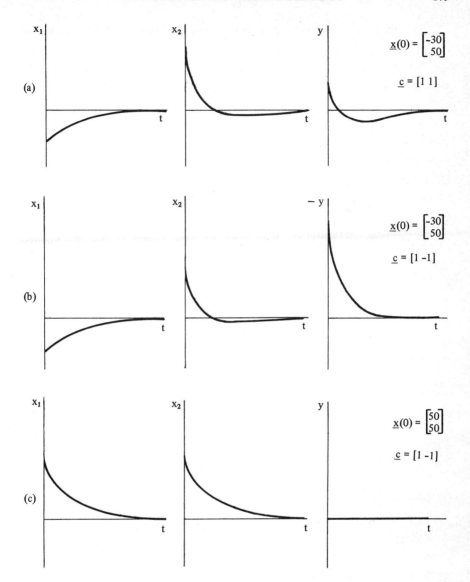

Fig. 6-12 Demonstration of an Unobservable Mode

(a) "Normal" case, both modes observable
(b) One mode unobservable, initial condition not along eigenvector
(c) One mode unobservable, initial condition along eigenvector

$$G(s) = \frac{k_3 + k_4 (s + 1)}{(s + 1)(s + 2)}$$

As expected, pole-zero cancellation will occur when $\underline{B}$ is aligned with either eigenvector, $(k_3 = 1, k_4 = 1)$ or $k_3 = 0$.

State Vector Reconstruction

A problem closely related to the observability question is state vector reconstruction. Many systems have fewer output variables than state variables, often as few as one, but during the operation of the system we might like to know its internal state. Knowledge of the internal state is sometimes desired for purely informational purposes, but, more often, it is used as part of the application of feedback control algorithms that utilize the additional information to improve controller performance.

It is clear that the output signal alone does not provide enough information to compute the state variables directly. In the cases we have been studying above, for example, there are two state variables and a single output. Trying to compute the state variables directly would be equivalent to solving a single equation for two unknowns. We can extricate ourselves from this dilemma by examining the hypothetical situation in which we have access to the output variable y and its time derivative, $dy/dt = Dy$. Differentiating the output equation, $y = \underline{C} x$ (assuming $\underline{D} = \underline{0}$)

$$Dy = \underline{C} D\underline{x} \qquad\qquad\qquad (6\text{-}81)$$

Assuming a free system, i.e., $u = 0$ or $\underline{B} = \underline{0}$, we can substitute for $D\underline{x}$ from the state equation, $D\underline{x} = \underline{A} x$, so Dy becomes

$$Dy = \underline{C} \underline{A} x \qquad\qquad\qquad (6\text{-}82)$$

As the key step in this process, we construct a vector consisting of y and Dy, $\begin{bmatrix} y \\ Dy \end{bmatrix}$. Noting that both the output equation, $y = \underline{C} x$, and the equation for Dy, Eq. (6-82), are written as functions of $\underline{x}$, we can write the following combined equation:

$$\begin{bmatrix} y \\ Dy \end{bmatrix} = \begin{bmatrix} \underline{C} \\ \underline{C}\,\underline{A} \end{bmatrix} \underline{x} \qquad\qquad\qquad (6\text{-}83)$$

where the coefficient matrix, written above in partitioned form, will always be an nxn square matrix. We can then solve for $\underline{x}$ from the measurements y and Dy if the coefficient matrix is invertible (i.e., has a nonzero determinant)

$$\underline{x} = \begin{bmatrix} \underline{C} \\ \underline{C}\,\underline{A} \end{bmatrix}^{-1} \begin{bmatrix} y \\ Dy \end{bmatrix} \tag{6-84}$$

We have generated a solution for reconstructing the state vector from output information for the case of a second order free system, but there are still two open questions that must be answered before we can attempt to apply it:

1) Is the coefficient matrix of Eq. (6-83) invertible?

2) How do we get Dy?

As a tentative answer to question (1) we would expect that taking the inverse of the coefficient matrix is always possible unless the system is unobservable. If the system is unobservable, no amount of manipulation involving y will enable us to compute the full internal state because information about one or more of the modes is simply not there. Thus, in addition to answering question (1), we have also deduced an alternative test for observability: if the coefficient matrix of Eq. (6-83) is nonsingular, then the system is observable. (See Ref. [3].) This new test for observability is superior to the method used earlier in this section because it does not require knowledge of the system's eigenvalues or eigenvectors in order to apply it. For example, applying this to the same sample system we have been studying

$$\underline{A} = \begin{bmatrix} -1 & 0 \\ 1 & -2 \end{bmatrix}$$

with $\underline{C} = [0 \quad 1]$ (an observable output coefficient matrix)

$$\begin{bmatrix} \underline{C} \\ \underline{C}\,\underline{A} \end{bmatrix} = \begin{bmatrix} 0 & 1 \\ 1 & -2 \end{bmatrix} \qquad \begin{bmatrix} \underline{C} \\ \underline{C}\,\underline{A} \end{bmatrix}^{-1} = \begin{bmatrix} 2 & 1 \\ 1 & 0 \end{bmatrix} \tag{6-85}$$

On the other hand, if $\underline{C} = [1 \quad -1]$ (a coefficient matrix that, as we have seen, leads to an unobservable system)

$$\begin{bmatrix} \underline{C} \\ \underline{C}\,\underline{A} \end{bmatrix} = \begin{bmatrix} 1 & -1 \\ -2 & 2 \end{bmatrix} \qquad \det \begin{bmatrix} 1 & -1 \\ -2 & 2 \end{bmatrix} = 0$$

We have frequently mentioned that it is impossible to build an exact time differentiator, that is, an element whose transfer function is s. The immediate answer to question (2) is therefore that we cannot exactly generate Dy from y. We can, however, generate an approximation to Dy. If we use an element whose transfer function is $s/(1 + Ts)$, a realizable transfer function as long as $T \neq 0$, and if we make T small, we can get an approximation to a differentiator. A state equation for implementing this transfer function is

$$Dw = -\frac{1}{T}w + \frac{1}{T}u$$
$$z = -\frac{1}{T}w + \frac{1}{T}u$$
(6-86)

where w is the state variable, u the input and z the output. For our case, the input u will be y and the output z will be an approximation to Dy. The approximation gets better as T gets smaller but, for practical reasons, we should not make T any smaller than necessary: although the theoretical accuracy does indeed increase, the noise sensitivity also increases as T is decreased.

We will now test this method of state reconstruction by continuing our analog simulation of the same second order system treated above. With the $\underline{A}$ matrix as given just above Eq. (6-85) and $\underline{C} = [0 \quad 1]$, we get the coefficient matrix for calculation of $\underline{x}$ from y and Dy as given by Eq. (6-85)

$$\underline{x} = \begin{bmatrix} 2 & 1 \\ 1 & 0 \end{bmatrix} \begin{bmatrix} y \\ Dy \end{bmatrix}$$
(6-87)

We have approximated Dy by building an analog model of Eq. (6-86) with T = 0.1. Fig. 6-13 shows the results of the analog computer simulation. The results shown in the top part of each graph are the actual x_1 and the estimate of x_1 using Eq. (6-87); since y measures x_2 directly, no approximation for x_2 is necessary (note that the second row of the coefficient matrix in Eq. (6-87) contains just a one). The results shown in Fig. 6-13(a) show that the estimation of x_1 is very accurate; the two curves are nearly identical. The error curve, with its ordinate scale magnified by a factor of ten relative to the x_1 plots, shows that the maximum error is about 2 volts and dies away as the system reaches equilibrium. Parts (b) and (c) of the figure are simple sensitivity studies of this method. In (b), we insert an initial error of 10% (5 volts) in the initial condition of the estimated x_1. As can be seen, the error is quickly reduced. The estimation scheme is much more sensitive to errors in the coefficients of the

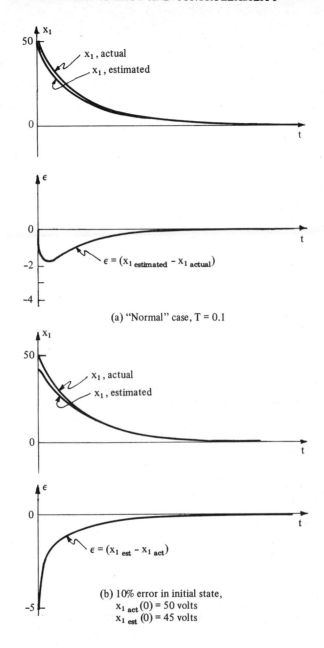

(a) "Normal" case, T = 0.1

(b) 10% error in initial state,
$x_{1\ act}(0) = 50$ volts
$x_{1\ est}(0) = 45$ volts

Fig. 6-13 Output of State Estimator, (a) Normal case, (b) Sensitivity to error in initial state, (c) Sensitivity to error in coefficients

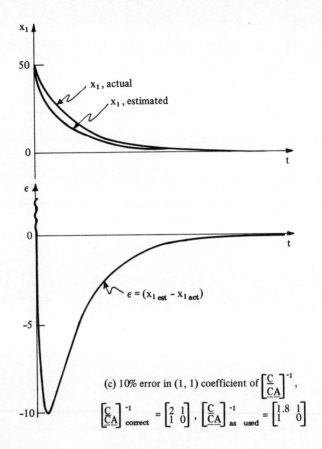

(c) 10% error in (1, 1) coefficient of $\left[\dfrac{C}{CA}\right]^{-1}$,

$$\left[\frac{C}{\underline{CA}}\right]^{-1}_{\text{correct}} = \begin{bmatrix} 2 & 1 \\ 1 & 0 \end{bmatrix}, \quad \left[\frac{C}{\underline{CA}}\right]^{-1}_{\text{as used}} = \begin{bmatrix} 1.8 & 1 \\ 1 & 0 \end{bmatrix}$$

Fig. 6-13 continued

estimation formula. The result in (c) of the figure was produced by changing the coefficient in the first row and first column of the matrix in Eq. (6-87) by 10% to 1.8. In this case, the error is much larger and grows to a maximum before it starts decreasing.

No measurement in a real system is ever completely free of noise. To test the sensitivity of this state estimation method to noise, we have added a small noise signal from an analog noise generator to the measured variable y before putting it through the approximate differentiator or the state estimator. These results are shown in Fig. 6-14. The upper curve shows the actual x_1 (the smooth curve) and the output of the estimator. The estimated output follows the trend of the actual state variable very closely but with a large noise

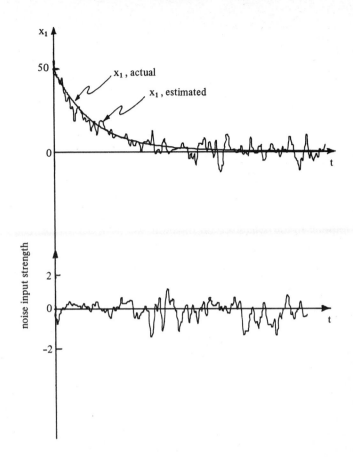

Fig. 6-14 Sensitivity of State Estimation Method to Noise

top: actual and estimated values of x_1
bottom: noise input, y signal used in the state estimator is the original y signal plus
this noise signal

component added on. The lower curve shows the noise signal magnified by a factor of ten. Note that the magnitude of the noise component in the output of the estimator is roughly ten times the magnitude of the noise component of the measured variable y. The noise sensitivity can be decreased by using a larger value for T in the approximate differentiator, but at the expense of accuracy in the state estimation.

As we have seen, this simple method for state estimation works very well under controlled conditions. Under real operating conditions, more sophisticated methods may be necessary, particularly methods that are less sensitive to errors in our knowledge of the system's state equation (i.e., errors in our knowledge of $\underline{A}$, $\underline{B}$, $\underline{C}$ and $\underline{D}$ that lead to errors in the estimation algorithm), errors in initial state and noise.

Model Reference Adaptive Methods

The state reconstruction problem discussed above is a special case of observation techniques in which we utilize a system model. The scheme is shown conceptually in Fig. 6-15. The model is typically implemented on an analog or digital computer using whatever information we have about the real system's coefficient matrices $\underline{A}$, $\underline{B}$, $\underline{C}$ and $\underline{D}$ and the system inputs. An estimate of the system's inaccessible states may be obtained from the state vector of the model, which is known. To improve the accuracy of the estimate continuously, the response $\hat{\underline{y}}$ of the model is checked against the real system's response $\underline{y}$. The error, $\underline{\epsilon}(t) = \underline{y}(t) - \hat{\underline{y}}(t)$, is used to modify the model or the model input. Two important examples of such systems are the dynamic observer (Ref. [4]), which is used for estimating the state of a system for which the initial state is unknown, and the Kalman filter (Ref. [3]), which is used to estimate the state of a system in a noisy environment.

These methods, which are called *model reference adaptive* methods (Ref. [5]), all exploit the principle of feedback, which is the main theme of the next chapter.

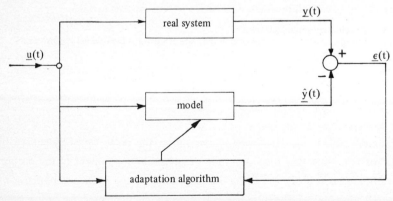

Fig. Fig. 6-15 A Model Reference Adaptive System

SUMMARY

The Laplace transformation provides the primary theoretical basis for the analytical simplifications that are possible when we deal with single-input—single-output, linear systems. The material in the early part of the chapter introduces Laplace transforms and shows how linear differential equations can be transformed into algebraic equations in the s domain. Inverse transformation, by table look-up, provides a means of transforming the algebraic solution obtained in the s domain back into the time domain.

The transfer function follows directly from the Laplace transformation of the system differential equations and is an extemely compact, easy to manipulate means of describing linear systems. The qualitative properties of a system's response pattern can often be deduced from its transfer function by inspection once we understand the mathematical basis connecting the two.

Block diagrams (or signal flow graphs) bridge the important gap between schematic diagrams of a system and mathematical models. They represent the topological relationships among the actual system components and act as graphical manifestations of the system equations.

The concepts of observability and controllability are important in systems described by transfer functions because of possibilities of pole-zero cancellation. They can also be useful in system design by providing guidance in the choice and placement of instruments and actuators.

REFERENCES

1. M. F. Gardner and J. L. Barnes, *Transients in Linear Systems*, John Wiley and Sons, Inc., New York, 1942

2. F. E. Nixon, *Handbook of Laplace Transformation: Tables and Examples*, Prentice-Hall, Inc., Englewood Cliffs, N. J., 1960

3. Y. Takahashi, M. Rabins and D. Auslander, *Control*, Addison-Wesley, Reading, Mass., 1970

4. D. G. Luenberger, "Observers for Multivariable Systems", *IEEE Transactions on Automatic Control*, Vol. AC-11, No. 2, pp. 190-197, April, 1966

5. I. D. Landau, "Model Reference Adaptive Systems – a Survey (MRAS) – What is Possible and Why?", *ASME Quarterly Transactions Journal of Dynamic Systems, Measurements and Control*, Vol. 94, Series G, No. 2, pp. 119-132, June, 1972

PROBLEMS

6-1 In a linear system described by the state equation

$$\frac{d}{dt}\underline{x}(t) = \underline{A}\,\underline{x}(t) + \underline{B}\,\underline{u}(t)$$

the input vector has a final value (meaning it is a sustained input of magnitude $\underline{h}$)

$$\lim_{t\to\infty}\underline{u}(t) = \underline{h}$$

Determine the final value of the state by the final value theorem

$$\lim_{t\to\infty}\underline{x}(t) = \lim_{s\to 0}s\underline{X}(s)$$

State the condition(s) for the final value to exist.

6-2 A linear system is given by

$$\frac{d}{dt}\underline{x}(t) = \begin{bmatrix} -2 & 0 \\ 5 & -3 \end{bmatrix}\underline{x}(t) + \begin{bmatrix} 1 \\ -2 \end{bmatrix}u(t)$$

Using the Laplace domain approach, obtain (a) the solution matrix, (b) the free response $\underline{x}(t)$ for $\underline{x}(0) = \begin{bmatrix} 2 \\ -3 \end{bmatrix}$ and (c) $\underline{x}(t)$ for zero initial state and a unit step input.

6-3 In the previous problem, let $\underline{x}(0) = \underline{0}$, $u(t)$ be a unit step input and the distribution vector given by $\underline{B} = \begin{bmatrix} 1 \\ -2 \end{bmatrix}$. (a) Find the forced response by convolution. (b) What are the steady state values of $x_1(t)$ and $x_2(t)$, i.e., as $t\to\infty$? How do these values compare to the equilibrium values of $x_1(t)$ and $x_2(t)$ found by setting $\dot{x}_1(t)$ and $\dot{x}_2(t)$ equal to zero in the state equations? How does this material relate to the final value theorem?

6-4 A system is described by the following state and output equations:

$$\frac{d}{dt}\underline{x}^*(t) = \begin{bmatrix} -3 & 0 \\ 0 & -5 \end{bmatrix}\underline{x}^*(t) + \begin{bmatrix} 0 \\ 1 \end{bmatrix}u(t)$$

and

$$\underline{y}(t) = \begin{bmatrix} 2 & 0 \\ 0 & 3 \end{bmatrix}\underline{x}^*(t)$$

Find (a) the system solution matrix, (b) the signal flow diagram in the s domain, including initial conditions, (c) the transient response for $x_1^*(0) = +2$ and $x_2^*(0) = -3$, (d) the forced response for $u(t) =$ a unit step and (e) the system transfer function matrix $\underline{G}(s)$.

6-5 A new set of state variables $\underline{x}(t)$ is defined in terms of the $\underline{x}^*(t)$ state variables of the preceding problem by

$$\underline{x} = \underline{T}\,\underline{x}^*$$

where

$$\underline{T} = \begin{bmatrix} 0.5 & 1 \\ 0.5 & 0 \end{bmatrix}$$

Find (a) the state equations for the new state variables $\underline{x}(t)$, (b) the signal flow diagram for these equations in the time domain, (c) the initial conditions on $x_1(0)$ and $x_2(0)$ corresponding to $x_1^*(0) = +2$ and $x_2^*(0) = -3$ from Prob. 6-4 and the transient, force-free response of $\underline{x}(t)$ and (d) the system transfer function matrix $\underline{G}(s)$.

6-6 In the general form of a rational transfer function, Eq. (6-65), the number of poles is n and the number of zeroes is m. For a step input response of the system with zero initial state, show that the slope of a tangent drawn to the response curve at $t = 0$ is (a) zero if $m \leqslant (n - 2)$, (b) finite if $m = (n - 1)$ and (c) infinite if $m = n$.

6-7 A single-input–single-output relation is given by

$$\frac{Y(s)}{U(s)} = \frac{s + 2}{s^3 + 3s^2 + 4s + 6}$$

Dividing the numerator and the denominator by s^3 and introducing a dummy variable Z, it is possible to convert the transfer function into the following form

$$\frac{Y(s)}{U(s)} = \frac{Z/s^2 + 2Z/s^3}{Z + 3Z/s + 4Z/s^2 + 6Z/s^3}$$

or

$$Y(s) = Z/s^2 + 2Z/s^3 \qquad U(s) = Z + 3Z/s + 4Z/s^2 + 6Z/s^3$$

Introduce the state variables by

$$Z/s = X_3 \quad X_3/s = Z/s^2 = X_2 \quad X_2/s = Z/s^3 = X_1$$

and obtain the state and output equations. Draw a signal flow graph.

6-8 The equation of motion of an inverted pendulum for a small deviation angle θ (radians) from its upright position (see Fig. P-3-6) is given by

$$\frac{d^2\theta}{dt^2} = \frac{g}{l}\theta$$

Using the Laplace domain approach, obtain a relationship between initial displacement θ_0 and initial (angular) velocity ω_0 for which the final state will be the upright equilibrium position. Is this equilibrium position stable?

6-9 Fig. P-6-9 shows a thermal system where: w = product of the flow rate and specific heat of the flowing fluid; C_1 and C_2 = heat capacitance of the fluid in the tanks; x_1 and x_2 = temperature deviations and u = heat input. There is no heat loss, the heat capacitance of the tank wall is negligible, complete mixing occurs in the tank and the inlet temperature of the fluid is zero. Temperature deviation in the first tank is taken as an output, $y = x_1$. Obtain the transfer function of the system and discuss controllability and observability of the system.

6-10 Water used for cooling enters into a reservoir at a temperature $(50 + u_1)$ degrees Centigrade, where u_1 is a temperature deviation. The flow rate is $(5 + u_2)$ metric tons per minute, where u_2 is a deviation in the flow rate. The reservoir holds 100

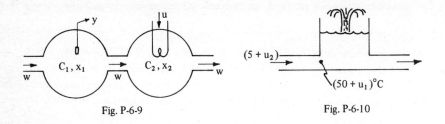

Fig. P-6-9   Fig. P-6-10

tons of water. It has a spray for cooling. When the spray is operating and the ambient temperature is $10°C$, the outgoing water temperature is $40°C$ when incoming temperature is $50°C$. Assume that the total heat rejection by the spray is proportional to the temperature difference of the ambient air and the reservoir water (the latter, in turn, must be equal to the outgoing water temperature when the heat capacitance of the pond is lumped; see Prob. 3-3). Ignore the evaporation loss and obtain the transfer functions between u_1, u_2 and the reservoir temperature deviation x.

6-11 A test structure of mass m_2, spring constant k and damper constant b is erected on a platform of mass m_1 and the latter is subject to a vertical driving force u (Fig. P-6-11). The system is for testing the effect of an earthquake or vibration on the test structure. Obtain the transfer function from the applied force u to the platform acceleration, $y = D^2 x_1$.

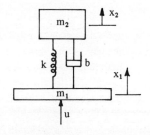

Fig. P-6-11

6-12 Cold slurry entering from the left is heated by a flame in a rotary kiln, Fig. P-6-12(a). For a step increase in fuel flow, the flame gets longer so that temperature at the exit end, P, will momentarily drop but eventually go up as shown in Fig. P-6-12(b). Obtain a transfer function that will qualitatively fit the system. Is this a *black box* approach?

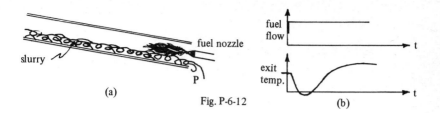

(a)

Fig. P-6-12

(b)

6-13 A moving average h(t) of a signal f(t) over a prescribed time interval T is defined by

$$h(t) = \int_{t-T}^{t} f(\tau)d\tau$$

Obtain the transfer function of the moving average operation.

6-14 In Example 6-3, discuss the response pattern $dx(t)/dt = 0$ at $t = 0$ if the input step size h is chosen equal to $2x(0)$. Discuss how you might use this discovery on real systems.

CHAPTER 7
CONTROL
AND FEEDBACK
SYSTEMS

Feedback control systems with a wide variety of structures and operating characteristics have evolved in nature. They range in complexity and speed from the slow, simple phototropic (light following) motion of a plant to the human brain which, in its function as a controller, scientists and engineers believe uses prediction algorithms, noise filtering, adaptive control and other sophisticated control algorithms just discovered in recent years. As in nature, a control system designer must choose from many possible control system types to achieve a solution that meets the performance specifications at minimum cost. The purpose of this chapter is to explore the field of control systems from this design point of view; first we look at classification and types of control systems and then at a particular configuration that is useful in many control problems. Like other dynamic systems, both analytic and computer simulation techniques are applicable to control system design. Some special mathematical formulations covering an important class of control systems are examined in this context. Then we look at some unusual control applications and, finally, at an advanced control algorithm utilizing full knowledge of the system's state.

7.1 A VIEW OF MANMADE CONTROL SYSTEMS

Probably the oldest example of automatic control may be found in the water clock which Ktesibios in Alexandria is believed to have built during the first half of the third century B.C. (Ref. [1]). A water tank without any leak integrates water inflow. If the inflow rate is kept constant, the level in the tank

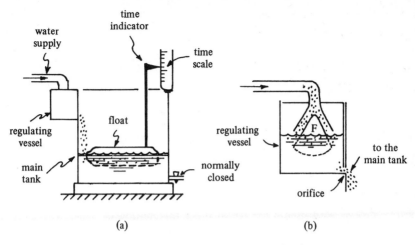

Fig. 7-1 Water Clock and its Regulating Vessel

will give a measure of time, Fig. 7-1(a). Therefore, in order for the water clock
to be accurate, it is crucial to keep the rate of water trickling into the tank
constant. Overflow vessels (weirs) were undoubtedly used for this purpose in
antiquity, but they waste large amounts of water and are messy. Ancient Arabic
records indicate a cone shaped float, F in Fig. 7-1(b), seems to have been used
by Ktesibios for a more elegant solution to the problem. The float will regulate
the water supply, throttling the inflow with rising level. If our interpretation of
the ancient record is correct, this must be the oldest known *feedback control*
device; here the controlled variable (the level in the regulating vessel) is fed back
to the input (water supply) side to maintain a constant level, hence a constant
flow through the orifice to the main tank.

Other devices making use of the principle of feedback have appeared from
time to time, although the various designers do not seem to have had any explicit
understanding of the principle. In the fifteenth century, the Dutch, who used
wind power extensively for pumping water out of their below-sea-level country
and for grinding grain, sought to make more efficient use of their windmills by
adding an auxiliary propellor at right angles to the main wind vanes. This auxiliary power source operated a gear train which turned the main wind vanes so
that they faced into the wind. This early example of automation (the job of
turning the windmill into the wind had previously been done manually) is also
an example of automatic control because the placement of the auxiliary vanes
at right angles to the main vanes guaranteed that they would only be actuated

when the windmill was not facing into the wind. A second example of a position controller was the ship's steering engine, invented in the nineteenth century to enable a steersman to position the large rudder of the more massive ships then being constructed. Interestingly, Norbert Wiener used the Greek word for steersman (kybernet) in naming the general science of feedback systems, natural and manmade, *cybernetics*.

Another important early control development was the steam engine governor perfected by Watt in the eighteenth century. The steam engines of the day changed speed whenever the load or steam pressure changed. Watt's governor consisted of a set of flyballs connected to the main power shaft of the engine. As the speed of the engine increased, the centrifugal force on the flyballs caused them to fly out further. Watt used a linkage to make this motion of the flyballs close the engine's steam valve, thus causing the engine to slow down. If the engine speed decreased, the opposite reaction would occur and the engine's speed would increase. The use of a flyball as a feedback element proved tremendously successful and is still used in the fuel control system of most modern jet engines. Pneumatic power was harnessed for the control of temperatures, pressures and flows in the emerging petroleum and chemical processing industries of the early twentieth century. Then, in the 1930's, in the communications industry and during World War II, the electronics revolution caused an explosion in control system technology. The advent of electronic amplifiers in instrumentation and communications made it possible for designers to achieve an intuitive understanding of the nature of feedback. At about the same time, Wiener explored its profound significance (Ref. [2]).

Today automatic control is so diversified, and often so completely integrated into the system itself, that it escapes definitive classification (see Ref. [3] for a selected bibliography). We can, however, define several broad categories of control systems and illustrate them by means of simple examples.

First, *closed loop* versus *open loop*. Closed loop systems contain feedback, that is, a measurement of the system's output is used in the regulation of the input to the system, thereby keeping the output closer to its desired value. Open loop systems lack feedback. A home heating system containing a thermostat, which measures the room's temperature and turns the furnace on or off, is a closed loop system. A system in which only the fuel flow can be set is open loop because there is no measurement made of the system's output, the room temperature. The level control of Ktesibios (Fig. 7-1(b)) is a closed loop system whereas the temperature compensation used in some pendulum clocks, which counteracts changes in the effective length of the pendulum caused by thermal expansion or contraction to prevent changes in the clock's speed when the temperature changes, is open loop because there is no measurement of the clock's output, its speed.

Secondly, self-operated controllers versus those with separate power sources. The Watt governor is self-operated. The motion of the flyballs, which are connected to the main power shaft of the engine, is used directly to operate the main steam valve of the engine and thus alter the speed back towards the desired or *set point* value. The size of the flyballs determines the power drawn from the engine shaft and the power available to operate the steam valve. Most of today's automatic controllers are equipped with auxiliary power supply units; the controllers are defined by the type of power they use — hydraulic, pneumatic or electronic.

Thirdly, the name of the variable being controlled (the *controlled variable*) may identify a control system. For instance, Fig. 7-1(b) shows a level control system. Likewise, there are flow rate, temperature, pressure, pH, voltage, electric current, neutron density controllers, etc. in the process and power industries. The name *servomechanism* (from the Latin word for slave) is used for mechanical position control systems. For instance, a radar tracking antenna is driven by a servomechanism, as are aircraft control surfaces.

The desired value (i.e., the set point) of the controlled variable may be kept constant or may be varied. For example, the set point is constant in the Ktesibios system (Fig. 7-1(b)) and in the Watt governor whereas it changes in a radar tracking servo. Automatic control that will repeat programmed changes is used in automated manufacturing processes and machine tool controls. Automatic control is sequential in some cases in which logical operations dominate, for example, as in automatic elevators, some robots and the automatic start-up/shut-down of plants.

Let us take modes of control as the fifth item for classification. A thermostat for room temperature control operates in an on-off (or *bang-bang*) mode. A contactor type electric servomotor may have three states of operation: clockwise and counterclockwise rotation at a fixed speed and stop. These are all discontinuous mode controllers. The float in Fig. 7-1(b), on the other hand, has a continuous mode between its two end positions, thus throttling the water flow. In general, continuous control gives smoother operation than does the discontinuous mode. In addition, the time mode of the controller may be either continuous or discrete. For instance, the control action generated by an on-line digital computer is discrete in time.

Up to this point, we have illustrated each item of our informal classification with simple examples. When several controls are combined, however, complexity arises. A temperature control system in a process, for instance, may have a pneumatic servomechanism operating on a steam valve under the command of the temperature controller. In a boiler combustion controller, a control signal from the main line steam pressure controller (or the master controller) will change the set point of a fuel flow rate controller. This is a cascade control system. The fuel flow, in turn, must have a matching flow in the combustion air so that the air flow controller maintains its set point at a fixed ratio to the fuel flow set point, which is known as a ratio control. Such vertical (cascade) and horizontal (like ratio) formations can build up into a hierarchy. The low level controllers in a hierarchy system are mostly for local (and short term) control whereas the higher ones are for global (and longer time span), often supervisory operations, such as readjusting, coordinating and adapting low level control actions for overall optimization of some sort. The relation is somewhat like our higher level brain (a supervisory controller) deciding to walk in a certain direction versus the lower level neuro-muscular control system (local control) coordinating the walking activity.

7.2 FEEDBACK STRUCTURE

Feedback is not a monopoly of automatic control engineers. Common feedback phenomena are seen in biological, ecological (predator-prey, for example), societal, economical (for example, boom and depression cycles based upon the classical Keynesian viewpoint) and engineering systems. Since the 1930's, the use of feedback has been a well established technique in electronic amplifiers. In fact, classical control techniques, based upon transfer functions and frequency response concepts (see Chapter 8), have their origin in the theory of feedback amplifiers. To see a basic property of feedback systems in its purest form, consider the network shown in Fig. 7-2(a), where the relations are presented in the Laplace domain. Signal $E(s)$ is given by $E(s) = I(s) - B(s)$ where $I(s)$ and $B(s)$ are input and feedback signals, respectively. This actuating signal $E(s)$, amplified, becomes the output signal $O(s)$

$$O(s) = k\,E(s) \qquad \text{where } k = \text{amplifier gain} \tag{7-1}$$

With the output thus established, the feedback signal is given by $B(s) = H(s)O(s)$ where $H(s)$ is the transfer function of the feedback (measurement) network. Substituting for $B(s)$ in $E(s) = I(s) - B(s)$

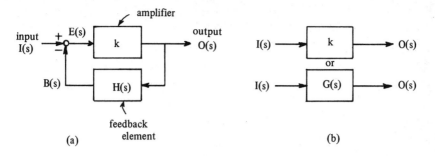

Fig. 7-2 Closed Loop (a) versus Open Loop (b) System

$$E(s) = I(s) - H(s)O(s) \qquad (7\text{-}2)$$

so that, eliminating $E(s)$ from the two expressions, we find the input to output relation

$$\frac{O(s)}{I(s)} = \frac{k}{1 + kH(s)} \qquad (7\text{-}3)$$

This is a fundamental relation in control system work since it relates the transfer function of the closed loop system to the transfer functions of each of the system components. If k is a high gain, $k|H(s)| \gg 1$, then

$$\frac{O(s)}{I(s)} = \frac{1}{H(s)} \qquad (7\text{-}4)$$

The amplifier gain k is not involved in the final relation (7-4), showing that this feedback system is insensitive to the forward path (E to O in Fig. 7-2(a)) parameter. The amplifier is not required to be highly accurate or time invariant; it could be nonlinear and time varying. This is the *raison d'être* of the (negative) feedback structure. The analog computer is an example of a high gain amplifier with feedback. As shown in Fig. 4-8, the input-output voltage relations are independent of the characteristics of the operational amplifier. On the other hand, the input-output relation of an open loop system (Fig. 7-2(b)) is naturally influenced by the element's parametric changes.

In automatic control systems, the closed loop and open loop configurations correspond to feedback control and feedforward (or compensation), respectively. How do they compare to each other? If properly applied, feedforward control can generate a corrective action promptly. However, the disturbance must be measured to produce a matching corrective action. The performance of this scheme thus depends on the accuracy of the measurement and the nature of the feedforward element. The error in a feedforward controller is not checked. Therefore, the performance may deteriorate with time because of parameter drifts. Some time lag in the response is unavoidable in a feedback loop. However, the value of the controlled variable is always checked against its desired value. There is no need to measure the disturbances (although measuring the disturbance and feeding forward to initiate a feedback control action promptly would improve the control quality). In short, a feedback control system is flexible. It can even cope with unanticipated disturbances.

Self-regulation, the tendency of a system to level off at an equilibrium operating level, can be explained in terms of feedback. In a leaking tank, for example, the net flow, which is the difference of inflow and outflow, Fig. 7-3(a), is integrated (i.e., accumulated) in the tank and determines the level in the tank. The level, in turn, affects the leaking flow, which forms a path (in the block diagram) backwards to the input side of the tank; it is thus a feedback system. Because of the feedback, the "demand" (or load or outflow) curve in Fig. 7-3(b) has a plus slope when plotted against level h, like the corresponding M line in Fig. 1-3. The supply characteristic of the water tank, however, is different from the B curve in Fig. 1-3; it is horizontal, meaning that the supply flow is independent of the water level. The intersection of the two, point P in Fig. 7-3(b), is a stable equilibrium point.

A forest fire or bomb explosion is regenerative, characterized by positive feedback, as indicated conceptually in Fig. 7-3(c), where fire, the output, causes higher temperatures and induces draft, which increases the combustion rate, once the chain reaction is triggered by ignition (the input).

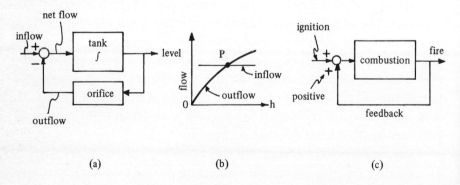

(a)   (b)   (c)

Fig. 7-3 Self-regulating (a, b) versus Autocatalytic (c) Reaction

A feedback loop has a tendency to generate its own loop oscillation (a loop with only one storage element, like the single leaking tank system, is an exception). One example is a spring-mass system in which the spring force on the mass is proportional and opposite to the deflection of the mass so that it acts as a position controller of the mass. The interaction of elements in the loop generates an oscillation. A self-generated loop oscillation is sometimes observed in *homeostasis* (built-in feedback control action for self-regulation in biological systems).

7.3 AUTOMATIC CONTROL SYSTEMS

The general form of Fig. 7-4 is normally accepted as the canonical configuration of an engineering feedback control system. It depicts a causal sequence along a closed loop. A system represented by the diagram could be linear or nonlinear, although, rigorously speaking, block diagram algebra only applies to linear systems. In particular, the Laplace domain variables and transfer functions shown in the figure are strictly limited to linear systems.

The set point (also called the reference input or command) is one of the inputs to the closed loop system. It sets the value desired for the system's output, the controlled variable. The reference input may stay constant or it may be changed (see Sec. 7.1). Since the control object may be subject to disturbing effects and load changes from its environment, the disturbance in Fig. 7-4 is

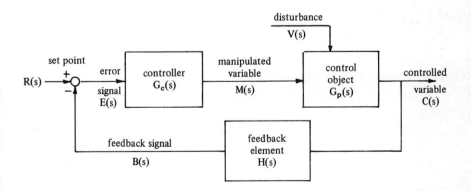

Fig. 7-4 Control System Block Diagram

also considered as an input to the closed loop system. The output (the value of the controlled variable) is fed back via a feedback element (a measuring instrument or a component for performance improvement). Its output, the feedback signal, is then checked against the set point and the difference (error) actuates the controller which, in turn, applies a controlling input (the manipulated variable) to the control object.

The system structure represented by the block diagram in Fig. 7-4 is causal. In many cases (especially in some typical process control systems), this causality is close to the causal relationships between the hardware components in the system. For instance, many sensing elements that measure the value of the controlled variable are unilateral; that is, most instruments are designed so that they will have virtually no loading effect on the control object (such an instrument has a high input impedance). Note, however, that the float F in Fig. 7-1(b) does directly affect the level; for this case, the block diagram representation (Fig. 7-4) does not apply because the feedback element is not causally isolated from the controlled output — they are bilaterally coupled. A similar argument applies to the path from the controller to the object. The block diagram of Fig. 7-4 implies an isolation between the manipulated variable and the error signal. This is true, for example, if the manipulated variable is a signal from a controller to a power operated valve in a process control system. Because of the amplifiers present in the controller and the low power necessary to actuate the valve, signals cannot propagate in the "wrong" direction, that is, against the arrows. This is not always the case, however. Recalling Ktesibios' clock, because the float acts as the feedback element, controller and actuator all rolled into one, there can be no isolation between these signals.

There are many systems where several loops are mutually coupled (Sec. 7.1). J. Forrester's urban model (Ref. [4]) is an extreme case in which nine reservoirs (state variables) representing various levels of housing, men and their working place (job) are all coupled to each other by flow variables and the flows are subject to nonlinear constitutive relations. What Forrester claims is that the system's dynamic behavior often defies an intuitive guess. Here, it is difficult to spot any oscillations dominated by a single loop. However, as Wiener pointed out (Ref. [2]), there are many complex systems that are characterized by single loop feedback. For instance, the hormone cycle (homeostasis) in humans (Ref. [5]) is associated with time periods of weeks and months and may be separated from, say, the eyeball servomechanism's tracking behavior of moving objects simply because of their entirely different time scales. The conceptual single loop structure of Fig. 7.4 can thus apply to a variety of problems,

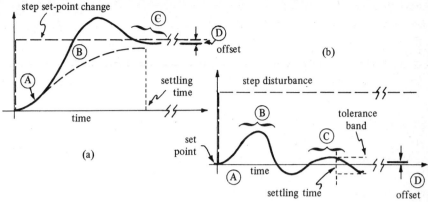

Fig. 7-5 Step Input Response (in the Controlled Variable) of a Control System

at least as a first approximation.

The step input response pattern of a single loop feedback control system gives crucial information about the system's control performance. For this reason, it is often used as part of a control system's specification. Depending on the purpose of the control system, the reference input can be a step (if it is a servomechanism for tracking, for example) or the disturbance can be a step (as in a process control with constant set point). Four crucial parts of the response are marked as regions A, B, C and D in Fig. 7-5. When an equilibrium at zero initial state is broken by a step application, the response starts after some delay or lag, region A. In part (b) of the figure, the response is caused by a disturbance (hence not caused by M(s) but by V(s) in Fig. 7-4). If a disturbance hits the control object at a point close to its sensing element, the response starts sooner and goes up to a higher overshoot (peak) in region B than does the response to, for example, a set point change which is separated from the sensing element by many lag effects (i.e., capacitance C's and resistance R's). The magnitude of the maximum overshoot is a measure of performance in region B. An indication of the speed of response may be also obtained for a step reference input ((a) of the figure) by observing the time at which the peak occurs. We can avoid overshoot by letting the rise level off, as indicated by the dashed line, trading off reduced speed of response. The dominant period and decay of the loop oscillation are observed in region C. A control system may have no residual error or, as shown in region D, it may have an *offset* (a steady-state error).

The *settling time* is the time at which the response becomes completely bounded by a tolerance band as shown. It should be noted here that in many cases (particularly in process control problems) control performance as measured by the response of a particular controlled variable is often only an indirect measure of success. In some cases, the real variable of interest is too difficult to measure, as in a sugar refinery where a particular crystal formation is the ultimate goal of temperature control. In other cases, the ultimate goal has global significance and depends on maintaining control in many local control loops.

7.4 CONTROL SYSTEM SIMULATION

Often the best way to obtain the step response of a control system, or any other time response that might be important for the particular application, is to use the techniques described in Chapter 4 to simulate the system's behavior. This is especially valuable in the design stages when the actual system may not even exist. Simulation can also be a useful procedure even when the real system does exist if experiments on the actual system are difficult to perform, as in biological systems, very expensive, as when a large refinery would have to be out of production for the duration of the experiment, or when the time constants of the system are so long that repetitions of the experiment to find the effects of parameter variation would be too lengthy.

Ktesibios' level control device is an ideal demonstration of control system simulation. The level control and a blowup of the region around the tip of the float are shown in Fig. 7-6. We start by selecting state variables for this system. The float can have two modes of energy storage: kinetic energy due to its velocity and potential energy due to the spring-like interaction between the float and the water. To characterize these energy storage modes, we can choose the velocity V and the position y of the float as state variables. A third energy storage mode is associated with the liquid height h in the tank, so we will use it as the third state variable. Let's start from the top and work down, deriving the system's state equations.

First we assume that the pressure in the main water supply conduit is an input. That is, the amount of flow that goes to the water clock is not large enough to have any significant effect on the supply pressure. This does not mean, however, that we consider the water supply pressure to be constant. It can change because other users on the line draw more or less water at different times during the day or because of general water supply conditions. One of the primary purposes of this study is to see how well the clock keeps time in the

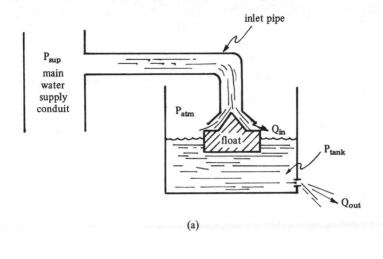

(a)

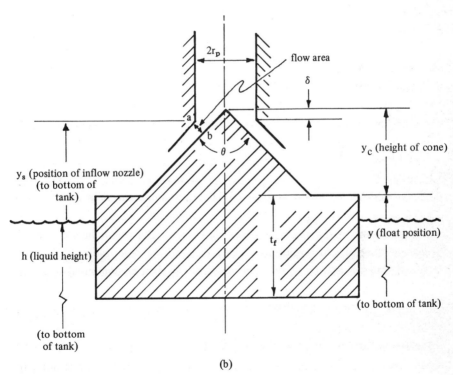

(b)

Fig. 7-6 Water Level Regulator from Ktesibios' Clock

face of such changes. The flow rate of water into the tank is governed by the supply pressure, the flow resistance in the pipe leading to the tank, the position of the float and the atmospheric pressure P_{atm}. We assume that the end of the flared part of the inlet pipe exit is always open to the atmosphere and that atmospheric pressure is constant. For turbulent flow, the flow rate depends on the square root of the pressure drop

$$Q_{in} = K_{in}(P_{sup} - P_{atm})^{1/2} \tag{7-5}$$

Since flow reversals are not possible here, we can use the simple square root rather than the signed square root (SST) function we used in Chapter 3. The value of K_{in} is modulated by the float position, most particularly by the value of the minimum flow area, shown in Fig. 7-6(b). We will assume that as long as the flow area is greater than the area of the inlet pipe, the flow rate is governed completely by the value of K_{in} determined from pipe size, water viscosity, etc. Designating this value by K_{pipe}, we assume that the overall flow coefficient K_{in} decreases linearly from K_{pipe} to zero according to the ratio of flow area to inlet pipe area, that is

$$K_{in} = K_{pipe} \qquad \text{for } A_{flow} \geq A_{pipe}$$
$$K_{in} = K_{pipe} \frac{A_{flow}}{A_{pipe}} \qquad \text{for } A_{flow} < A_{pipe} \tag{7-6}$$

This relationship is shown in Fig. 7-7(a). To compute the flow area, we note that it is the surface area of the frustrum of a cone obtained by rotating the line a–b shown in Fig. 7-6(b) through 360° about the center line shown. The frustrum of a cone of revolution is characterized by a larger radius r_1, a smaller radius r_2 and a height h_{cone}. The surface area can then be computed from

$$A_{flow} = \pi(r_1 + r_2)[h_{cone}^2 + (r_1 - r_2)^2]^{1/2} \tag{7-7}$$

Designating the cone angle of the float θ, the cone dimensions can be computed from

$$r_1 = r_{pipe}$$
$$r_2 = \frac{1}{2}\delta\left[\sin\theta + \frac{r_{pipe}}{\delta}(1 - \cos\theta)\right]$$
$$h_{cone} = \frac{1}{2}\delta\left[\frac{r_{pipe}}{\delta}\sin\theta - (1 - \cos\theta)\right] \tag{7-8}$$

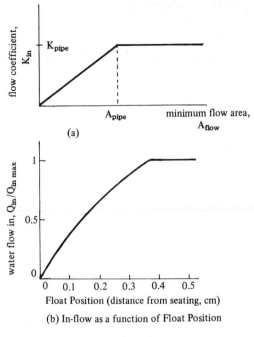

(a)

(b) In-flow as a function of Float Position

Fig. 7-7 Water Inflow Characteristics

where δ is the height of the tip of the cone over the point at which the flare of the inlet pipe begins

$$\delta = (y + y_c) - y_s \tag{7-9}$$

(see Fig. 7-6(b) for definition of the y's). From Eqs. (7-5) through (7-9), we can compute the inflow Q_{in} as a function of float position and supply pressure. Fig. 7-7(b) shows the normalized water flow as a function of the float position parameter δ for a cone angle of $90°$.

Continuing, we can now develop the relationships for the forces on the float. There are two downward forces: gravity and the force applied from the water flowing in and striking the float; an upward force due to buoyancy and a viscous damping force whose sign changes with the sign of the float velocity. As sign conventions, we define velocity and displacements as positive in the upward direction and forces on the float to be positive if they act upward. The gravity force is

$$F_g = -W = -Mg \tag{7-10}$$

As a first approximation for the force applied by the inflowing water on the float, we will assume that it is constant and equal to the force when the float completely shuts the flow off, that is

$$F_{flow} = -P_{sup}A_{pipe} \tag{7-11}$$

The buoyant force is equal to the weight of water displaced by the float. For a sufficiently light float shaped as shown in Fig. 7-6(a), the cross-sectional area of the portion under water is constant, so the weight of water displaced is a linear function of the submerged depth

$$F_{buoy} = \rho_w g A_{float}[t_f - (y - h)] \tag{7-12}$$

The viscous damping force will always oppose the motion of the float. Assuming that linear damping applies

$$F_{damp} = -bV \tag{7-13}$$

where b is a constant coefficient and V is the vertical velocity of the float.

We can now apply Newton's 2-nd law to the float

$$M\frac{dV}{dt} = F_{buoy} + F_g + F_{flow} + F_{damp}$$
$$= \rho_w g A_{float}[t_f - (y - h)] - Mg - P_{sub}A_{pipe} - bV \tag{7-14}$$

where M is the mass of the float. Dividing through by M and noting that the first term can be considerably simplified by substituting for M, which is equal to $\rho_{float}t_f A_{float}$, we obtain

$$\frac{dV}{dt} = \frac{\rho_w}{\rho_{float}} g\left(1 - \frac{y - h}{t_f}\right) - g - \frac{P_{sub}A_{pipe}}{M} - \frac{b}{M} V \tag{7-15}$$

This is the first of the three state equations we need to describe this system. The second follows immediately from the definition of velocity as the derivative of displacement

$$\frac{dy}{dt} = V \tag{7-16}$$

where y is the vertical displacement of the float. Eq. (7-16) is thus the second state equation.

The third state equation comes from a consideration of the factors that contribute to changes in the height of water in the tank. Three factors affect water height: 1) water flow out of the tank, 2) water flow into the tank and 3) vertical motion of the float. The equation for the time rate of change of h is

$$\frac{dh}{dt} = \frac{Q_{in}}{A_{free}} - \frac{Q_{out}}{A_{free}} + H_{fm} \tag{7-17}$$

where A_{free} is the free surface area of the tank (i.e., the total cross-sectional area of the tank minus the cross-sectional area of the float, $A_{tank} - A_{float}$) and H_{fm} is the component of dh/dt due to float motion. Q_{in} is determined by Eqs. (7-5) to (7-9). Using a square root law for the flow out of the tank since the pressure drop for the outflow, $P_{tank} - P_{atm}$, will be determined by the height of water in the tank, we have

$$Q_{out} = K_{out}h^{\frac{1}{2}} \tag{7-18}$$

The change in height due to float motion can be derived by imagining that the water being displaced because of velocity V of the float is being added to a tank have a surface area A_{free}. The rate at which water is being displaced is $V \cdot A_{float}$, so

$$H_{fm} = -\frac{V A_{float}}{A_{free}} \tag{7-19}$$

The minus sign is necessary because a positive (upwards) V yields a negative (downwards) rate of change of h. Substituting into Eq. (7-17) yields

$$\frac{dh}{dt} = \frac{Q_{in}}{A_{free}} - \frac{K_{out}h^{\frac{1}{2}}}{A_{free}} - \frac{V A_{float}}{A_{free}} \tag{7-20}$$

This completes the set of state equations. The state vector is

$$\underline{x} = \begin{bmatrix} V \\ y \\ h \end{bmatrix}$$

and the state equations are Eqs. (7-15), (7-16) and (7-20), with Eqs. (7-5) to (7-9) used as auxiliary equations to compute Q_{in}.

Next, the computer simulation. Because of the nonlinearities in the flow equations, digital simulation will prove easier to apply than analog simulation. The simulation algorithm, using the Euler variant method (Sec. 4.1), follows. Aside from name changes to suit computer requirements, most of the statements come directly from the state and auxiliary equations. The algorithm is:

```
      REAL M, KIN, KOUT
      read in values for parameters and
          initial states: DT, TFINAL,
          DENRAT, G, RPIPE, TF, M,         – DENRAT is the ratio of
          B, PATM, YC, YS, THETA,             the density of water to
          KPIPE, KOUT, AFLOAT,                the average density of the
          ATANK, VZERO, YZERO,                float.
          HZERO
      APIPE = 3.1416*RPIPE**2
      AFREE = ATANK – AFLOAT
      DELMAX = RPIPE/TAN(THETA/2.0)
      T = 0.0
      V = VZERO
      Y = YZERO
      H = HZERO
  100 CONTINUE
      print or plot results
      if PSUP varies, compute its value
          here
      YSUB = (Y–H)/TF                       – YSUB is a measure of the
      IF(YSUB .LT. 0)YSUB = 0                  fraction of the float that
      IF(YSUB .GT. 1.0)YSUB = 1                is submerged, which must
                                               be between zero and one.
      V = V+(DENRAT*G*(1–YSUB)–G             – Eq. (7-15)
          –PSUB*APIPE/M–B*V/M)*DT
      Y = Y+V*DT                            – from Eq. (7-16)
      DELTA = Y+YC–YS                       – from Eq. (7-9)
      IF(DELTA .LT. DELMAX)GO TO            – If δ is greater than δ_max,
          200                                  the cone has seated and
                                               cut off the inflow com-
                                               pletely.
```

```
      AFLOW = 0.0
      QIN = 0.0
      Y = DELMAX+YS−YC
      V = 0.0
      GO TO 300
200   HCONE = 0.5*DELTA*((RPIPE/        — These three are from Eqs.
          DELTA)*SIN(THETA)−(1.0−         (7-8).
          COS(THETA)))
      R2 = 0.5*DELTA*(SIN(THETA)+
          (RPIPE/DELTA)*(1.0−COS
          (THETA)))
      IF(R2 .LT. 0)GO TO 260
      R1 = RPIPE
      AFLOW = 3.1416*(R1+R2)*SQRT      — Eq. (7-7)
          (HCONE**2+(R1−R2)**2)
      IF(AFLOW .GT. APIPE)GO TO 275    — from Eq. (7-6)
250   KIN = KPIPE*(AFLOW/APIPE)        — from Eq. (7-6)
260   QIN = KIN*SQRT(PSUP−PATM)
      GO TO 300
275   QIN = KPIPE*SQRT(PSUP−PATM)
300   CONTINUE
      H = H+(QIN−KOUT*SQRT(H)−V*       — from Eq. (7-20)
          AFLOAT)*DT/AFREE
      T = T+DT
      IF(T .LE. TFINAL)GO TO 100
      STOP
      END
```

The series of IF statements check for three conditions that affect how the inflow Q_{in} will be computed. The first check is to see if the cone is completely submerged or out of the water. The second checks whether the cone has been pushed directly against the inlet pipe, cutting the inflow to zero. The last is to see if the minimum flow area is greater than the inlet pipe area. If it is, the inlet flow rate depends only on K_{pipe}; if the minimum flow area is less than the area of the pipe, the flow rate is computed from K_{in}.

Results of the simulation and some typical parameter variations that might be used in a design optimization study are shown in Fig. 7-8. As we can see from the responses, the motion of the float can interact with the water flow

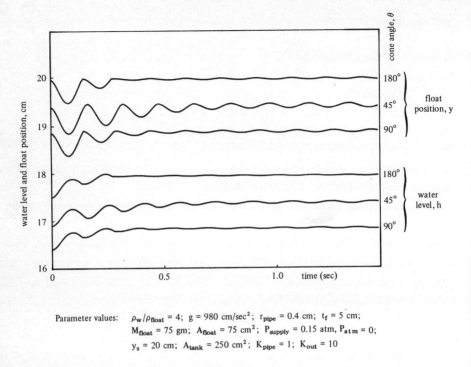

Parameter values: $\rho_w/\rho_{float} = 4$; $g = 980$ cm/sec^2; $r_{pipe} = 0.4$ cm; $t_f = 5$ cm;
$M_{float} = 75$ gm; $A_{float} = 75$ cm^2; $P_{supply} = 0.15$ atm, $P_{atm} = 0$;
$y_s = 20$ cm; $A_{tank} = 250$ cm^2; $K_{pipe} = 1$; $K_{out} = 10$

Fig. 7-8 Simulated Response of Water Clock Level Control System to a 33% Increase in Supply Pressure

part of the system; that is, float motion causes an immediate change in water level. We can see that the oscillations in the figure are caused primarily by the float-water interaction by noting that whenever there is a downward float motion there is a corresponding upward change in the water level. This interaction limits the performance of the controller, but, because of the low cost and simplicity of the design, it could be an optimum solution to the problem.

Further design work on this problem would start with parameter variation studies. One such study is shown in Fig. 7-8, where the cone angle of the float has been varied. These results indicate that higher cone angles (i.e., a flatter top to the float) give better results for supply pressure change. Another such study might be to vary the float size. A smaller float would respond much faster and have less interaction with the water, but the size of the inlet pipe would have to be reduced (otherwise the smaller float would not have enough buoyant force to counteract the downward force from the inflowing water). This would reduce the overall speed of response of the system. An important aspect of these kinds of parameter studies is that all the parameters can interact. That is, the optimum float angle probably changes as a function of float size and of other parameters that are changed. In order to prevent the number of trials from becoming overwhelming, the designer must use his intuition to restrict the search to a region in the parameter space that is likely to yield a good compromise.

If Ktesibios had transistors at his disposal in designing the water clock, he could have used amplifiers in the system, reduced the size of the float so that it no longer interfered with the water flow dynamics, converted the float's motion into an electrical signal and amplified that signal, perhaps using an analog computer type of circuit. An analog computer circuit would have acted as the controller, computing the desired flow of water, and the electrical signal it produced could have operated a power actuated flow valve. Such a system would have improved controller performance but would have been more expensive and complicated than the original design.

7.5 LINEAR CONTROL LAWS

We did not pay much attention to the canonical feedback structure of Fig. 7-4 in the simulation studies in the preceding section. Instead, we made a digital computer simulation directly from a set of constitutive relations without trying to mold the relations into a block diagram for closed loop control; the tank water and float interaction would have made such an attempt futile anyway. Since we utilized digital simulation, there was no need to linearize the equations describing the float action.

In the following, and in the next section, however, attention is focused on the single loop feedback structure of linear elements. Fig. 7-4 is simplified even further into the direct feedback form given in Fig. 7-9 for the purpose of gaining general insight into feedback loop dynamics, which is possible through an analytical approach to linear systems. Following simple algebraic steps that parallel Eqs. (7-1) through (7-4), the *closed loop transfer functions* of the direct feedback system are:

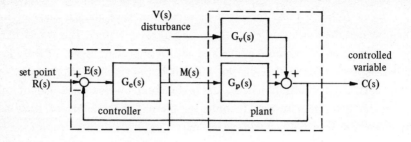

Fig. 7-9 A Direct Feedback System

for reference input (with $V(s) = 0$):
$$\frac{C(s)}{R(s)} = \frac{G(s)}{1 + G(s)} \qquad \frac{E(s)}{R(s)} = \frac{1}{1 + G(s)} \qquad (7\text{-}21)$$

and

for disturbance input (with $R(s) = 0$):
$$\frac{C(s)}{V(s)} = \frac{G_V(s)}{1 + G(s)} \qquad \frac{E(s)}{V(s)} = \frac{-G_v(s)}{1 + G(s)} \qquad (7\text{-}22)$$

$G(s)$ in these equations is given by

$$G(s) = G_p(s)G_c(s) \qquad (7\text{-}23)$$

We call such a product of transfer functions in a loop the *open loop transfer function*.

A common form of $G_c(s)$ that relates the manipulated variable $M(s)$ to the error signal $E(s)$ is called a *linear control law*. There are at least four basic laws.

Proportional action (P-action):
$$G_c(s) = k_c \qquad (7\text{-}24)$$

Integral action (I-action):
$$G_c(s) = \frac{k_i}{s} \qquad (7\text{-}25)$$

Proportional plus integral action (PI-action):
$$G_c(s) = k_c (1 + \frac{1}{T_i s}) \qquad (7\text{-}26)$$

Proportional plus integral plus derivative action (PID-action):

$$G_c(s) = k_c(1 + \frac{1}{T_i s} + T_d s) \qquad (7\text{-}27)$$

where k_c and k_i are gains and T_i and T_d are I-action and D-action time constants, respectively. These are usually adjustable controller parameters.

P, PI and PID actions are normally implemented in industrial instruments by means of the feedback principle shown in Fig. 7-2 and Eq. (7-4). $H(s)$ is simply a gain (k_b) for P-action, like the resistor feedback network in an analog computer gain element. A resistive-capacitive network is required to implement PI-action. $H(s)$ for PI control has the general form

$$H(s) = k_b(1 - \frac{1}{Ts + 1}) \qquad k_b = \text{feedback gain} \qquad (7\text{-}28)$$

so that its inverse, $H(s)^{-1}$, will produce a P and an I in linear combination, Eq. (7-26). If the feedback transfer function is replaced by a single lag form

$$H(s) = \frac{k_b}{Ts + 1} \qquad (7\text{-}29)$$

$H(s)^{-1}$ will give a PD-action, $k_c(T_d s + 1)$. Strictly speaking, this is unrealizable (see Eq. (6-67)); substitution of Eq. (7-29) into Eq. (7-3), however, is realizable. The PD-control law, $k_c(T_d s + 1)$, is an idealized form of a realizable PD-action. One way to implement PID-action is to couple PI and PD controls in series so that their transfer functions multiply. An I-action (Eq. (7-25)) can be realized by making the velocity of the motor that drives the final control element (control valve) proportional to its input signal, $E(s)$.

P-action is the most simple and basic of all the control laws. We saw it in the Ktesibios system (Fig. 7-1(b)) and in James Watt's first speed governor (about 1750). With P-action, which is symbolically sketched in Fig. 7-10, the engine speed must change to alter the flyball position and, thus, to change the steam valve opening. This implies that the engine must run at a speed lower than the set point under a heavy load while the speed will be above the set point at a lighter load. For example, a heavy load will require more steam to maintain the set point speed, but, to get this extra steam, the speed governor will have to operate at a speed lower than the set point. This *offset* in equilibrium value of the controlled variable from its set point is unavoidable in any P-control system.

Let us use a linear approximation for the engine system and estimate the

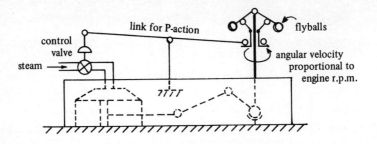

Fig. 7-10 The Watt Steam Engine Governor

offset caused by a load change. By Newton's 2-nd law

$$(\text{moment of inertia}) \cdot \frac{dn}{dt} = (\text{engine torque}) - (\text{load torque})$$

where n is engine speed (rpm). Denoting small deviations of the speed, engine torque and load torque from the normal equilibrium state by $C(s)$, $M(s)$ and $V(s)$ (in the s domain), respectively, we have

$$sC(s) = k_p[M(s) - V(s)] \qquad\qquad\qquad (7\text{-}30)$$

where the engine gain k_p represents the shaft and load inertia. The P-action is $M(s) = k_c E(s)$, where $E(s)$ is the change in speed error[†] and $M(s) = k_c E(s)$ is the resulting change in engine torque (caused by the control valve movement as shown in Fig. 7-10). We thus have

$$G_p(s) = \frac{C(s)}{M(s)} = \frac{k_p}{s} \qquad G_v(s) = \frac{C(s)}{V(s)} = -\frac{k_p}{s} \qquad G_c(s) = \frac{M(s)}{E(s)} = k_c$$

The open loop transfer function is

$$G(s) = G_p(s)G_c(s) = \frac{k_p k_c}{s}$$

so that, by Eq. (7-22)

---

† It is customary to designate a particular set of operating conditions, i.e., load and speed, as "normal" and to designate the speed error at this point as zero. $E(s)$ is thus the change in engine speed error as the operating condition deviates from normal.

$$\frac{E(s)}{V(s)} = \frac{k_p}{s + k_p k_c} \tag{7-31}$$

The offset for a unit step increase in load torque, $V(s) = 1/s$, can be estimated by the final value theorem, Eq. (6-12), applied to Eq. (7-31)

$$\lim_{t \to \infty} e(t) = \text{offset} = \lim_{s \to 0} sE(s) = \frac{k_p}{s + k_p k_c}\bigg|_{s=0} = \frac{1}{k_c} \tag{7-32}$$

This indicates that the engine speed is lower than its set point when the load torque is increased above normal and higher than the set point when the load torque is decreased below normal.

Application of the final value theorem shows that the engine governor system has no offset for a step change in set point, $R(s) = 1/s$. However, for a system with an open loop transfer function of the form

$$G(s) = \frac{k_p k_c}{Ts + 1}$$

(a liquid level control, for example), using Eq. (7-21) and the final value theorem, we find that

$$\text{offset due to a unit change in set point} = \frac{1}{1 + k_p k_c} \tag{7-33}$$

This implies that the equilibrium level will be lower than its set point value when the set point is moved up from the normal value for which the control system has been pre-adjusted. Analyses of offset shown here for load and set point upsets may be generalized, if necessary, for the general form of the transfer function, Eq. (6-65).

The offset in the first-generation Watt governor spurred engineers to devote a half century of trial and error research and development work in the quest of a better governor. First, speculating that the offset due to load change might be eliminated if the steam valve (steam control valve) is kept moving (or *floating*) as long as there is still an error, they tried I-action. The attempt failed because the system "hunted," that is, developed a sustained oscillation in engine speed. With hindsight, we understand this problem by substituting $G_p(s) = k_p/s$ and $G_c(s) = k_i/s$ into Eq. (7-21); we then have

$$\frac{C(s)}{R(s)} = \frac{k_i k_p}{s^2 + k_i k_p} \tag{7-34}$$

which is an undamped oscillator. It is possible, however, to apply I-action to some other systems. If it is applied to a water level system, $G_p(s) = k_p/(Ts + 1)$, which has self-regulation, Eq. (7-21) will give the following closed loop transfer function:

$$\frac{C(s)}{R(s)} = \frac{k_i k_p}{Ts^2 + s + k_i k_p} \tag{7-35}$$

This transfer function describes a damped second order system. The system is asymptotically stable. In addition, computing $E(s)/R(s)$ or $E(s)/V(s)$ by Eqs. (7-21) and (7-22) and applying the final value theorem, we find that the I control of the level control system will have no offset. Simple I-action, implemented by a rugged hydraulic regulator, can be used, for instance, for temperature or pressure control of outdoor furnaces that have strong self-regulation. The temperature will level off (without control) due to natural heat loss. In general, however, PI-action is better than I-action alone for many systems.

PI-action, Eq. (7-26), was the final solution in the speed governor system; it was implemented by a dashpot (damper) and spring ingeniously inserted in the linkage that connects the flyball-governor and steam valve. Applying

$$G_p(s) = \frac{k_p}{s} \qquad G_c(s) = k_c(1 + \frac{1}{T_i s})$$

in Eqs. (7-21) through (7-23), we find that

$$\frac{C(s)}{R(s)} = \frac{k_p k_c(1 + T_i s)}{T_i s^2 + k_p k_c T_i s + k_p k_c} \tag{7-36}$$

The system is asymptotically stable. It is easy to confirm that there will be no offset.

A further refinement in control performance was achieved just after the turn of the 20th century when D-action was introduced into control laws. D-action, added to either P or PI-action, improves recovery (or response speed) (see Fig. 7-5) because D-action detects the trend of change and thus, in a way, anticipates the future. Independent use of a D-action, however, is meaningless because it responds only to the time rate of a change of the error.

To summarize, the three basic components of the linear control laws can be seen to have the following meanings: P-action responds to the present (or current) situation, while all of the past history, integrated, appears in I, and the D-action attempts to speculate about the future. If these three laws seem familiar, perhaps it is because they are found in human behavior as well as in engineering systems. Especially since Wiener's work (Ref. [2]), many papers have been published on man-machine systems. Experiments to identify the "human operator transfer function" were carefully designed to eliminate such "unwanted" complexities of man as adaptation and learning. A setup that is still frequently used is an oscilloscope display of a "dancing" spot which an operator is required to track — the spot motion being so random that the human operator never learns to adapt himself to a pattern. Many results in various countries over a long period of time seem to agree, except for minor details, that the human transfer function in extremely simple man-machine operation is basically a PID system with a dead time of a fraction of a second.

We have seen that application of feedback can cause oscillations in systems with nonoscillatory open loop responses. This tendency towards oscillatory, or even unstable, operation is an important aspect of closed loop system design, so we will examine it next.

7.6 STABILITY AND DYNAMICS OF LINEAR FEEDBACK SYSTEMS

The simple block diagram of a closed loop system, Fig. 7-9, is reduced even further in Fig. 7-11, where the open loop transfer function G(s) defined by Eq. (7-23) is the only block contained in the closed loop path. This simple structure is a good approximation for a large number of control systems. It provides a clear demonstration of some of the important dynamic properties of control systems. Applying the general form of Eq. (6-65) to G(s)

$$G(s) = \frac{B(s)}{A(s)} \tag{7-37}$$

the eigenvalues of the control object and controller ($G_p(s)$ and $G_c(s)$ in Fig.

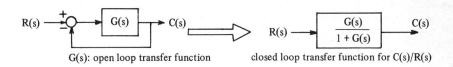

G(s): open loop transfer function   closed loop transfer function for C(s)/R(s)

Fig. 7-11 Block Diagram of a Basic Closed Loop System

7-9) are given as the roots of Eq. (6-66), restated

$$A(s) = 0 \qquad\qquad (7\text{-}38)$$

The roots of the open loop characteristic equation, Eq. (7-38), are called the *open loop poles*. According to Eqs. (7-21), (7-22) and Fig. 7-11, the characteristic equation of the closed loop system is

$$G(s) + 1 = 0 \qquad\qquad (7\text{-}39)$$

or, substituting Eq. (7-37)

$$A(s) + B(s) = 0 \qquad\qquad (7\text{-}40)$$

is the closed loop characteristic equation. The roots of this equation are called the *closed loop poles*.

To see the relation between the open loop and closed loop poles, let us consider a third order open loop transfer function with a triple real pole λ, where λ must be negative for the open loop system to be asymptotically stable. Therefore, the open loop transfer function is

$$G(s) = \frac{K}{(s - \lambda)^3} \qquad\qquad (7\text{-}41)$$

where K is a gain. The modes of the open loop system are $e^{\lambda t}$, $te^{\lambda t}$ and $\frac{1}{2}t^2 e^{\lambda t}$ (from Eqs. (6-33) and (6-34)), so that no oscillation will appear. Its unit step input response for zero initial state will have a typical S-shape pattern when λ is negative.

By Eqs. (7-39) and (7-40), the closed loop characteristic equation for this example is

$$(s - \lambda)^3 = -K \qquad\qquad (7\text{-}42)$$

The closed loop poles, designated by p_1, p_2 and p_3, are related to the open loop parameters (λ and K) by

$$(s - p_1)(s - p_2)(s - p_3) = (s - \lambda)^3 + K = 0 \qquad\qquad (7\text{-}43)$$

This cubic equation can be solved graphically. As shown in Fig. 7-12(a), $(s - \lambda)$

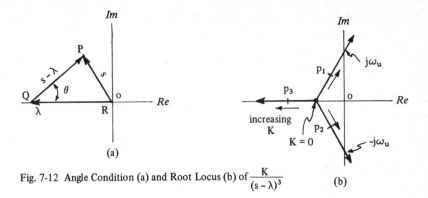

Fig. 7-12 Angle Condition (a) and Root Locus (b) of $\dfrac{K}{(s-\lambda)^3}$ (b)

is a vector in the complex plane for an arbitrarily chosen value of s. In this figure, s is point P or vector RP (where R is the origin) and λ for a negative real value is represented by vector RQ, so that QP is the vector $(s - \lambda)$. Let θ be the angle of this vector. When $(s - \lambda)$ is multiplied by itself twice to get $(s - \lambda)^3$, the product vector will have an angle of 3θ. This product, according to Eq. (7-42), must be a negative real quantity for all positive values of K, so that the product must have an angle of $\pm 180°$, or more generally, $\pm 180° \pm 360°$, hence

$$3\theta = \pm 180°, \pm 180° \pm 360° \quad \text{thus } \theta = \pm 60° \text{ or } \pm 180° \qquad (7\text{-}44)$$

Therefore, the three roots p_1, p_2 and p_3 (the closed loop poles) of Eq. (7-43) must lie on the three lines that radiate from the λ point (Fig. 7-12(b)).

Root Locus

Curves which show root location (straight lines for our example) are generally called *root loci* because the roots (closed loop poles) will "move" on those curves as the value of a parameter (K in our example) is varied. Since the length PQ in Fig. 7-12(a) is the vector magnitude $|(s - \lambda)|$ and the magnitude condition of Eq. (7-42) is

$$|(s - \lambda)|^3 = K$$

the closed loop poles p_1, p_2 and p_3 in Fig. 7-12(b) will move away from the center point λ as K is increased. This implies that the closed loop system will have an oscillatory mode (Table 5-1, second row) due to the pair of conjugate complex, closed loop poles (p_1 and p_2). Moreover, the closed loop system will reach a *stability limit* at some value of gain, $K = K_u$, when the two root-locus branches cross the imaginary axis at $p_1 = j\omega_u$ (Fig. 7-12(b)). The period of cycling at this critical condition is

$$P_u = \frac{2\pi}{\omega_u} \tag{7-45}$$

Even though the open loop system is stable, the closed loop system will generate an oscillation of increasing amplitude and hence become unstable when the loop gain K is increased beyond it critical value K_u.

D-action, when its parameter T_d is properly tuned, will speed up signal transmission in a loop and thus improve the stability of a closed loop system. To illustrate the stabilizing effect of D-action, we shall assume a control object $G_p(s)$ with a triple negative real pole λ and a PD controller $G_c(s) = k_0(T_d s + 1)$. If T_d is tuned to a value of $-1/\lambda$ (which is positive since λ is negative), the open loop transfer function will have the form

$$G(s) = \frac{K}{(s - \lambda)^2}$$

The root locus for this system is shown in Fig. 7-13(a). Since the system is simpler than the third order system of Eq. (7-42), the root locus can be determined by solving directly the quadratic closed loop characteristic equation

$$s^2 - 2\lambda s + (\lambda^2 + K) = 0$$

The roots (closed loop poles) are shown in Fig. 7-13(a)

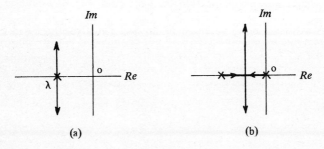

(a)   (b)

Fig. 7-13 Root Locus of a Second Order System (Arrows show direction of increasing K and crosses indicate where K=0)

$$p_{1,2} = \lambda \pm j\sqrt{K} \quad \text{where } j = \sqrt{-1} \tag{7-46}$$

Since the negative real part of λ of the conjugate complex closed loop poles does not depend on the loop gain K, theoretically the closed loop system will never reach a stability limit. In practice, however, excessive D-action (too high a value for T_d) may deteriorate control quality and jeopardize loop stability. Also, the pole-zero cancellation (by tuning T_d to $-1/\lambda$ in this example) requires caution because it will make the system either uncontrollable or unobservable (Sec. 6.8).

I-action, on the other hand, will introduce a state variable of its own into a system, thus contributing to a time lag in the loop. It tends, therefore, to induce loop oscillation and weaken the loop stability. Consider a first order control object $G_p(s) = k/(Ts+1)$ whose pole is $\lambda = -1/T$. The closed loop system will never oscillate under P control. Under I control, however, the second order, open loop transfer function

$$G(s) = \frac{K}{s(s - \lambda)} \tag{7-47}$$

will yield the following quadratic closed loop characteristic equation:

$$s^2 - s\lambda + K = 0 \tag{7-48}$$

and hence the pair of closed loop poles

$$p_{1,2} = \frac{1}{2}(\lambda \pm \sqrt{\lambda^2 - 4K}) \tag{7-49}$$

The roots are negative real for $0 < K \leqslant \dfrac{\lambda^2}{4}$, they are critically damped at $K = \dfrac{\lambda^2}{4}$ and loop oscillation will appear when K becomes larger than $\dfrac{\lambda^2}{4}$ (Fig. 7-13(b)).

The root locus patterns presented in the last two figures were all so simple that it was possible to derive them analytically. In general, however, a digital computer root-finding routine (Ref. [6]) or a graphical technique based upon complex-vector angle and magnitude conditions (Ref. [7]) can be used for their construction.

Parameter Tuning

The linear closed loop dynamics presented so far illustrate the trade-off

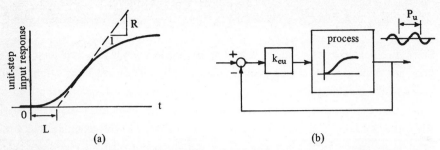

(a)   (b)

Fig. 7-14 Process Parameters for Ziegler-Nichols Rules (Process is shown by its signature in (b))

problem in control system design: closed loop stability will be jeopardized when the control is too tight (for instance, an excessive loop gain in Fig. 7-12), while control will not be effective if the action is too weak (for instance, a low P-action gain will result in excessive offset in Eqs. (7-32) and (7-33)). Ziegler and Nichols, while working on industrial control problems, arrived at a set of semi-empirical rules for tuning controller parameters (Ref. [8]). Their first set of rules is based on process *signature* − an open loop step response curve, which is not oscillatory in most industrial process control systems. Two parameters, the maximum slope R and the *lag time* L, defined in Fig. 7-14(a) for a unit step input, are measured on an experimentally obtained response record or from an analytical (or numerical) result. The process is not subject to feedback control, so the parameters R and L will represent open loop dynamics. In terms of these, for P control, Ziegler and Nichols recommend the gain

$$k_c = \frac{1}{RL} \qquad (7\text{-}50)$$

as an optimum.

Their second method is based on the response of a closed loop system, Fig. 7-14(b), where the process is under P control, and its gain k_c is at the stability limit k_{cu}, so that the loop has sustained oscillation of a period P_u, Eq. (7-45). The pair k_{cu} and P_u may be determined by a real test (if the system already exists) or estimated by calculation (see below) or computer simulation. Ziegler and Nichols recommend

$$k_c = \frac{1}{2} k_{cu} \qquad (7\text{-}51)$$

as the optimum adjustment for a P control. The control parameters they recommend for PI and PID controllers are:

for PI-action:

$$k_c = \frac{0.9}{RL} \qquad T_i = 3.3L \tag{7-52}$$

or $\quad k_c = 0.45k_{cu} \qquad T_i = 0.83P_u \tag{7-53}$

for PID-action:

$$k_c = \frac{1.2}{RL} \qquad T_i = 2L \qquad T_d = 0.5L \tag{7-54}$$

or $\quad k_c = 0.6k_{cu} \qquad T_i = 0.5P_u \qquad T_d = 0.125P_u \tag{7-55}$

The P-action gain for PI-action is 10% lower than the case of P-action only because of the destabilizing effect of the I-action. It is about 20% higher in PID-action due to the stabilizing effect of the D-action. The closed loop response curves (Fig. 7-5) with the optimum tunings will have a damped oscillation with an amplitude ratio of 1/4 or less per cycle (i.e., the amplitude decreases by a factor of 4 for each cycle). This optimum is a nice midway point between an excessively oscillatory but fast response and a stable but slow response. Generally, a final refinement in tuning is desirable to suit one's specific control job.

Stability Limit Estimation

A quick estimate of the stability limit of a control loop is sometimes useful as a guide for feedback system design. There are several methods available for testing the stability of a linear system without solving the characteristic equation. One of these, the Routh method, is presented in the appendix. Another, from which the stability limit oscillation conditions (k_{cu} and P_u in Fig. 7-14(b)) can be computed directly, is suitable if a linear model can be simplified to an order lower than about 7. The general approach can be illustrated using Eq. (7-42) as an example, where the closed loop characteristic equation is

$$(s - \lambda)^3 + K = 0$$

that is

$$s^3 - 3\lambda s^2 + 3\lambda^2 s - \lambda^3 + K = 0 \tag{7-56}$$

Substituting $s = j\omega_u$, $s^2 = -\omega_u^2$, $s^3 = -j\omega_u^3$ and $K = K_u$ into Eq. (7-56)

$$-j\omega_u^3 + 3\lambda\omega_u^2 + 3\lambda^2 j\omega_u - \lambda^3 + K_u = 0 \tag{7-57}$$

Collecting real and imaginary parts, we obtain two equations for two unknowns

$$\text{Im:} \quad -\omega_u^3 + 3\lambda^2\omega_u = 0 \tag{7-58}$$

$$\text{Re:} \quad 3\lambda\omega_u^2 - \lambda^3 + K_u = 0 \tag{7-59}$$

Solving Eq. (7-58) for ω_u

$$\omega_u = \sqrt{3}\ \lambda \tag{7-60}$$

The negative root, $-\sqrt{3}\ \lambda$, is the other part of the conjugate pair. Substituting Eq. (7-60) into Eq. (7-59)

$$K_u = -8\lambda^3$$

If the control object (open loop) is stable, λ will be negative and K_u, the gain at the stability limit, positive. For this case, as for most systems with stable open loop characteristics, the system becomes unstable if the gain is increased beyond K_u, as we saw in Fig. 7-12(b).

This approach applies in general to a closed loop system's characteristic equation written in polynomial form. There can be only one unknown parameter, like K_u in the example, but the frequency of oscillation ω_u is also found. This approach is useful for most normal control systems which have an oscillation at their stability limit. However, there are some exceptional systems that show a regenerative instability (a positive real closed loop pole) when the stability limit is trespassed.

The linear theory and simplified techniques presented here and in the previous chapter are convenient to use for getting a general idea about a closed loop system's behavior. They are inadequate, however, for describing the behavior of a system completely. Various factors excluded in the process of idealization (linearization and simplification), like nonlinearities (valve saturation, in particular), nonzero initial state, etc., may sometimes drastically alter the final results from the linear first approximation. A follow-up or parallel study by computer simulation is normally recommended.

7.7 CONTROL OF NONTECHNICAL SYSTEMS

Feedback is central to the functioning of the natural world (Ref. [2]). As technology and man's understanding of technology have grown, it has also become apparent that technological systems depend on feedback to operate properly. Furthermore, with population increase and economic growth, application of feedback control to economic and societal problems via government (e.g., planned economy, federal reserve, etc.) has become common. As we have seen above, systems with feedback are more prone to instability than those without feedback. The current environmental crisis, in which man's heavy use of the earth's resources has severely disrupted natural ecological loops, is a reflection of this principle.

As dynamic system and control theory is extended to encompass wider varieties of systems (Refs. [4] and [9]), basic concepts that we use to understand physical systems (like thermodynamics and electrical circuit theory) are not so obvious, or even available.

This dilemma suggests two possible complementary paths of action: first, we can use the existing theory at whatever level is applicable to solve problems arising out of today's increasing concern about the effects of technology, conservation of natural environment, ecology, etc. Second, we can fuse engineering analysis with basic material in the discipline involved. The goal of this fundamental research is the production of new theory; an underlying "physics" or "chemistry" that will establish fundamental laws from which general theory can be derived.

We will address ourselves here mainly to the first route, trying to use what we know of dynamic system and control theory to shed some light on problems of broader interest. In most cases, the parts of dynamic system theory that can be used most readily are identification of state variables and functions, system equation formulation and some preliminary analysis, causality computation and application of numerical and analog techniques. In the two examples that follow, we will explore two problems involving population dynamics, each with a different goal. In the first example, we want to assure the survival of a species threatened by overexploitation, whales. In the second, we would like to control the population of a species we think is overexploiting us, insect pests.

Though whaling as a subject of literature and adventure is associated with the 19th century, the industrial revolution hit whaling in the middle of the 20th century. Harpoons with explosive heads, SONAR, helicopters and factory ships with their fleets of catcher boats have multiplied the yearly kill of whales by several hundred-fold to the point where conservationists are predicting the possible extinction of many species of whales (the 150-ton blue whale, the biggest of them all, has been commercially extinct for several years). The example below illustrates the type of model that can be used to predict what levels of whale hunting will assure maintenance of adequate population levels while optimizing long-term yields for the whaling industry.

The Whale Problem

In this problem, only one fundamental law is apparent — that of population conservation. This was already given by Eq. (1-1), restated here in a slightly different form

$$\frac{dN}{dt} = B - M$$

where N is the total population of a species or group, B is the number of births per unit time and M is deaths per unit time. This is thus a single state variable lumped model of whale population. As shown in Fig. 7-15(a) (Fig. 1-3 redrawn here), B and M are closely tied to the total population N. In Fig. 7-15(b), population under N_1 is "underpopulation" where the birth rate stays low because individuals cannot find mates or suffer from "loneliness," lack of protection for infants, etc. Population above N_2 is "overpopulation" where B will level off and M goes up, due to general crowding problems.

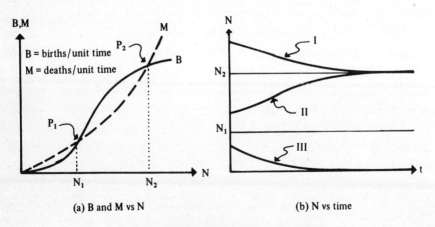

(a) B and M vs N   (b) N vs time

Fig. 7-15   Equilibrium Populations, N_1 and N_2

The whaling industry is a large-scale, technological enterprise subject to the same potential economic and financial market conditions and regulatory control as other industries. For the purpose of this problem, however, we want to simplify the description of the industry so we can isolate its effect on whale population. We will presume that the important characteristics of the whaling industry are the size and vigor of the fleets and the regulatory controls imposed on their hunting activities. A possible use of a whale population model would be to estimate current population and predict population for several years ahead so that whaling companies and regulatory agencies have a more rational basis for decision-making (a kind of feedforward-feedback scheme).

Let us assume that the mortality due to hunting M_h can be expressed as a fraction (h for hunting) of the total population

$$M_h = hN$$

but with an upper limit (saturation) that depends on the abilities of the fleet to process and store whale products. We can write this as

$$M_h = LS\,(hN, K_{max})$$

where LS is the lower-selector function (i.e., the output is the lower of the two values) and K_{max} represents the maximum number of whales that the fleet can process per unit time (a year). Note the implicit assumption here that all whales (including the species we are modeling) are equally desirable to the hunters. Whalers, however, go after the biggest and most lucrative whales first (for this reason, the blue whales have now been hunted almost to extinction and hunting pressure has switched to fin, sei and sperm whales).

Before doing a computer simulation of this system, we must express the constitutive relations in forms that can be used in a computer program. Two common ways of doing this are *interpolation* between discrete data points and *curve fitting*. Curve fitting, which we will use here, is the process of guessing algebraic functions which will suitably approximate the observed constitutive relations. It is important to keep in mind that the particular algebraic functions used have no significance in themselves — they are not the result of any theoretical considerations but rather expressions created to fit experimental data. As such, curve fitted functions have no validity outside the range of the data to which they have been fitted. Theoretically derived results can be used with caution for extrapolation or prediction.

The curve fits given below are for hypothetical data. The general procedure that we follow is to find a function that has the correct shape, write it with undetermined coefficients and then use some numerical procedure to find the set of coefficients that gives the best fit to the data. For the birth curve B in Fig. 7-15, which is S-shaped (called a sigmoid curve), a combination of two exponentials will give the right shape

$$B = A_1 e^{-aN} + A_2 e^{-bN} + C \tag{7-61}$$

The numbers for our hypothetical case could be

$$A_1 = -8000 \qquad a = 0.69 \times 10^{-4} \qquad A_2 = 4000 \qquad b = 1.38 \times 10^{-4}$$
$$C = 4000 \tag{7-62}$$

The death curve M in Fig. 7-15 can be fit with a second order polynomial

$$M = A_1' N + A_2' N^2 \tag{7-63}$$

where M is natural deaths per year. With hypothetical numbers, we get

$$M = 0.875 \times 10^{-2} N + 1.70 \times 10^{-6} N^2 \tag{7-64}$$

Simulated results are given in Fig. 7-16. The first results shown in (a) and (b) of the figure are for the whales in their natural state, not hunted by man. The curve in (a) shows an increase towards a stable population of about 50,000 (P_2 in Fig. 7-15). If the population ever gets too low (Fig. 7-16(b)), the species will become extinct. Both the passenger pigeon and the buffalo, once two of the dominant species in North America, succumbed in a manner described by the S-shaped curve.

In Fig. 7-16(c), we show the simulated results if hunting is considered and, by implication, a suggested means of controlling hunting to assure survival of the species. If values of h = 0.1 and K_{max} = 4,000 represent the current capacity of our hypothetical whaling fleet, the hypothetical whale species will become extinct in about thirty years (estimates for some of the species currently being heavily hunted run as low as five to ten years for commercial extinction, that is, too few to be worth hunting). If hunting is limited according to population by artificially changing the catch coefficient h, we see that stable populations can be maintained. To put catch limitations into practice, an estimate of

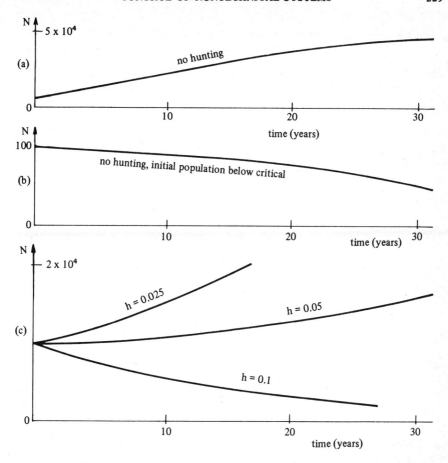

Fig. 7-16 Simulated Population Dynamics for Whales, Without (a, b) and With (c) Hunting

population (feedback signal) that all the parties concerned can agree is accurate must be available.

Control of Insect Pest Population

Insects and man never have hit it off. Modern farmers use large quantities of chemicals in their efforts to keep the insects from eating too much of the crop. Unfortunately, the chemicals have two side effects that are limiting their usefulness: 1) the insects keep evolving strains that are more resistant to the insecticides and 2) the chemicals themselves are often doing damage to wildlife and humans. Using a simple model, we will explore one of the proposals for biological control of insect population — the controlled release of sterilized males to lower the insect birth rate.

Biological control might involve creating such a calculated upset in the life cycle of the species or introducing some natural enemy. To determine the effectiveness of the control mechanism chosen and to avoid boomerang effects, feasibility studies should include very careful modeling and simulation. In the case of the massive release of sterile males into the insect population, the newcomers must eat their share of food and take up their share of space but produce no offspring. Since, sexually, they act exactly like normal males, the birth rate goes down according to the percentage of the male population that is sterile. In subsequent generations, if still more sterile males are released, the birth rate goes down still further because there are fewer females.

We need at least three state variables to model this system: N_m for the number of normal males, N_{sm} for the number of sterile males and N_f for the number of females. The total population is thus

$$N = N_m + N_{sm} + N_f \qquad\qquad (7\text{-}65)$$

Since we are dealing with a hypothetical situation, instead of using actual populations for the state variables, we will normalize all of the numbers around a magnitude of one.

The assumed birth and death rate curves are shown in Fig. 7-17. These are the curves that apply to the undisturbed population before we have applied any control mechanisms to it. Insects, because of their vulnerability to predators and environmental conditions, display an ability to reproduce very rapidly once their

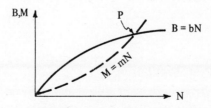

Fig. 7-17 Birth and Death-rates for Insects

population has been depleted. Thus the birth curve rises rapidly from $N = 0$. In fact, some species may have a birth curve that is higher for low population levels. The death rate is again assumed to be dependent on the total population, that is, density dependent.

We will use the following curve-fit expressions for births and deaths:

$$B' = (1 - e^{-0.391N})\frac{N_f}{N} \tag{7-66}$$

and

$$M = 0.0031N^2 + 0.0093N \tag{7-67}$$

where B' is the birth rate including the effects of infant mortality and normal predation but not any controls and M is the death rate. We assume that the offspring are half male and half female and thus the factor N_f/N is $1/2$ in a natural population. The actual birth rate is lower than B' because of the sterile males in the population. We can use the following expression for the birth rate in the presence of sterile males:

$$B = \frac{N_m}{N_m + N_{sm}} B' \tag{7-68}$$

Note that the factor used in B approaches one as N_{sm} approaches zero.

The following algorithm is used to compute population as a function of time:

```
        REAL NM, NSM, NF, N
        read in parameters and initial
            conditions: DT, TFINAL,
            NMZERO, NSMZERO,
            NFZERO
        T = 0.0
        NM = NMZERO
        NSM = NSMZERO
        NF = NFZERO
100  CONTINUE
        N = NM+NSM+NF
        print or plot results
        BPR = (1.0−EXP(−0.391*N))*NF/N    − from Eq. (7-66)
        B = (NM/(NM+NSM))*BPR              − from Eq. (7-68)
        D = 0.31E−2*N**2 + 0.93E−2*N       − from Eq. (7-67)
        NM = NM+(B/2.0−NM*D/N)*DT          − Births are divided by two,
```

```
compute REL here
N = NM+NSM+NF
BPR = (1.0−EXP(−0.391*N))*NF/N
B = (NM/(NM+NSM))*BPR
D = 0.31E−2*N**2 + 0.93E−2*N
NSM = NSM+(REL−NSM*D/N)*DT
N = NM+NSM+NF
BPR = (1.0−EXP(−0.391*N))*NF/N
B = (NM/(NM+NSM))*BPR
D = 0.31E−2*N**2 + 0.93E−2*N
NF = NF+(B/2.0−NF*D/N)*DT
T = T+DT
IF(T .LE. TFINAL)GO TO 100
STOP
```

assuming that there are an equal number of males and females born. Deaths are proportioned according to percentage of total population. REL is an input, the number of sterilized males released per unit time.

All of the studies are based on an initial population equal to the stable equilibrium population, point P in Fig. 7-17, approximately N = 10. The first strategy we examine is to continuously (step input) release sterile males. As we see from Fig. 7-18(a), this strategy is not very effective in reducing the total population because a large number of sterile males must be released continuously to keep the normal population down. If, however, the economic damage is done by the larvae rather than the adult insect, this strategy will be quite effective because the number of larvae is proportional to the number of normals, which is very low.

An alternate strategy is to release large numbers of sterile males in timed bursts (impulse input). Fig. 7-18(b) shows that this can be far more effective although the population is very high for a short time after the release. This method would be effective for the case in which most of the damage is done by the pest over a short time, for instance, after a fruit has matured and before it is picked. With proper timing, this method can be used to keep the damage to a minimum.

7.8 CONTROL WITH STATE VECTOR FEEDBACK

Thus far in this chapter, we have dealt with single-input—single-output systems — control systems in which only one measurement, that of the controlled variable, is made and only one system input or actuator is available. If we in-

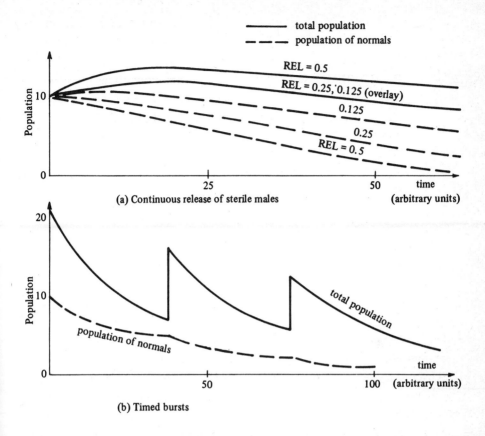

Fig. 7-18 Insect Population with Two Control Schemes

crease the amount of information available by adding extra measuring instruments or increase the amount of control by adding extra actuators, we can improve the quality of control. This concept is the basis for multi-variable control (Ref. [10]). We will now examine a simple case of a system with state vector feedback; that is, all of the state variables are measured and are available to the controller but there is still only a single actuator. This case is practical to examine because it is usually much less expensive to add measuring instruments to a system than it is to add actuators. It will also give us a feeling for the kind of control performance improvement we can expect when using multi-variable control. More theory and a better knowledge of the plant's dynamics are usually required for effective design of state vector feedback controllers.

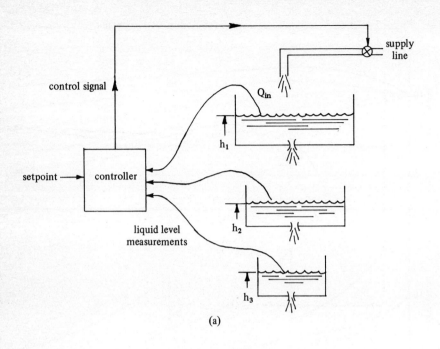

(a)

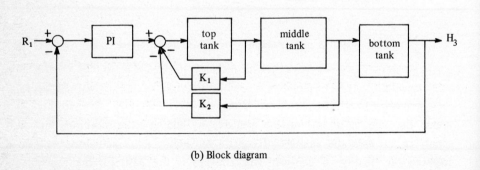

(b) Block diagram

Fig. 7-19 Three Tank System

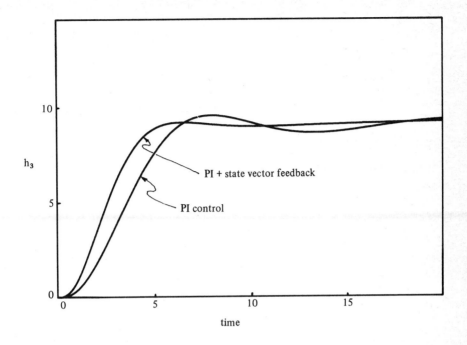

Fig. 7-20 Closed Loop Response of Three Tank System

Consider the three tank system of Fig. 7-19(a). In common applications of, say, PI control to this system, only the liquid height in the bottom tank, the one whose level is being controlled, is measured. This signal is used by the controller to compute the control signal. The curve marked "PI control" in Fig. 7-20 gives a simulated response for a PI controller for this system (all tanks empty at $t = 0$). Intuition tells us, however, that if information about the liquid height in the two upper tanks is also used to compute the control signal, better control performance should result. For instance, if the bottom tank is empty but the upper tanks are full to the brim, a much lower inflow is called for than if all of the tanks are empty. The PI controller has no information about the states of the other tanks, though, so its performance must be a compromise: a large overshoot would result in the first case and a very slow response in the second. The curve marked "PI control + state vector feedback" is the simulated response using the same PI controller but with added proportional terms for each of the other measured liquid levels, Fig. 7-19(b). This response has less oscillation and shorter settling time than the PI control alone and is thus a much better controller. Designing the state vector feedback controller (i.e., specifying its gains), however, is more difficult than designing the PI controller because it has four gains to be set instead of just two (the proportional and integral terms of the PI control plus two proportional gains for the terms from the upper two tank levels).

Looking at the responses in Fig. 7-20, we note an interesting pattern: adding the state vector feedback to the PI control has an effect on the system response that is similar to the effect of adding D (derivative) action to a PI controller. Recalling from Sec. 6.8 that differentiation is required to reconstruct a state variable which is not directly measured, we see that adding D-action to a controller is equivalent to reconstructing one state variable and using it in the controller. In the three tank example shown above, two extra state variables are used; it would require double differentiation to compute both of them from a single output, an extremely noisy operation in most real systems, although satisfactory controller performance might be obtained by using a more sophisticated model reference adaptive system.

SUMMARY

Closing the loop on a system gives it very special properties. We exploit these properties to design automatically controlled systems that can operate effectively in changing environments and under some conditions that were not anticipated when the system was designed. To achieve such performance improvement takes extra design effort. Stable components, combined in a feedback configuration, can sometimes yield a closed loop system with unstable behavior.

Feedback control is not found solely in the technological domain. It occurs naturally in many systems. We can use it in the control of other natural and manmade nontechnological systems and it can help us understand the behavior of natural systems that affect us. As long as man's demands were low, only the open loop, stable behavior of the ecological systems with which he interacted was obvious. As man's demands have increased, however, we have begun to note the closed loop behavior of these systems with their possibilities for instability.

Many control systems can be modeled by the canonical, single loop feedback structure. When this is true, assuming that the system is not strongly nonlinear, we can refer to a large body of knowledge based on years of previous experience in control system design by applying P, PI or PID control laws. Furthermore, if a linear model of the control system can be developed, we can rely on a great deal of mathematical and empirical theory created specifically for estimating stability properties and parameters for control systems.

REFERENCES

1. O. Mayr, *The Origins of Feedback Control* (translation from German), MIT Press, Cambridge, Mass., 1970, pp. 4-9

2. N. Wiener, *Cybernetics*, Technology Press (now MIT Press), Cambridge, Mass., 1947

3. R. K. Kaminski, "An Instrumentation Library for Managers, Engineers and Technicians, Pt. 1, Measurement, Control and Mathematics," *Instrumentation Technology*, Jan. 1972, pp. 65-70

4. J. W. Forrester, *Urban Dynamics*, MIT Press, Cambridge, Mass., 1969

5. D. M. Auslander and D. C. Sharma, "Study of Certain Clinical Disorders Related to the Biosynthesis and Regulation of Steroid Hormones by Computer Simulation," *Progress in Cybernetics*, Gordon and Breach, 1970

6. J. L. Melsa and S. K. Jones, *Computer Programs for Computational Assistance in the Study of Linear Control Theory*, McGraw-Hill, New York, 1973

7. J. G. Truxal, *Automatic Feedback Control System Synthesis*, McGraw-Hill, New York, 1955

8. J. G. Ziegler and N. B. Nichols, "Optimum Settings for Automatic Controllers," *ASME Transactions*, Vol. 64, No. 8, 1942, p. 759; "Process Lags in Automatic Control Circuits," *ASME Transactions*, Vol. 65, No. 5, 1943, p. 433; "Optimum Settings for Controllers," *ISEJ*, June 1964, pp. 731-734

9. K. E. F. Watt, *Ecology and Resource Management*, McGraw-Hill, New York, 1968

10. Y. Takahashi, M. Rabins and D. Auslander, *Control*, Addison-Wesley, Reading, Mass., 1970, Chap. 10

PROBLEMS

7-1 Using a conceptual block diagram with a feedback loop, explain temperature self-regulation in an electric light bulb.

7-2 Consider the control system shown in Fig. 7-9, where the plant transfer function $G_p(s)$ is given by Eq. (6-65), and a proportional controller, $G_c(s) = k_c$, is used. (a) Determine the offset for a unit step reference input (no disturbance). (b) Assume $G_v(s) = G_p(s)$ in Fig. 7-9 and obtain the offset for a unit step disturbance input (zero set point). (c) If the reference or disturbance input is not a step but a gradual change that will eventually approach a final value (= 1), do we get an offset different from (a) or (b)?

7-3 Show that a series coupling of PI and PD control laws yields a PID-action. Obtain controller parameters, k_c', T_i' and T_d' of this PID-action in terms of the original PI and PD controller parameters.

7-4 The measured temperature y in Fig. P-6-9 is compared against a desired temperature r of the downstream tank, whose actual temperature is x_2. The heat supply u to the latter is controlled by a proportional action

$$u = k_c(r - y)$$

where k_c is the gain. Is this a feedback control system? For what kinds of disturbances is the control system effective? When it is effective, is there any offset?

7-5 A purely inertial system with force input and displacement output (i.e., a double integrator) has a positive feedback loop, meaning that the force will be increased in proportion to the increase in displacement. Sketch the root locus.

7-6 The displacement of a purely inertial system is controlled by a PID-action, where the manipulated variable is a force input to the inertial body. Compute the stability limit condition and sketch the root locus for a gain change (a change of k_c in Eq. (7-27) from zero to infinity).

7-7 Using the Routh array (see the Appendix), test the stability of a system represented by the following characteristic equation:

$$s^5 + 7s^4 + 18s^3 + 23s^2 + 17s + 6 = 0$$

7-8 The depth of an underwater spherical vehicle is to be controlled by letting in or pumping out water at a rate proportional to the depth error (i.e., the difference between the desired depth and the actual depth). Will this control scheme work? If, in addition to depth, the time rate of change of depth is available as a control signal, is it possible to design a better control system?

7-9 The double oscillator shown in Fig. P-7-9 is described by

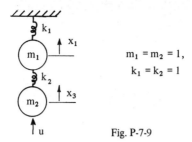

$$m_1 = m_2 = 1,$$
$$k_1 = k_2 = 1$$

Fig. P-7-9

$$\frac{d}{dt}\begin{bmatrix} x_1 \\ x_2 \\ x_3 \\ x_4 \end{bmatrix} = \begin{bmatrix} 0 & 1 & 0 & 0 \\ -2 & 0 & 1 & 0 \\ 0 & 0 & 0 & 1 \\ 1 & 0 & -1 & 0 \end{bmatrix} \begin{bmatrix} x_1 \\ x_2 \\ x_3 \\ x_4 \end{bmatrix} + \begin{bmatrix} 0 \\ 0 \\ 0 \\ 1 \end{bmatrix} u$$

where x_1 and x_3 are displacements and x_2 and x_4 are velocities. The open loop poles are given by the roots of the characteristic equation $|s\underline{I} - \underline{A}| = 0$ as

$$\pm 0.618j \qquad \pm 1.618j$$

It is desired to stabilize the system by a feedback

$$u = -kx_i$$

where u is the force acting on the lower mass, x_i is one of the state variables and k is a gain. Choose a state variable for this purpose. Sketch the root locus.

7-10 A reverse reaction process

$$G_p(s) = \frac{1 - \frac{1}{2}s}{(1 + s)(1 + \frac{1}{2}s)}$$

is under proportional control. Obtain (a) the stability limit, (b) condition(s) for double closed loop poles and (c) sketch the root locus.

7-11 The transfer function of a reverse reaction process, given in the preceding problem, can be expanded into partial fractions

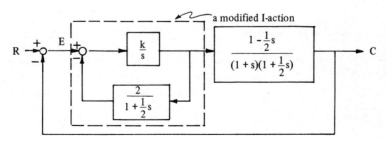

Fig. P-7-11

$$G(s) = \frac{3}{s+1} - \frac{2}{\frac{1}{2}s+1}$$

The negative component, $-2/(\frac{1}{2}s+1)$, that will produce the reverse reaction, is effectively cancelled out in Fig. P-7-11 by an inner loop around an I-action. (a) Is this control system more stable than the P control of the preceding problem? (b) Does this system have an offset for reference input? If so, how may it be eliminated?

7-12 Hot and cold fluid flows are fed into a mixing tank, where the mixed temperature θ will be controlled by manipulating the flow rate of the hot fluid. The heat balance equation for the plant is given by

$$C\frac{d\theta}{dt} = w_h\theta_h + w_c\theta_c - (w_h + w_c)\theta$$

where C is heat capacitance, w_h and w_c are the product of the flow rate and specific heat of the hot and cold fluids, respectively, and inlet temperatures θ_h and θ_c of the fluids are kept constant. Assume the numerical values are

$$C = 1 \qquad w_c = 1 \qquad w_h = 1 + u$$

where u is the controlling input which is described by an I-action law

$$\frac{du}{dt} = k(r - \theta)$$

where r is the set point and k is the gain. Using a graphical technique or computer, construct trajectories of the controlled process in the $u - \theta$ plane for $r = 0$ and $k = 2$.

7-13 A simple production marketing process is shown in Fig. P-7-13, where the price p of a product is determined by the difference of demand r and actual sales b times a scalar k_1, where the sales, in turn, are fixed by the price via a scalar multiplier k_4. The value of the multiplier is determined in such a way that the cash flow bp will be maximized. The production command m is proportional to an inventory level c and k_2p, where k_2 is a constant. The command is executed in a factory by a transfer function $1/(1 + Ts)$ and the difference of production flow and sales flow enters an inventory, which is an integrator k_3/s. Determine the optimal value for k_4 and compute the inventory level response for a unit step demand input change.

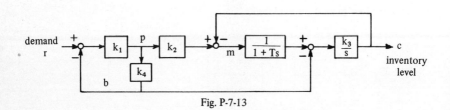

Fig. P-7-13

7-14 Suppose that the population of one species of wildlife is subject to the logistic equation

$$\frac{dN}{dt} = (K - \frac{N}{M})N$$

where K and M are positive constants. Also, suppose that the rate of harvest H(t) is
proportional to the population N(t), with a proportionality constant h

   H(t) = hN(t)

Investigate the equilibrium state(s) and its (their) stability for various values of the
hunting pressure h and, in particular, that hunting pressure for which the sustainable
yield (the equilibrium value of H(t)) will be maximum. Is it advisable to apply the
hunting pressure for the maximum sustainable yield?

7-15 Two species are competing against each other so that their population deviations x_1
and x_2 are described by the following linear equations:

$$\frac{dx_1}{dt} = r_1 x_1 - a_1 x_2 - h x_1$$

$$\frac{dx_2}{dt} = r_2 x_2 - a_2 x_1$$

where r_1 and r_2 are Malthusian terms, a_1 and a_2 are positive constants representing
the competition and a hunting pressure h is applied to the first species. Is it possible
to "stabilize" the dynamics by a proper choice of the hunting pressure?

CHAPTER 8
FREQUENCY RESPONSE

When a linear system is excited by a sinusoidal forcing function, we can expect the system output to be a sinusoid of the same frequency. As the frequency varies, so does the amplitude of the system output as well as its phase relative to the system input. *Frequency response* is the study of such amplitude and phase relations as a function of frequency. Frequency response techniques have been important system and component design tools since World War II when they were used extensively in weaponry and communications developments. We begin this chapter with some comments about linear and nonlinear mechanical systems under forced vibrations as a graphic means of introducing the frequency response viewpoint. Some basic relations are then presented for the general frequency response problem, following which Nyquist and Bode plots are introduced. Digital computation and analog simulation of frequency response problems are next discussed. The stability of single loop feedback systems is then investigated by interpretation and application of the Nyquist stability theorem. The chapter closes with discussion of the limit cycle behavior observed in some nonlinear systems.

8.1 FORCED MECHANICAL VIBRATION

One way to identify the unknown dynamics hidden inside a black box (spring-mass pair in our example, Fig. 8-1) is to shake it, applying a reciprocating motion as an input and feeling the force reaction as a response (i.e., output). This is a kind of frequency response test. In studying a linear system's

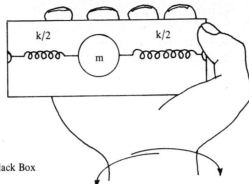

Fig. 8-1 Testing a Black Box

frequency response, we consider its *sinusoidal steady-state* input-output relation.

An idealized spring-mass system with a sinusoidal forcing function (Fig. 8-2(a)) has been studied in many textbooks and its mathematical model is well known. The equation of motion for a sinusoidally changing force applied to the mass is

$$mD^2 x(t) + kx(t) = F_1 \sin(\omega t) \tag{8-1}$$

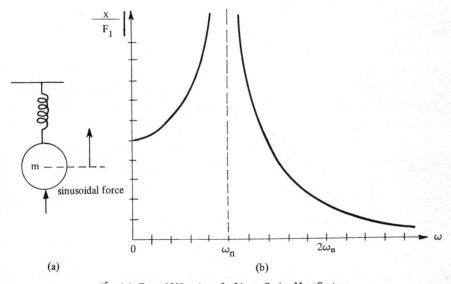

Fig. 8-2 Forced Vibration of a Linear Spring-Mass System

where m is the mass, k is the spring constant and $x(t)$ is the displacement of the mass from an equilibrium position (plus for up). On the right side, F_1 is the force amplitude and ω is the (circular) frequency of the harmonic input (for brevity, we assumed a sine function instead of cosine or sine and cosine combined).

The sinusoidal steady-state response $x(t)$ for this system is easily obtained by substituting into Eq. (8-1) a trial solution.

$$x(t) = X \sin(\omega t) \tag{8-2}$$

Thus

$$-m\omega^2 X + kX = F_1$$

hence

$$X = \frac{F_1}{k - m\omega^2} = \frac{F_1}{m(\omega_n^2 - \omega^2)} \tag{8-3}$$

where

$$\omega_n = \sqrt{k/m}$$

is known as the *natural (circular) frequency* of the system. The amplitude ratio, $|X/F_1|$ is plotted in Fig. 8-2(b). The singularity at the resonance point $\omega = \omega_n$ will vanish if a linear damping term $bDx(t)$ (no matter how small b is) is added on the left side of Eq. (8-1) due to the introduction of some energy dissipation to the system of Fig. 8-2(a).

Since the system of Eq. (8-1) is not asymptotically stable (see Section 5.3 and Table 5-1) when it completely lacks damping, undamped sinusoidal motion at its natural frequency, due to an initial transient, will persist. This makes it impossible to realize a pure sinusoidal steady-state due to a forcing input at another frequency unless a specific initial state is chosen when the sinusoidal forcing starts. To illustrate this point, let us take a moment to consider a first order system

$$Dx(t) = ax(t) + bu(t) \tag{8-4}$$

where $bu(t) = \sin(\omega t)$ for $0 < t$. By means of Eq. (5-31), we find that

$$x(t) = e^{at}x_0 + e^{at} \int_0^t e^{-a\tau} \sin(\omega \tau)\, d\tau$$

where

$$\int_0^t e^{-a\tau} \sin(\omega\tau)\, d\tau = \frac{e^{-a\tau}}{a^2 + \omega^2} \left[-a\sin(\omega\tau) - \omega\cos(\omega\tau)\right]\Big|_0^t$$

$$= \frac{e^{-at}}{a^2 + \omega^2} \left[-a\sin(\omega t) - \omega\cos(\omega t)\right] + \frac{\omega}{a^2 + \omega^2}$$

so that

$$x(t) = e^{at}x_0 + \frac{1}{a^2 + \omega^2}\left(-a\sin(\omega t) - \omega\cos(\omega t) + \omega e^{at}\right) \tag{8-5}$$

where the first term after the equal sign is the free response and the second is the forced part of the response. If the system is asymptotically stable, a is negative so that

$$\lim_{t\to\infty} \left(x_0 + \frac{\omega}{a^2 + \omega^2}\right) e^{at} = 0 \tag{8-6}$$

and the response x(t) will converge to the sinusoidal steady-state

$$x_{ss}(t) = -\frac{a\sin(\omega t) + \omega\cos(\omega t)}{a^2 + \omega^2} \tag{8-7}$$

The sinusoidal steady-state would be reached from the outset (regardless of the value of a) if the initial state is chosen to be

$$x_0 = \frac{-\omega}{a^2 + \omega^2} \tag{8-8}$$

so that Eq. (8-7) is satisfied right away — but such a pinpoint choice is generally impossible. A similar analysis for second order systems indicates that there are particular values of initial displacement and velocity for which the sinusoidal steady-state is established immediately. Thus for an undamped osciallator, the sinusoidal steady-state can only be realized if the precise initial conditions are imposed. The sinusoidal steady-state will establish itself eventually for a very lightly damped system, but the time necessary for the transient response to die away may be too long for practical consideration.

Nonlinear Vibration

A spring-mass-damper system

$$mD^2x + F_{damp} + F_{spring} = \text{force input} \tag{8-9}$$

is nonlinear when the damping force F_{damp} is not proportional to velocity Dx and/or the spring force F_{spring} is not proportional to deflection x. Let us consider an undamped system ($F_{damp} = 0$) where the spring force deviates from Hooke's proportionality law. One type of nonlinear spring characteristic is shown in Fig. 8-3(a), where the spring gets stiffer when deflection is increased. We assume, by curve fitting, a cubic form

$$F_{spring} = k_1 x + k_3 x^3 \qquad\qquad (8\text{-}10)$$

The quadratic term $k_2 x^2$ does not appear because the spring force must be an odd function of deflection x. With this nonlinear spring, Eq. (8-1) becomes

$$mD^2 x + k_1 x + k_3 x^3 = F_1 \sin(\omega t) \qquad\qquad (8\text{-}11)$$

This is known as the Duffing equation after G. Duffing who first discussed the problem. Its general solution is unknown. Such is often the case in nonlinear systems; the analytical form of a differential equation may look simple, but the simplicity is usually deceptive. To find a periodic (particular) solution in analytical form for nonlinear systems is often extremely difficult and very few have been found so far. The graphical method in the state plane (see Sec. 3.4) or a computer may be applied to obtain a transient solution, which may or may not converge to a periodic steady-state (i.e., particular periodic solution).

Here we shall assume that the nonlinear effect due to $k_3 x^3$ in Eq. (8-10) is slight so that the resulting steady-state motion is close to being simple harmonic as in Eq. (8-2). This satisfies Eq. (8-11) only at time points where $\sin(\omega t) = 0$, that is

$$\text{at } \omega t = 0, \pi, 2\pi, \ldots$$

We now find the values of the displacement amplitude X such that the trial (approximate) solution of Eq. (8-2) will also satisfy Eq. (8-11) at instants of time when $\sin(\omega t) = 1$, that is

$$\omega t = \frac{\pi}{2}, \frac{3\pi}{2}, \frac{5\pi}{2}, \ldots$$

so that Eq. (8-11) at these points will reduce to

$$-m\omega^2 X + k_1 X + k_3 X^3 = F_1 \qquad\qquad (8\text{-}12)$$

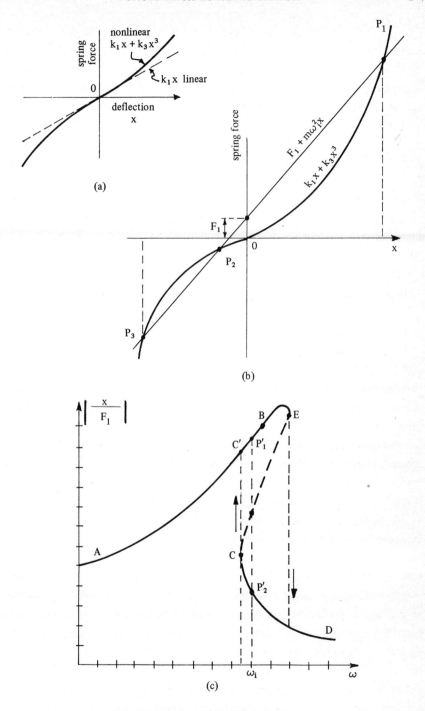

Fig. 8-3 Relations for a Nonlinear Spring

Since this is cubic in X, we solve it graphically, as shown in Fig. 8-3(b). The intersections of a fixed curve $k_1 X + k_3 X^3$ and a line $F_1 + m\omega_i^2 X$ for some fixed value ω_i, shown by points P_1, P_2 and P_3 in the figure, will give the value(s) of X_i that satisfy Eq. (8-12) at $\omega = \omega_i$. Repeating the process for various values of ω_i, we obtain Fig. 8-3(c). Since at some values of ω, like ω_i in Fig. 8-3(b), there are three "solutions" (P_1 through P_3), three points P_1' through P_3' will appear at a single frequency (vertical line) in the curve of Fig. 8-3(c). Such multiplicity causes the "jump" phenomenon. If the driving frequency is gradually decreased from D in the figure, the response amplitude X will increase along curve DC and, at C, the amplitude will jump to C'. If the driving frequency is increased from A, the response amplitude X will increase along the higher curve AB. With damping (which was neglected in the above computation), the amplitude at resonance is limited as indicated by the dotted curve BE and the amplitude jumps from E to E' as the frequency is further increased. Therefore, the states from C to E are not attainable (Ref. [1]).

8.2 BASIC RELATIONS IN THE FREQUENCY DOMAIN

The forced vibration of a mechanical system presented in the last section is just one example of the frequency response technique; the technique is widely applied to various kinds of systems in the field of dynamic systems and control. As we shall see in this chapter, the concept and technique of frequency response opens a new domain — the *frequency domain* — for dealing with single-input—single-output dynamic systems. Let us begin with a few simple but general and important observations.

In Section 8.1, it was shown by Eqs. (8-4) through (8-7) that a sinusoidal input-output steady-state (which we shall simply call steady-state in the following) can be reached in reality only when a linear system is asymptotically stable.

A nonlinearity causes complications in a frequency response relation, such as the case of the hardening spring of Section 8.1 leading to the jump phenomenon. Saturation, as in the case of a valve (or any static element), is another simple but important nonlinearity. Consider a control valve (Fig. 8-4(a)) where the input (control) is an electronic or pneumatic signal transmitted from a controller or a remote transmission device and the output is the steady-state valve opening. We will ignore the dynamics involved between the input and the output and assume that the relation is linear between the two ends (this is

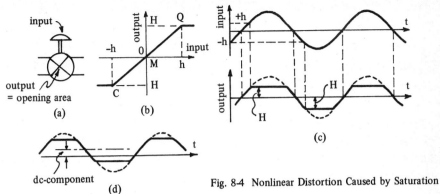

Fig. 8-4 Nonlinear Distortion Caused by Saturation

seldom true in reality) — one completely closed and the other fully open (points C and Q in Fig. 8-4(b)). Consider now that a sinusoidal input is applied to the static system about the midpoint of its linear range (point M in Fig. 8-4(b)). The input-output amplitude ratio of the two sinusoids (like $|X/F_1|$ in Eq. (8-3)) will be equal to the system gain k (the slope H/h of line CMQ in Fig. 8-4(b)) as long as the signals remain in the linear range, that is, when input amplitude is equal to or less than h in Fig. 8-4(b). This is generally true for any linear system; the frequency response amplitude ratio and phase are independent of the input signal amplitude. However, this statement does not apply to nonlinear systems; nonlinear response characteristics depend on input amplitude, as is clear by inspection of the distorted output signal shown in Fig. 8-4(c).

If, moreover, the input base-level deviates from the midpoint, M in this example, the output waveform may appear as in Fig. 8-4(d); the distortion is not symmetric — consequently the mean value of the output will shift. Such a shift or bias is sometimes referred to as the *dc-component*. A nonsymmetric nonlinearity of this sort is utilized in the AC to DC converter of Example 4-3. A function multiplier is another example where a dc-component will appear in the output. Consider the nonlinear input-output relation

$$y(t) = u(t)^2 \tag{8-13}$$

where y(t) is output and u(t) is input. For a sinusoidal forcing function u(t) = sin(ωt), the output will be

$$y(t) = \sin^2(\omega t) = \frac{1}{2}\left[1 - \cos(2\omega t)\right] \tag{8-14}$$

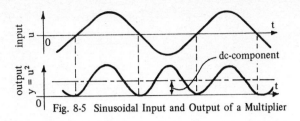

Fig. 8-5 Sinusoidal Input and Output of a Multiplier

Here, the constant component 1/2 is the dc-component. As shown in Fig. 8-5, the output frequency is twice its input frequency; this nonlinearity therefore introduces a higher harmonic component.

Another important observation is the fact that a static linear relationship will never introduce phase difference between an input and an output. Intuitively we see that the same is true for the nonlinear elements in Figs. 8-4 and 8-5, although we must be cautious when referring to phase when the wave form is distorted as in Fig. 8-4(d) or "distorted" from its input waveform to a higher harmonic as in Fig. 8-5. Some multiple valued nonlinearities, like hysteresis, will introduce phase difference, however.

Below, we consider only linear systems until Sec. 8.6, where we resume discussion of some other nonlinear elements. A slight distortion in output waveform due to system nonlinearity, which often appears in response records of a real system, should be smoothed out to a pure sinusoidal form in order to apply the frequency response technique. This approximation is related to the tangential linearization of Fig. 3-11 and Eq. (5-40) and is applicable as long as the error remains acceptable. The approximation is not permissible if reality calls attention to some behavior that stems from the nonlinearity (like the jump phenomenon in Sec. 8.1 or the limit cycle we shall discuss in Sec. 8.6).

Frequency Transfer Functions

We now focus our attention on linear dynamic elements. To deal with the frequency response of linear dynamic elements, it is highly advisable to use $e^{j\omega t}$ in place of $\sin(\omega t)$ or $\cos(\omega t)$, for it simplifies computations considerably. As shown in Fig. 8-6(a), $e^{j\omega t}$ is a unit vector in the complex plane, rotating about the origin with an angular velocity ω (radians/time) and $\sin(\omega t)$ and $\cos(\omega t)$ are its imaginary (or vertical) and real (or horizontal) components, respectively. Likewise the vector in (b) of the figure will represent sinusoidal signals in the form $A\sin(\omega t + \phi)$ or $A\cos(\omega t + \phi)$, where A is amplitude and ϕ is phase angle

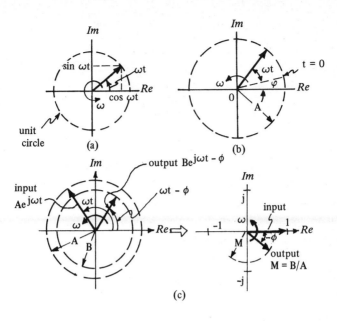

Fig. 8-6 Frequency Response in the Complex Plane

(radians). A sinusoidal steady-state of a linear dynamic object is shown in Fig. 8-6(c). Since the angular velocities ω of the two vectors (input and output) are the same, we do not lose information or generality by "fixing" the input vector on the positive real axis and showing the output vector in a fixed (phase) location relative to the input vector. Moreover, since the frequency response amplitude ratio and phase shift are independent of the input amplitude (for linear systems), we may consider the input amplitude to be unity so that output amplitude will represent an output/input amplitude ratio. With these permissible simplifications for linear systems, the frequency domain input and output can be expressed by

$$\text{Input:} \qquad U(j\omega) = e^{j\omega t}$$
$$\text{Output:} \qquad Y(j\omega) = (Me^{j\phi})e^{j\omega t} \tag{8-15}$$

Linear dynamics of an object in the frequency domain are now represented by M, the output/input amplitude ratio (a nonnegative quantity), and a phase shift

ϕ (radians). The phase shift may be positive or negative. Both M and ϕ will normally depend on the forcing frequency.

Analytical relations for $M(\omega)$ and $\phi(\omega)$ are very closely related to a system's transfer function G(s). To derive the relation, it is most convenient to consider a forcing input in the form of the first of Eqs. (8-15) instead of using sines and cosines. With this form, we can make use of the unique property of an exponential function of time

$$\frac{d}{dt} e^{j\omega t} = De^{j\omega t} = j\omega e^{j\omega t}$$

so that the operator D plays the role of $j\omega$. Furthermore, as shown in Sec. 6.1, the derivative operator D can be replaced by the Laplace domain parameter s that appears in transfer functions. Therefore

$$D \to s \to j\omega$$

and thus, by definition of a transfer function, which was expressed by Eq. (6-39), the frequency domain input and output are related by

$$\frac{Y(j\omega)}{U(j\omega)} = G(j\omega) \tag{8-16}$$

where $G(j\omega)$, a transfer function whose s is replaced by $j\omega$, is called the *frequency transfer function*.[†] From Eqs. (8-15) and (8-16), we conclude that

$$\begin{aligned}
\text{amplitude ratio:} \quad & \left| Y(j\omega)/U(j\omega) \right| = M = \left| G(j\omega) \right| \\
\text{phase shift:} \quad & \underline{/\,Y(j\omega)/U(j\omega)} = \phi = \underline{/\,G(j\omega)}
\end{aligned} \tag{8-17}$$

where $\left| G(j\omega) \right|$ and $\underline{/\,G(j\omega)}$ are magnitude and phase, respectively, of a vector $G(j\omega)$ in a complex plane as indicated in Fig. 8-7.

To illustrate the general relation of Eq. (8-17), let us first consider an integrator

$$G(s) = \frac{k}{s} \tag{8-18}$$

The frequency response for this case can be easily deduced without resorting to

---

† This useful substitution is the result of applying the Fourier transformation and is strictly valid only for asymptotically stable systems.

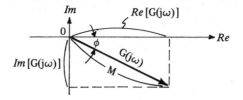

Fig. 8-7 A Complex Vector G(jω)
(Phase angle φ in the figure is negative)

Eq. (8-18). Since an integrated value of a sinusoidal input about zero mean is expected to reach its maximum point, Q in Fig. 8-8(a), when a positive half cycle of the input ends (point **P** in the figure), the input-output phase difference must be either −90° or +270°. However, an output never precedes an input. The phase shift must be negative, that is, a phase lag of −90° or

$$\phi = -\frac{\pi}{2} \tag{8-19}$$

The magnitude ratio is found by the rule $\int \sin(\omega t)dt = -(1/\omega)\cos(\omega t)$ or $\int \cos(\omega t)dt = (1/\omega)\sin(\omega t)$ as

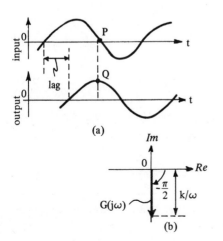

(a)

(b)

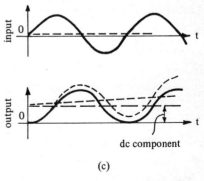

dc component

(c)

Fig. 8-8 Frequency Response of an Integrator

$$M = \frac{k}{\omega} \tag{8-20}$$

where k is the gain of the integrator. In frequency response work, however, M (i.e., $|G(j\omega)|$) is generally referred to as the system gain. The results, Eqs. (8-19) and (8-20), agree with what we obtain from Eq. (8-18) by a direct substitution of $j\omega$ for s

$$G(j\omega) = \frac{k}{j\omega} = -\frac{jk}{\omega}$$

This is a negative imaginary vector as shown in Fig. 8-8(b), which confirms the results given by Eqs. (8-19) and (8-20). This applies to a sinusoidal steady-state, but what would happen in a transient? A *start-up* process of a frequency response test is shown in Fig. 8-8(c), where the input sine wave begins at time zero. According to Eq. (5-31), where a = 0 and b = k in the state equation Dx = ax + bu, so that, for zero initial state, $x_0 = 0$, the response is

$$x(t) = \int_0^t k\cdot\sin(\omega\tau)\,d\tau = \frac{k}{\omega}\,[-\cos(\omega\tau)]\Big|_0^t = \frac{k}{\omega}\,[1 - \cos(\omega t)] \tag{8-21}$$

As shown in Fig. 8-8(c), the response will have a dc-component ($= k/\omega$) because a transient component will not decay away for a marginally stable system like this ("zero real part" in Table 5-1). Moreover, the dc level will build up (or *creep up*) when a sinusoidal input has a slight amount of dc-component drift, as shown in exaggeration by the dotted lines. From this, we see that care must be exercised when applying frequency response theory to systems that are not asymptotically stable.

The next example for our frequency response considerations is a first order stable transfer function, Eq. (6-63), familiar to us from our leaking tank example

$$G(s) = \frac{k}{1 + Ts} \tag{8-22}$$

We substitute $j\omega$ for s, then multiply numerator and denominator by $(1 - j\omega T)$ to rationalize (move the imaginary part from denominator into numerator)

$$G(j\omega) = k\,\frac{1 - j\omega T}{(1 + j\omega T)\,(1 - j\omega T)} = k\,[\frac{1 - j\omega T}{1 + (\omega T)^2}]$$

Thus

and

Real part: $Re\ [G(j\omega)] = \dfrac{k}{1 + (\omega T)^2}$

Imaginary part: $Im\ [G(j\omega)] = \dfrac{-k\omega T}{1 + (\omega T)^2}$

$\qquad$ (8-23)

Referring to Fig. 8-7

amplitude ratio: $M = |G(j\omega)| = \sqrt{[Re\ G(j\omega)]^2 + [Im\ G(j\omega)]^2}$

phase shift: $\phi = \underline{/\ G(j\omega)} = \tan^{-1}\dfrac{Im\ G(j\omega)}{Re\ G(j\omega)}$

$\qquad$ (8-24)

For our system, these become

$$M = \frac{k}{\sqrt{1 + (\omega T)^2}} \qquad \phi = -\tan^{-1}(\omega T) \qquad (8\text{-}25)$$

As shown by Eq. (8-6) (where a = −1/T), the transient component will decay away, eventually leaving only the sinusoidal steady-state response because the system is asymptotically stable.

Before carrying our discussion any further, we shall review some of the basic relations of complex variables that are useful for our purposes. Consider a ratio F of two complex quantities

$$F = \frac{c + jd}{a + jb} \qquad (8\text{-}26)$$

where a through d are real and $j = \sqrt{-1}$ so that $j^2 = -1$. The magnitude of F is then given by

$$|F| = \sqrt{\frac{c^2 + d^2}{a^2 + b^2}} \qquad (8\text{-}27)$$

The phase $\underline{/F}$ is equal to a phase difference of numerator angle γ and denominator angle α.

$$\underline{/F} = \gamma - \alpha = \tan^{-1}\frac{d}{c} - \tan^{-1}\frac{b}{a} \qquad (8\text{-}28)$$

The angles are shown in Fig. 8-9, where a through d are assumed to be positive for the purpose of simple illustration. We arrive at the same results by a slightly different approach in which Eq. (8-26) is rationalized by a multiplication of numerator and denominator by (a − jb)

Fig. 8-9 Vector Representation
of Complex Quantities

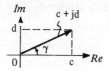

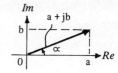

$$F = \frac{(a - jb)(c + jd)}{(a - jb)(a + jb)} = \frac{(ac + bd) + j(ad - bc)}{a^2 + b^2}$$

so that

$$Re\ F = \frac{ac + bd}{a^2 + b^2} \qquad Im\ F = \frac{ad - bc}{a^2 + b^2} \qquad\qquad (8\text{-}29)$$

and

$$|F| = \sqrt{(Re\ F)^2 + (Im\ F)^2} = \sqrt{\frac{c^2 + d^2}{a^2 + b^2}}$$

which is Eq. (8-27). The phase is

$$\underline{/F} = \tan^{-1}\left[\frac{Im\ F}{Re\ F}\right] = \tan^{-1}\left[\frac{ad - bc}{ac + bd}\right]$$

which looks different from Eq. (8-28) but is actually identical to the former result. The identity of the two forms may be proved by noting the following arctangent rule:

$$\tan^{-1}(x) \pm \tan^{-1}(y) = \tan^{-1}\left[\frac{x + y}{1 + xy}\right] \qquad\qquad (8\text{-}30)$$

that applies when

$$-\frac{1}{2}\pi < [\tan^{-1}(x) \pm \tan^{-1}(y)] < +\frac{1}{2}\pi \qquad\qquad (8\text{-}31)$$

In general, caution is required in both analytical and numerical computations when the quadrants of phase angles exceed the $\pm\frac{\pi}{2}$ range.

8.3 FREQUENCY RESPONSE DIAGRAMS

The frequency domain behavior of both an integrator and a stable first order object (Eqs. (8-20) and (8-25)) indicates that the amplitude ratio M decreases as the forcing frequency is increased, eventually converging to zero. The response amplitude thus gets smaller and smaller as the forcing oscillation gets faster. We eventually approach a frequency which will produce practically no response at all. We see such a phenomenon in many physical and nonphysical systems. For instance, an electric heating element in a kitchen stove connected to a 60 Hz source does not show any flicker in its temperature although the Joule's heat generation, being proportional to the square of the current, must be oscillating at a rate of 120 Hz (see Fig. 8-5). Here the heat fluctuation is averaged out in the heat capacitance of the element, so that its temperature is governed only by the dc-component of the fluctuating rate of heat generation. Systems like this, in which only some low frequency components of its input will pass through the system and thus appear as its output, are generally called *low-pass filters*. The frequency range the filter will pass is referred to as the *bandwidth* of the system. For example, a brick house with heavy outside walls may have a frequency bandwidth of from zero (i.e., dc-component) to about one cycle per day. For outside temperature input, day and night temperature fluctuations average out almost completely so that room temperatures remain cold throughout the day in winter and hot throughout the night in summer (when no air conditioner is installed). An automobile suspension system (Fig. 2-2) is designed to act as a low pass filter and thus maintain riding comfort despite road irregularities of short wavelength (i.e., high frequency input), although a suspension spring may produce a resonance peak as in Fig. 8-2 when the shock absorber (damper) is defective. Day by day local events normally do not affect long term social trends as long as there is no persistent element (dc-component) in the events. However, if an instability is hidden in the system in the form of a dormant $e^{\lambda t}$ mode, $0 < \lambda$, even a small event may "ignite" (excite or give an initial value to) the system, resulting in an unbounded response which may end in catastrophe.

The heuristic observations made above indicate the necessity of observing frequency response behavior not just for one forcing frequency but also over some frequency range that will match the purpose of one's analysis or design.

We need frequency response information over the entire frequency span ($\omega = 0$ to ∞) in order to obtain a complete description of a linear dynamic object which is represented by a transfer function. There are two common graphical formats for representing frequency response information: a polar form called the *Nyquist diagram* and a semi-log form called the *Bode diagram*.

Nyquist Diagram

The Nyquist diagram is a plot of the complex-valued function $G(j\omega)$ for ω = 0 to ∞, hence a direct extension of Fig. 8-7, which was limited to a single value of ω. The end point of the complex vector $G(j\omega)$ will generate a locus in the complex plane when ω is changed; such a locus is called the *Nyquist locus* (or vector locus). The Nyquist theorem, published in 1932, relates the Nyquist locus of an open loop transfer function to the system's closed loop stability (see Sec. 8.5, the appendix and Ref. [2]).

We shall first present some simple examples of the Nyquist locus. We see in Fig. 8-8(b) that the vector locus of an integrator will completely coincide with the negative half of the imaginary axis of the $G(j\omega)$ plane, Fig. 8-10(a). The arrow in the figure shows the direction in which ω is increasing. The locus should have ω scaled along the plot for a complete description, but the scale is often omitted. The next simple example is the first order system of Eq. (8-22), which in the frequency domain with s = $j\omega$, is

$$G(j\omega) = \frac{k}{1 + T(j\omega)}$$

whose locus is the semi-circle shown in Fig. 8-10(b). Letting x = *Re* $G(j\omega)$ and y = *Im* $G(j\omega)$ in Eq. (8-23), it can be proved that

$$(x - \tfrac{1}{2}k)^2 + y^2 = (\tfrac{1}{2}k)^2$$

This is the equation of a circle with a radius of $(1/2)k$ centered at $+(1/2)k$ on the real axis. Since y (the imaginary part) is always negative, as seen from Eq. (8-23), we take the lower half of the circle. Such an analytical approach to determine the Nyquist plot pattern is not generally recommended, however, because locus patterns are usually too complex for analytical representation.

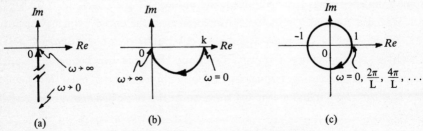

Fig. 8-10 Some Simple Nyquist Locus Patterns

The last simple example is a delay, Eq. (6-79)

$$G(j\omega) = e^{-j\omega L} \qquad\qquad (8\text{-}32)$$

As we saw in Fig. 8-6(a), this yields a unit circle. A sinusoidal input u(t) into a delay line, Fig. 6-11, will generate a travelling wave in the line. Its wave length is

wave length h = (velocity)·(period of input oscillation)

$$= v \cdot \frac{2\pi}{\omega}$$

The input-output phase will match when (length of line l)/(wave length h) = (integer n). Eliminating h from the two conditions and replacing l/v by the dead time L, we obtain the following expression for input-output phase matching:

$$\omega = \frac{2n\pi}{L} \qquad n = 1, 2, 3, \ldots$$

In Fig. 8-10(c), we see that the locus returns to its starting point (+1 on the real axis) at these frequency points.

Fig. 8-11 is an example of plotting experimental data on a Nyquist diagram (Ref. [3]). Input in this system, for which dogs were used in the original exper-

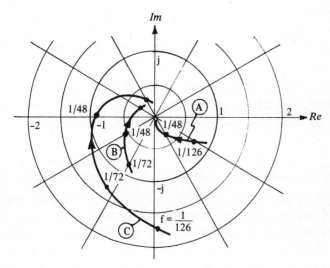

Fig. 8-11 Nyquist Plots of the Cerebral Ischemic Pressure Response; H_s = 60 mmHg for A, 40 mmHg for B, and 30 mmHg for C. Frequency f is Cycles per Sec.

iments, is a sinusoidally changing cerebral perfusion (blood) pressure around variously chosen constant (i.e., dc) mean pressure levels: A, B and C in the figure for constant pressure levels H_s ranging from 60 to 30 mm Hg. A small amplitude (± 10 mm Hg) was chosen as the input sinusoidal amplitude to justify a linear analysis of a system with nonlinear static characteristics. The resulting systemic arterial blood pressure (a slightly distorted sinusoidal pressure super-imposed on a constant mean pressure) is the output. According to the Nyquist stability theorem which we shall discuss more fully in Sec. 8.5, a closed loop system will generate undamped loop oscillations when its open loop vector locus passes through the -1 point in the clockwise direction. In the figure, the three curves at three different mean pressures H_s gradually approach the critical -1 point as the mean pressure H_s is lowered. From this diagram, and for this case, it can be deduced that the ischemic pressor response system would lapse into a sustained loop oscillation (cycling) if the feedback loop were closed at the mean pressure $H_s = 20$ mm. The oscillating frequency will be identical with the cross-over frequency at which the vector locus crosses the -1 point, namely f = (approximately) 1/50, or one cycle every fifty seconds in this particular example.

Bode Diagram

The Nyquist diagram presentation is convenient, especially for a problem like this in which a black box approach (like Fig. 8-1) is taken for an open loop system where closed loop stability is the main question. However, the Bode format is generally better suited to deal with lumped parameter objects for either plotting experimental data or presenting computed frequency response.

The two first order systems we saw in Figs. 8-10(a) and (b) are represented by Bode plots in Fig. 8-12. As shown in the figure, the horizontal axis of the diagram is frequency ω to a logarithmic scale. The amplitude ratio, labelled "gain," is also plotted as a logarithmic unit (decibels, db) on the left side ordinate scale, but phase shift, labelled "phase," is a linear scale (degrees) on the right side ordinate scale. The decibel scale is popular in acoustics, where it is the ratio of a sound wave's pressure level to a standard pressure. Typical noise levels are 130 db for a jet plane take-off and 30 db for conversation in a living room. A noise level of 40 db or more would probably be considered "noise pollution" by the average listener. In general, a dimensionless number N is converted into decibels by

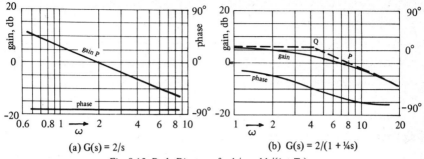

(a) G(s) = 2/s

(b) G(s) = 2/(1 + ¼s)

Fig. 8-12 Bode Diagrams for k/s and k/(1 + Ts)

$$20 \log_{10} N = \text{decibels} \tag{8-33}$$

so that

N	0.01	0.1	1	10	100
$20 \log_{10} N$ (db)	−40	−20	0	+20	+40

There is no physical reason for the decibel unit to be used to express amplitude in the Bode diagram. A logarithmic scale may be used without converting the amplitude ratio into decibels; therefore, log-log graph paper could be used for the gain plot. However, using decibels, semi-log paper can be used for both the gain and phase plots, as shown in Fig. 8-12.

The gain plot of an integrator (Eq. (8-20)) is a straight line in the Bode diagram, Fig. 8-12(a), at a slope of 20 db decrease in gain per decade increase in frequency. The position of the straight line may be fixed by point P where ω = k, so that the gain is one (zero db) at this point. The phase is −90° for all frequency, Eq. (8-19).

The next example, G(s) = k/(1 + Ts) in Fig. 8-12(b), has a plot which combines characteristics of a static element and an integrator. It behaves approximately like a static system at very low frequency

$$G(j\omega) = \frac{k}{1 + T(j\omega)} \rightarrow k \quad \text{when } \omega \rightarrow 0 \text{ or } \omega << \frac{1}{T} \tag{8-34}$$

The gain at low frequency is thus asymptotic to $20 \log_{10} k$ (db), where k = 2 in this example, so that (0.3010)20 = 6 db in Fig. 8-12(b). The phase is asymp-

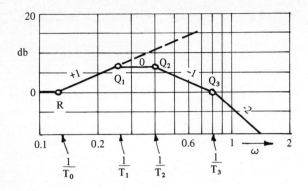

Fig. 8-13 Straight Gain Asymptotes for a Factored Transfer Function ($T_0 = 8$, $T_1 = 4$, $T_2 = 2.5$, and $T_3 = 1.25$, where $-1/T_0$ is a zero, and $-1/T_1$, $-1/T_2$ and $-1/T_3$ are poles)

totic to zero at the left end of the figure since a real constant contains no phase shift. The system acts almost like an integrator at high frequency

$$G(j\omega) = \frac{k}{1 + T(j\omega)} \rightarrow \frac{k}{T(j\omega)} \quad \text{when } \omega \rightarrow \infty \text{ or } \frac{1}{T} \ll \omega \qquad (8\text{-}35)$$

The high frequency gain asymptote (the dashed line QP with slope −20 db/ decade in Fig. 8-12(b)) crosses the 0 db level at point P where $\omega = k/T = 2/(1/4) = 8$, while the phase becomes asymptotic to −90° for high frequency. The two gain asymptotes cross at point Q in the figure, where $\omega = 1/T = 4$ is called a *corner frequency*, and Q is a corner or break-point.

Making use of the straight line gain asymptotes, we can sketch a gain profile in the Bode format. For example, Fig. 8-13 is a sketch of the gain for the factored transfer function

$$G(s) = \frac{1 + T_0 s}{(1 + T_1 s)(1 + T_2 s)(1 + T_3 s)} \qquad (8\text{-}36)$$

where $T_0 > T_1 > T_2 > T_3$. For this system, the gain asymptote is flat at low frequency up to the first corner point R; then it has an upwards slope because $T_0 s$ in the numerator will dominate the overall behavior. This slope, called a plus one (+1) slope, is at a rate of 20 db up in a one-to-ten span of ω (20 db/decade). It lasts until corner point Q_1 since $T_1 s$ in the denominator, with its −1 slope effect, cancels the +1 slope, so that a zero slope (flat) exists until the next corner point Q_2. Then a -1 slope occurs, due to the $(1 + T_2 s)$ factor in the denominator and, after the last corner point Q_3, a -2 slope finally appears. The phase of this system is asymptotic to $0°$ at low frequency where it behaves like a constant and asymptotic to $-180°$ at high frequency where it approximates a double integrator, k/s^2.

The characteristic feature of the Bode diagram — straight asymptotes — also appears in some unfactored transfer functions. Let us consider a linear damped mechanical vibration system

$$(mD^2 + bD + k)x = \text{force input}$$

where

$$x = \text{displacement (see Sec. 8.1)}$$

A canonical form of the transfer function for this system is

$$G(s) = \frac{K}{s^2 + 2\zeta\omega_n s + \omega_n^2} \tag{8-37}$$

where $K = 1/m$, ζ = damping factor and ω_n = undamped natural frequency, $\omega_n = \sqrt{k/m}$ and $\zeta = b/(2\sqrt{km})$. Letting $s \to j\omega$

$$G(j\omega) = \frac{K}{(\omega_n^2 - \omega^2) + 2j\zeta\omega_n\omega} \tag{8-38}$$

so that the low frequency behavior in the range $\omega \ll \omega_n$ is static as in Eq. (8-34). It is asymptotic to a double integrator K/s^2 at high frequency, so that the gain slope is -2 and the phase is asymptotic to $-180°$ (see the righthand side of Fig. 8-14). At the corner frequency $\omega = \omega_n$ (point P in Fig. 8-14), Eq. (8-38) reduces to

$$G(j\omega) = \frac{K}{2j\zeta\omega_n\omega} \tag{8-39}$$

This is a single integrator (see Fig. 8-12(a)); hence the plots here have a -1 slope and $-90°$ phase, as shown by the dashed line through point Q with -1 lope and the phase curve passing through point R where the phase lag is $-90°$ n Fig. 8-14. Moreover, the curve is tangent to the -1 slope line at Q, near the resonance peak because

$$\frac{1}{4\zeta^2\omega_n^2\omega^2} \geq \frac{1}{(\omega_n^2 - \omega^2)^2 + 4\zeta^2\omega_n^2\omega^2} \qquad \text{for all } \omega$$

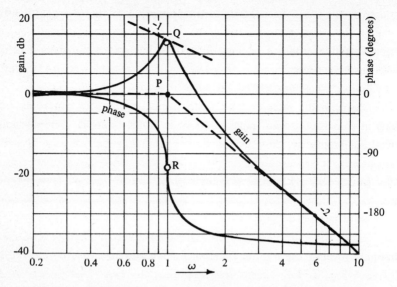

Fig. 8-14 Bode Diagram of a Damped Oscillator, $\omega_n = 1$, $\zeta = 0.1$, and $k = 1$

The Bode plots (like Figs. 8-12 and 8-14) make us wonder whether both gain and phase are necessary for a complete description of a dynamic system. It may be that just one of the two would be sufficient because the gain slope and phase are related to each other by the following simple rule:

$$
\begin{array}{lccccc}
\text{for } G(s) = & k/s^2 & 1/s & k & s & \\
\text{gain slope:} & -2 & -1 & 0 & +1 & \text{etc.} \qquad (8\text{-}40)\\
\text{phase shift:} & -180° & -90° & 0° & +90° &
\end{array}
$$

H. W. Bode gave a complete answer to this question in 1945 in his book on the diagrams he originated. His theorems state that either a gain or phase curve is sufficient for complete description of a transfer function, as long as all poles and zeros of the transfer function are either negative real or conjugate complex with negative real part (zero real part or a pole at 0 is allowed). Systems that satisfy this condition are called *minimum phase systems*; otherwise the systems are nonminimum phase. He showed that a nonminimum phase system will have more phase lag than a minimum phase system that has the identical gain curve. Dead time (Fig. 8-10(c) and Eq. (8-32)) is nonminimum phase; its gain stays constant but its phase lag increases indefinitely as the frequency is increased. The reverse reaction process (Fig. 6-10) is nonminimum phase because of its positive zero. In general, caution is required to determine phase shifts of nonminimum phase systems; often it is advisable to go back to the structure of the complex vectors (as in Fig. 8-9) of the nonminimum phase factors and check them carefully.

Although it is theoretically possible to derive phase information from the gain curve and vice versa by the Bode theorems as long as a system is minimum phase, the process is so complicated that it is not practical. For practical purposes, gain and phase plots over some crucial frequency range are needed. For this purpose, the Bode format is generally simpler than the Nyquist plot, especially because of the straight line asymptotes and the additive property of the plot. Use of the log scale for gain and the linear scale for phase make complex vector multiplications simple graphical additions on the Bode diagram. Also, the Bode format for plotting experimental data has the merit that errors in gain and phase are separated in the plot; the two errors will be combined in the Nyquist plot (see Fig. 8-11). Despite the simplifications made possible by the Bode format, it is still tedious work to construct a Bode diagram manually with reasonable accuracy. To ease the task, computers can be used for frequency response computations, as we shall see in the next section.

8.4 FREQUENCY RESPONSE COMPUTATION AND SIMULATION

We shall first present one possible algorithm for the purpose of frequency response computation.[†] Consider, for this example, an unfactored transfer function given as a ratio of two polynomials in s. Substituting $j\omega$ for s in Eq. (6-65) where the numerator will be taken as order m, we obtain the following frequency transfer function:

$$G(j\omega) = \frac{(b_m - b_{m-2}\omega^2 + \cdots) + j(b_{m-1}\omega - b_{m-3}\omega^3 + \cdots)}{(a_n - a_{n-2}\omega^2 + \cdots) + j(a_{n-1}\omega - a_{n-3}\omega^3 + \cdots)}$$

$$= \frac{C + jD}{A + jB} \tag{8-41}$$

If, for instance, n = 4 and m = 3

---

† A complete Fortran program for Nyquist and Bode plots is given in Ref. [4].

$$C = b_3 - b_1\omega^2 \qquad D = \omega(b_2 - b_0\omega^2)$$
$$A = a_4 - a_2\omega^2 + \omega^4 \qquad B = \omega(a_3 - a_1\omega^2)$$

$$(8\text{-}42)$$

Recalling Eqs. (8-27) and (8-28), the required results are written as

$$|G(j\omega)| = \text{GAIN} = \sqrt{\frac{C^2 + D^2}{A^2 + B^2}}$$
$$\angle G(j\omega) = \text{PHASE} = \tan^{-1}[\frac{D}{C}] - \tan^{-1}[\frac{B}{A}]$$

$$(8\text{-}43)$$

A constant frequency increment $\Delta\omega$ is normally not desirable. The frequency response patterns in the Bode plots of the preceding section show that log increments fit far better. If, for example, 30 data points are desired over a frequency range of $\omega = 0.1$ to 10, letting $x = \log_{10}\omega$, the range is -1 to $+1$ in x for which

$$\omega = 10^x \qquad\qquad (8\text{-}44)$$

and x must have 30 equal increments. The algorithm may start, therefore, after specifying the coefficient values A1 through A4 and B0 through B3 in Eq. (8-42)

PI = 3.141592	
DO 10 K = 1,31	— counting 30 increments by integer number K
FK = K−1	— converting K into floating
X = (FK−15.0)/15.0	point number FK starting from zero, the number is shifted into the span x from −1 to +1
W = 10.0**X	— Eq. (8-44) where W is ω

Here, if needed, the frequency in rad/sec may be converted into cycles per second (CPS or Hz) by $f = \omega/(2\pi)$

$$\text{CPS} = W/(2.0*PI)$$

The period $P = (2\pi)/\omega$ may also be computed if necessary. Now $W2 = \omega^2$ and $W4 = \omega^4$ are computed by

W2 = W**2
W4 = W2**2

and thus A, B, C and D in Eq. (8-42) are

A = A4−A2*W2+W4
B = W*(A3−A1*W2)
C = B3−B1*W2
D = W*(B2−B0*W2)

— where a_4 and a_2 are specified in advance

Moving to Eq. (8-43)

GAIN = SQRT((C**2+D**2)/
    (A**2+B**2))

If decibel measure is desirable

DBGAIN = 20.0*ALOG(GAIN)

Since arctangents are given in radians, a conversion factor $(180/\pi)$ is needed to get the phase in degrees, so

PHASE = (180.0/PI)*(ATAN(D/C)
    −ATAN(B/A))

Here, a jump in the value of $\tan^{-1}$ may occur if, for instance, angle α in Fig. 8-9 increases and crosses the negative real axis (that is, α becomes greater than π). The computer output for this case will jump from a plus value of α (which is less than π measured counterclockwise) to a negative value (measured clockwise). To prevent such a jump, an IF statement is needed

ALFA = ATAN(B/A)
IF(ALFA .LT. 0.0)ALFA = ALFA+
    2.0*PI

These two statements must come before the final phase computation. Finally, one must specify either print or plot instructions

write or plot statement
10   CONTINUE
     STOP
     END

Where available, **COMPLEX** mode variables can be used to simplify the form of this algorithm.

A computer plot in the Bode format, if crucial frequency zones are properly covered with a reasonably chosen increment, may indicate some straight line gain asymptotes and/or peaks (due to conjugate complex poles) or notches (due to conjugate complex zeros) and, thus, shed light on a system's poles and zeros which are imbedded in the unfactored numerator and denominator polynomials.

We shall choose a typical process transfer function for the second example. A second order system with dead time is a simple but good approximation of an S-shaped process response signature

$$G(s) = \frac{ke^{-sL}}{(1 + T_1 s)(1 + T_2 s)} \tag{8-45}$$

where T_1 and T_2 are time constants, L is a dead time (delay) and k is a gain. A Bode diagram may be sketched by hand for this simple form when accuracy is not required. Such a preliminary check is a desirable way to choose a frequency range and increment for computation. Factored forms of the transfer function may be computed with an algorithm different from the preceding example, but the previous format may still be used by multiplying out the factors. The delay term in the numerator is

$$e^{-j\omega L} = \cos(\omega L) - j\sin(\omega L) = C + jD \tag{8-46}$$

where

$$C = \cos(\omega L) \quad D = -\sin(\omega L)$$

The denominator is

$$(1 + j\omega T_1)(1 + j\omega T_2) = (1 - T_1 T_2 \omega^2) + j(T_1 + T_2)\omega = A + jB \tag{8-47}$$

thus

$$A = 1 - T_1 T_2 \omega^2 \quad B = (T_1 + T_2)\omega$$

and

$$G(j\omega) = k \left[\frac{C + jD}{A + jB} \right] \tag{8-48}$$

Let us suppose that the Nyquist plot is desired. Then we must compute $Re[G(j\omega)]$ and $Im[G(j\omega)]$ in place of gain and phase. Using the general form of Eq. (8-29), we obtain

$$Re\ G(j\omega) = k\ [\frac{AC + BD}{A^2 + B^2}] \quad Im\ G(j\omega) = k\ [\frac{AD - BC}{A^2 + B^2}] \qquad (8\text{-}49)$$

The frequencies at which the data are required may be specified in advance in array form, $\omega(1) = 0.0$, $\omega(2) = 0.1$, etc. The desired frequency values can be specified by a DATA statement

```
      DATA W/0.0, 0.1, 0.25, 0.45, 0.7,
            1.0, 1.35, 1.75, 2.2, 2.7/
```

After stating the values of T1, T2 and EL (which is L), we can write

```
      DO 20 I = 1,10
      A = 1.0–T1*T2*W(I)**2          – these two are for Eq.
      B = T1*T2*W(I)                    (8-47)
      C = COS(W(I)*EL)               – Eq. (8-46)
      D = –SIN(W(I)*EL)
      REG = (A*C+B*D)/(A**2+B**2)    – Eq. (8-49), where k = 1 is
                                       assumed
      AIG = (A*D–B*C)/(A**2+B**2)    – AIG is Im G(jω)
      plot or print instruction
 20   CONTINUE
      STOP
      END
```

The result is shown in Fig. 8-15 for $T_1 = 1.0$, $T_2 = 2.0$ and $L = 0.5$.

If an open loop frequency response computation is being performed for the purpose of closed loop system design, it is easy to compute the closed loop frequency response simultaneously. Let

$$G(s) = \frac{C + jD}{A + jB} \qquad (8\text{-}50)$$

be the open loop transfer function for a closed loop unity feedback system as given in Fig. 7-11. Then the closed loop transfer function from reference input R(s) to controlled variable C(s) in the same figure is given by

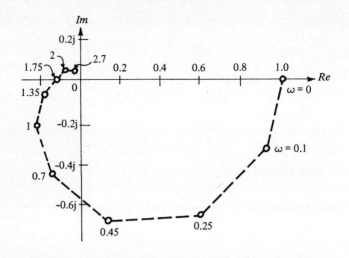

Fig. 8-15 Nyquist Diagram of a Second Order System with a Delay

$$G_{cl}(s) = \frac{C(s)}{R(s)} = \frac{G(s)}{1 + G(s)} = \frac{C + jD}{(A + C) + j(B + D)} \tag{8-51}$$

The form of Eq. (8-51) is very similar to the form of Eq. (8-50). They can be reduced to the same form by letting $A + C = A'$ and $B + D = B'$ in Eq. (8-51). Then Eq. (8-51) will reduce to Eq. (8-50). In order to compute Eqs. (8-50) and (8-51) simultaneously, we introduce a "switching" symbol F (or SW may be used) such that

$$F = 1.0 \;\; \text{for closed loop} \quad F = 0.0 \;\; \text{for open loop} \tag{8-52}$$

Then the closed loop transfer function, Eq. (8-51), will be

$$G_{cl}(s) = \frac{G}{1 + FG} = \frac{C + jD}{A' + B'} \tag{8-53}$$

where

$$A' = A + FC \quad B' = B + FD$$

By using F, the preceding algorithm can be modified to compute both open and closed loop frequency responses. However, if the closed loop system is unstable, the results computed in this manner will not be valid because the substitution $s = j\omega$ is not valid for unstable systems.

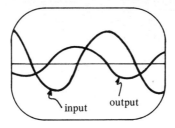

Fig. 8-16 Frequency Response at a Fixed Frequency on a Two-Channel Oscilloscope

Analog Simulation of Frequency Response

Frequency response computation on an analog computer is a kind of experimentation, that is, a frequency response test in itself. We feed a sinusoidal input into a simulated system that has been programmed on an analog computer. After waiting for the transient to die down (this will occur only if the system is stable), we then compare the system's steady-state sinusoidal output with its input to obtain the magnitude ratio and phase shift. A two-channel (i.e., dual trace) oscilloscope may be used for this purpose. Input and output sinusoidals may be frozen by adjusting the sweep speed (Fig. 8-16). A two-channel or multi-channel recorder may also be used with a slow speed analog computer to record the input and output. The sinusoidal input for this test may be taken from a sine wave generator or an oscillator circuit may be built (programmed) quite easily. According to Eq. (3-26), the state equation for an oscillator of frequency ω is

$$Dx_1 = -\omega x_2 \qquad Dx_2 = \omega x_1 \tag{8-54}$$

hence the signal flow graph shown in Fig. 8-17(a), from which the wiring in (b) of the figure will follow. Here the third operational amplifier, No. 3 in the figure, is needed for a sign change. The frequency of this circuit is

$$\omega^2 = \frac{k(R_4/R_3)}{(C_1 R_1)(C_2 R_2)} \tag{8-55}$$

so that the frequency may be changed by "pot" setting k or replacing R_3 and/or R_4. The amplitude of the sinusoidal signal appearing at V (or at any other terminal) in the figure depends on the initial voltage charged across either

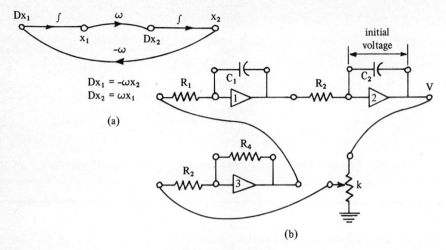

$$Dx_1 = -\omega x_2$$
$$Dx_2 = \omega x_1$$

(a)

(b)

Fig. 8-17 Oscillator Circuit

of the capacitors.

A difficulty in reaching sinusoidal steady-state, due to drift as shown in Fig. 8-8(c), will appear when integrators are involved in the system to be tested (one or more poles at s = 0 in G(s)). We make use of the relation given by Eq. (8-35) to avoid this difficulty by adding a high valued resistor element in parallel with the integrator capacitor. Effectively, this operational amplifier then acts as an integrator at all but the lowest frequencies at which the drifting signals are blocked.

There is no limit to the frequency range we can compute using a digital computer. An analog computer, on the other hand, is a real physical system. Consequently, there is a limit to the frequency range we can test on it. When the forcing frequency becomes too high for the system that is being tested, the output amplitude will drop down to a noise level and any further increase in forcing frequency will be meaningless. However, the range that can usually be tested is normally the range of importance.

As shown in Fig. 8-18, it is generally easy to test the frequency response of a closed loop system after testing its open loop frequency response. What is needed is a summer (Fig. 4-9(c)) at the input end of an open loop system G(s) and a piece of wire for the feedback from the output end back to the summer. A simple rule for assuring correct signs for negative feedback is that the total number of operational amplifiers connected in series around any loop must be odd (for instance three, as in Fig. 8-17(b)). This is because a sign change is

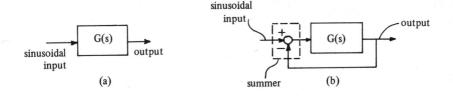

Fig. 8-18 From Open Loop to Closed Loop

introduced in each stage. Tests of a feedback control system in the time domain normally yield much information and insight. Controllers, like P, PI and PID given by the control laws, Eqs. (7-24) through (7-27), may be built using the feedback principle presented in Fig. 7-2. The resulting analog simulation will become a replica of a real electronic controller, incorporating such realities as saturation and nonzero initial values in the I action. Additionally, instabilities will be readily apparent and dynamic response patterns to various inputs can be tested on the same simulation.

8.5 STABILITY OF SINGLE LOOP FEEDBACK SYSTEMS

The frequency domain representation of a dynamic system provides us with much information, such as the system's behavior in the high frequency range, its bandwidth, resonance peak, behavior at low frequency and its static characteristic (or dc-behavior) at the zero frequency limit. The performance of a hi-fi unit, for instance, is generally expressed using an amplitude ratio (gain) versus frequency diagram. The frequency response technique is particularly important in linear feedback control system design. The design principle is based on the Nyquist theorem of input-output stability, which was originally developed for feedback amplifier design in the communications field. Application of the theorem was extended to servomechanism design in the 1940's, which triggered the rapid development of what is now called *classical control theory* – an expression which covers analytical and design techniques in terms of transfer functions, frequency response and the root locus.

To understand the Nyquist stability theorem, consider, in Fig. 8-19, that an open loop forced sinusoidal input signal is $E(j\omega_u)$. At this specific forcing frequency $\omega = \omega_u$, assume that the output sinusoidal signal $B(j\omega_u)$ happens to

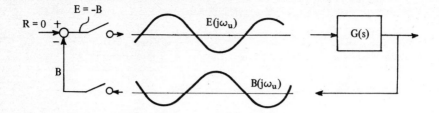

Fig. 8-19 An Oscillatory Stability Limit of a Closed-Loop System

have the same magnitude as the input and a phase shift of $-180°$ (i.e., $180°$ phase lag). The sinusoidal input-output relation will thus satisfy the condition

$$E(j\omega_u) = -B(j\omega_u) \qquad (8\text{-}56)$$

Let us now close the loop by closing the two switches in the figure, which connect the left side adder to the open loop system without any forcing input, that is, $R = 0$. Then the closed loop system must satisfy $E = R - B = -B$ for $R = 0$. This condition is satisfied by Eq. (8-56), which means that the closed loop system will oscillate with frequency ω_u in the absence of any forcing input from the outside unless the system is quiescent because of zero initial state. When the system has any nonzero initial value, its output B, fed back as E in the absence of R, will become an input to G. Thus, a circulation of information will begin. The initial transient of the circulation will converge to an undamped sinusoidal oscillation (of frequency ω_u) when all other closed loop modes are asymptotically stable (see Sec. 7.6).

According to Eq. (7-39)

$$G(s) + 1 = 0$$

is the characteristic equation of a closed loop system whose open loop transfer function is $G(s)$ and, according to the symbols used in Fig. 8-19, $G(s) = B(s)/E(s)$. We therefore see that for the specific condition where Eq. (8-56) will hold

$$G(j\omega_u) = \frac{B(j\omega_u)}{E(j\omega_u)} = -1$$

or

$$G(j\omega_u) + 1 = 0 \qquad (8\text{-}57)$$

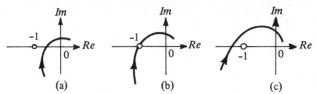

Fig. 8-20 Open Loop Vector Locus and Closed Loop Stability

that is, $s = j\omega_u$ is an eigenvalue (pole) of the closed loop system. On the other hand, $G(j\omega)$ for some range of interest of ω is the open loop frequency response that can be plotted on the complex plane as the Nyquist plot. Eq. (8-57) means that the vector locus in a Nyquist plot will pass through the -1 point at $\omega = \omega_u$, as sketched in Fig. 8-20(b). A closed loop system is therefore at its oscillatory stability limit when its open loop $G(j\omega)$ vector locus crosses the negative real axis of the Nyquist plane at the -1 point. This is the simplest statement of the Nyquist theorem.

When is the closed loop system stable? Recalling the discussion of Sec. 7.6, it can be deduced that a (normal or minimum phase) closed loop system will be stable when its open loop gain is reduced — for instance, cut to half of its stability limit value (see Eq. (7-51)). This will shrink the open loop vector locus, as shown in Fig. 8-20(a). Conversely, a closed loop system will usually be unstable if its open loop vector locus crosses the negative real axis on the left side of the critical -1 point as in part (c) of the figure. For a general statement and proof of the Nyquist theorem, see the appendix or Ref. [5], for instance.

How can we apply the theorem to feedback control system design? From the observations made above, we deduce that the distance from the -1 critical point C in Fig. 8-21(a) will give a measure of closed loop stability. The larger the distance CP, the more the margin of stability. Of course, in order for the closed loop system to be stable, the C point must be on the left side of the vector locus. Point G in the Bode plot, Fig. 8-21(b), is where $|G(j\omega)| = 1$ (i.e., 0 db) and is called the *gain crossover* while P is the *phase crossover* point where $\underline{/G(j\omega)} = -180°$. The stability margin in the Nyquist plane of Fig. 8-21(a) can be represented by *phase* and *gain margins* in the Bode diagram, labelled PM and GM in Fig. 8-21(b), respectively. The phase margin (PM) is the phase angle measured upward from $-180°$ at the gain crossover frequency at point G while gain margin (GM) is the gain in db measured downward from the 0 db level at the phase crossover frequency at point P. Negative margins (phase below $-180°$ at G or gain above 0 db at P) are meaningless, for they indicate instability as in

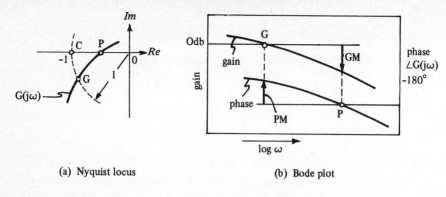

(a) Nyquist locus   (b) Bode plot

Fig. 8-21 Gain and Phase Crossover

Fig. 8-20(c). Phase margin of $30°$ or more and gain margin of 8 db or more are normally recommended (Ref. [2]). Note that excessive margins mean ineffective and weak control (Chap. 7). Therefore, this design criterion is interpreted to mean

or
$$\text{gain margin} = 8 \text{ db and phase margin may be more than } 30°$$
$$\text{gain margin may be more than 8 db and phase margin} = 30° \quad (8\text{-}58)$$

Since 1/2 is minus 6 decibels, the recommendation $k_c = (1/2)k_u$ in Eq. (7-51) yields 6 db gain margin. General guide rules like these must be refined for the requirements of each specific system.

The closed loop frequency response can be found by computer when the open loop frequency response is computed, as discussed in the previous section. There are also several graphical methods to obtain a closed loop frequency response from an open loop Bode or Nyquist plot, such as the Nichols chart (Sec. 9.4 of Ref. [5]). If a closed loop system is dominated by a pair of conjugate complex closed loop poles like p_1 and p_2 in Fig. 7-12(b) and, thus, a conspicuous damped oscillation characterizes the system's step response as shown in Fig. 7-5, the closed loop frequency response will have a peak in its gain (i.e., amplitude ratio) curve, just like the resonance peak Q in Fig. 8-14. Such a peak must not be permitted to be too high or else the system will be too underdamped, so that it is normally recommended (Ref. [2]) that

$$\left|\frac{C(j\omega)}{R(j\omega)}\right|_{max} \leqslant 1.3 \tag{8-59}$$

Stated in the frequency domain, the ideal goal of any feedback control system is

$$R(j\omega) = C(j\omega) \quad \text{hence } E(j\omega) = 0$$

for all frequencies ω and for all disturbance input $V(j\omega)$ (see Fig. 7-4). According to Eq. (7-21), the goal can be achieved only when the open loop gain is infinity for all frequencies, which is impossible without jeopardizing closed loop stability. Therefore, feedback control system design is a problem of finding a good compromise between control accuracy and closed loop stability. For instance, an I-control action will increase low frequency gain ($|G(j\omega)| \rightarrow \infty$ as $\omega \rightarrow 0$, Fig. 8-12(a)), eliminating offset. In exchange, however, a price is paid in closed loop stability because the $-90°$ phase shift introduced by the I-action may cut down the phase margin. A D-action, on the other hand, introduces phase advance (see Eq. (8-40)) in the open loop, thus improving phase margin. Using properly tuned D-action, it is possible to shift the gain and phase crossover points to the right (i.e., in the high frequency direction) in Fig. 8-21(b), resulting in a wider bandwidth in the system's closed loop frequency response, meaning quick recovery (or quick closed loop response) in the time domain behavior.

Generally, the time domain and the frequency domain are related to each other as shown in Fig. 8-22. The initial part of a transient response (from zero initial state) in the time domain, part A in the figure, is characterized by a number of delays and lags due mostly to $k/(1 + Ts)$ type dynamics, where T is

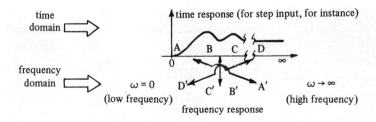

Fig. 8-22 Relations Between the Time Domain and the Frequency Domain

very small. Corresponding corner frequencies 1/T are thus in the high frequency end of the frequency domain, A'. This also ties into the initial value theorem, Eq. (6-13), where t → 0 corresponds to s (or ω) → ∞. The final value theorem, Eq. (6-12), is a dual; it ties t → ∞ with s (or ω) → 0. Point D in the time domain thus relates to D in the frequency domain in Fig. 8-22. A damped oscillation in the B to C range in the time domain will show up as a peak in gain (Fig. 8-14) located at B' to C' in the frequency domain.

8.6 LIMIT CYCLES

There are some phenomena that occur only in nonlinear systems. The jump phenomenon, presented in Sec. 8.1, is one such example. Limit cycle behavior is another important example. It is a self-excited periodic motion of a fixed amplitude and frequency. Rubbing noise, chatter in metal processing and room temperature fluctuation due to thermostat action are all considered to be limit cycles and could have deleterious effects. For instance, a limit cycle in a radar tracking servomechanism, caused by Coulomb friction (Eq. (2-12)) combined with backlash and elasticity in the mechanical transmission elements, may severely impair its performance. Since a limit cycle is periodic, we can obtain some insight into a limit cycle problem by using a frequency domain approach.

When input and output are in a periodic steady-state, the backlash plus Coulomb friction involved between an input (such as torque) and an output (velocity, for instance) is often approximately considered as a kind of hysteresis. A typical hysteresis is shown in Fig. 8-23(a). The relation follows A through B to C when input is increasing, then C via D back to A in the return motion.

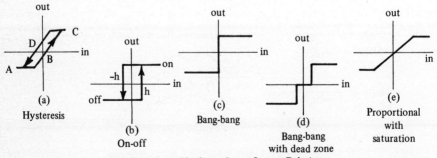

Fig. 8-23 Some Nonlinear Input-Output Relations

The area of the loop is often related to energy dissipation. Fig. 8-23(b) is a typical characteristic of an on-off thermostat, which will turn heat on when room temperature drops $h°C$ below its set point and cuts heat off at a temperature $h°C$ higher than the set point, hence a rectangular loop as shown. There is no loop in an ideal bang-bang controller, such as a contactor solid state switch which always causes a motor to rotate in one direction or another. If there is a "gap" in the switch (for instance, when a motor stops), a "dead zone" will appear as in (d) of the figure. As the number of switching steps is increased, the input-output relation will approach that of a linear proportional element, which is linear except for saturation end effects as in Fig. 8-23(e).

Since Fig. 8-23 is a "black box" expression of input-output relations, it looks simple, but it sometimes may be deceptive. Extremely complicated dynamic relations are hidden in a hysteresis phenomenon where past and recent behavior must be known to find present and future behavior. Even for the simple looking on-off action diagram, (b) of the figure, transient heating or cooling of a bimetal strip and its elastic reaction, internal and external friction and a triggering mechanism with its parametric changes are all involved. Parts (a) and (b) of Fig. 8-23 are therefore dynamic elements involving extreme simplification, applicable only for a periodic input-output problem. On the other hand, (c) through (e) are all static in that they are single-valued and involve no memory.

An approximate method is available to investigate limit cycles that may exist in a feedback loop. Consider a feedforward path in the loop that consists of a nonlinear element ($F(a)$ in Fig. 8-24) and a linear element ($G(j\omega)$ in the figure). Since our goal is to detect a condition under which a self-excited oscillation (a limit cycle) may exist, the feedback system is considered free. That is, R is set equal to zero, or no forcing from the outside is considered.

Let us suppose that the nonlinear element in Fig. 8-24 is subject to a sinusoidal input $ae^{j\omega t}$, where a is its amplitude. The output m(t) of the nonlinear element must have nonlinear distortion; that is, a sinusoidal component of

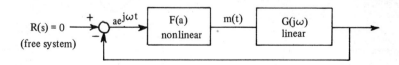

Fig. 8-24 Feedback Loop with a Nonlinear Element

frequency ω is distorted by other (high) frequency components. However, if the linear element $G(s)$ acts as a low pass filter and filters out practically all of the high frequency (distortion) components, only the original frequency (= ω) component will appear at its output. If that output has the same amplitude but is 180° out of phase with the input to the nonlinear element (i.e., output of $G(s)$ is $-ae^{j\omega t}$), such an oscillation can exist in the loop without any external forcing. This is the basic concept of the approximate method we shall present below.

The method requires an approximate description of a nonlinear element in the frequency domain. Let us derive such a description for the on-off action of Fig. 8-25(a) for the purposes of illustration. Response of the element to a sinusoidal input of amplitude a is a square wave, as shown in Fig. 8-25(b). The square wave of amplitude H is now approximated by a sine wave, as in part (c) of the figure. This approximation is based on a Fourier series expansion of the square wave, the sine wave shown of amplitude $4H/\pi$ being the first (or fundamental) component of the Fourier series. Because the frequencies of other components are higher than the first, we assume that the second and higher harmonics are insignificant when the linear part of the system ($G(j\omega)$) in Fig. 8-24) acts as a low pass filter. Nonlinear distortion thus ignored, it is now possible to describe approximately the nonlinear elements in terms of the input-output amplitude ratio and phase shift in the frequency domain. For our system, the description is

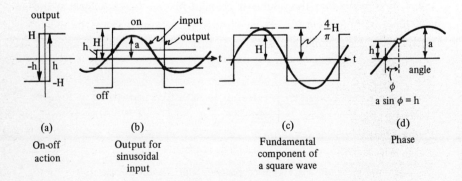

Fig. 8-25 Derivation of the Describing Function for On-Off Action

Gain (amplitude ratio): $|F(a)| = \dfrac{4}{\pi} \cdot \dfrac{H}{a}$

$$(8\text{-}60)$$

Phase shift: $\qquad \underline{/F(a)} = \phi = -\sin^{-1}\dfrac{h}{a}$

where the phase shift ϕ is obtained by the geometry shown in Fig. 8-25(d).

In general, an approximate description $F(a)$ of a nonlinear element in the frequency domain (like Eq. (8-60)) is called the *describing function* of the element; the approach we are taking is known as the *describing function method* and it is applicable to systems with only one nonlinearity. Note that the describing function does not depend on ω; instead, it is a function of the input sinusoidal amplitude "a". All of the complicated dynamic relations hidden inside a nonlinearity like a thermostat switch box are now represented by the phase lag given in Eq. (8-60).

We now apply the Nyquist theorem to the loop of Fig. 8-27(a), where the nonlinear element will be approximated by its describing function. Recalling Eq. (8-57) in the preceding section, the loop oscillation condition for a limit cycle of amplitude a_u and frequency ω_u is written as

$$1 + F(a_u)G(j\omega_u) = 0 \qquad\qquad (8\text{-}61)$$

where the second term on the left is the open loop transfer function. To find a pair of values a_u and ω_u that will satisfy this condition, it is convenient to rewrite the condition in the form

$$G(j\omega_u) = \dfrac{-1}{F(a_u)} \qquad\qquad (8\text{-}62)$$

and solve it graphically in the complex plane, where the left side, $G(j\omega_u)$, is a point on the vector locus for $G(j\omega)$. What is needed is a locus of $-1/F(a)$ (called an *amplitude locus*) for some range of "a" so that the solution of Eq. (8-62) will be given by an intersection of the two loci. Steps involved in constructing the amplitude locus for our system are shown in Fig. 8-26. We begin with vector $F(a)$, which was given by Eq. (8-60), in part (a) of the figure. A minus sign is introduced in (b) and then inverted in (c) where, by the geometry shown in the figure, we find that the amplitude locus is a straight line parallel to the negative real axis starting at $-\pi h/4H$ on the imaginary axis.

In Fig. 8-27(b), the amplitude locus of Fig. 8-26(c) and the Nyquist locus we obtained in Fig. 8-15 are combined for this on-off control system. The thermostat parameters are arbitrarily chosen such that $(\pi/4)\,(h/H) = 0.3$. The

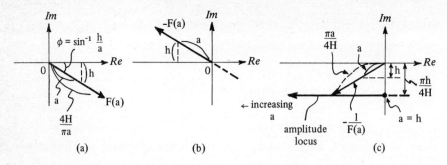

Fig. 8-26 Construction of the Amplitude Locus for On-Off Action

two loci intersect at point P so that the ω_u that satisfies Eqs. (8-60) and (8-61) is between 0.7 and 1.0. The amplitude locus will move closer to the negative real axis in Fig. 8-27(b) when the gap h of the thermostat is decreased, coinciding with the negative real axis at the limit h = 0 and the on-off action has no hysteresis. The limit cycle frequency at this limiting condition will be about 1.75, hence a period of about 1/2 of that at point P in the figure. The amplitude scale along the amplitude locus (increasing amplitude in the direction of the arrow) may be determined by the geometry shown in Fig. 8-26(c) for a given set of thermostat parameters h and H.

Let us say that $a = a_u$ at point P. What would happen if the amplitude a_u

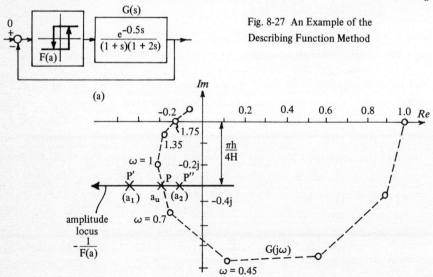

Fig. 8-27 An Example of the Describing Function Method

of the limit cycle is momentarily perturbed to some larger deflection a_1 or smaller value a_2? We know intuitively that the system will regain the original amplitude a_u in the absence of such perturbation, but does this approach give us some clue to the "stability" of a limit cycle? Although the describing function approach is basically inadequate to discuss any transient in the limit cycle build-up or decay, a clue to the stability or persistence of a limit cycle may be obtained. If the limit cycle amplitude is perturbed and slightly increased to a larger value a_1, by Eq. (8-60) we see that $|F(a_1)| < |F(a_u)|$, but $|F(a_u)G(j\omega_u)| = 1$ by Eq. (8-61) so that $|F(a_1)G(j\omega_u)| < 1$ in the vicinity of the phase crossover. Thus, the open loop transfer function $F(a)G(j\omega)$ will cross the negative real axis on the Nyquist plane on the right side of the -1 point, as shown in Fig. 8-20(a). The system is then stable in the sense that the loop oscillation will decay, which implies that the increased amplitude a_1 will decrease back towards a_u. A similar argument applies to a perturbation in the opposite direction, i.e., an amplitude a_2 which is smaller than a_u as at point P'' in Fig. 8-27(b). The overall open loop frequency transfer function $F(a)G(j\omega)$ will cross the negative real axis on the left side of the -1 point when a is a_2, meaning instability. Hence, the loop oscillation will grow, so that $a_2 \rightarrow a_u$. If the direction of the amplitude locus in Fig. 8-27(b) were reversed, increasing amplitude "a" from left to right along the amplitude locus, then the intersection P would be an unstable limit cycle. Its amplitude will either decay or increase away from the intersection point due to the slightest perturbation. One must investigate the general pattern of trajectories in state space to answer such questions as "how does a stable limit cycle build itself up in a start-up transient?" or "what transient will follow when an unstable limit cycle starts decaying?".

What do we gain by applying the describing function approach to a nonlinear closed loop system? For simple nonlinear control systems (such as the bang-bang type), this approach often gives a quick, first approximation value of the system's performance in terms of its loop oscillation amplitude and frequency. However, the application is not limited to discontinuous control systems; it applies to many systems which include a single nonlinearity. The accuracy of the approximation depends upon the low pass filtering characteristic of the linear part, $G(s)$. For instance, the method does not work well when $G(s)$ is only first order, $k/(1 + Ts)$, because the attenuation of the gain (amplitude ratio) at high frequency is still not enough to filter out the nonlinear distortion. Needless to say, a follow-up study using a computer is highly desirable after most describing function analyses.

SUMMARY

In addition to providing information about the sinusoidal steady-state response of a system to a sinusoidal forcing function, the frequency response method also is an important and convenient tool for component and system design under arbitrary inputs. Using the Nyquist stability criterion, we are able to apply frequency response design methods to the specification of systems that must be stable for any kind of forcing function.

The physical feel for frequency response tests of mechanical and electrical components leads directly to some basic formulations in the frequency domain. These formulations of frequency response data, in turn, yield alternative graphical representations — Nyquist or polar plots and Bode diagrams. Means for sketching or carefully computing these various diagrams have been discussed, as well as analog computer simulation approaches for achieving the same results.

The application of the Nyquist stability criterion permits us to design a system, either graphically or analytically, with a prescribed margin of stability. By utilizing open loop frequency transfer functions, we are able to choose controller parameters such that desirable closed loop system performance is assured.

Nonlinear systems may also be handled conveniently in the frequency domain, either directly in some straightforward cases as for the jump phenomenon situation discussed at the start of the chapter or by the describing function approximation discussed at the end. The limit cycle analysis which results from the latter permits us to better understand the amplitude and frequency characteristics of the bothersome self-sustained oscillations exhibited by numerous nonlinear systems.

REFERENCES

1. R. F. Steidel, Jr., *An Introduction to Mechanical Vibrations*, J. Wiley, New York, 1971

2. R. Oldenburger (ed. by), *Frequency Response*, McMillan, New York, 1956

3. K. Sagawa et al., "Elicitation of Theoretically Predicted Feedback Oscillations in Arterial Pressure", *American Journal of Physiology*, Vol. 203, No. 141, 1962

4. J. L. Melsa and S. K. Jones, *Computer Programs for Computational Assistance in the Study of Linear Control Theory*, McGraw-Hill, New York, 1973

5. Y. Takahashi, M. Rabins and D. Auslander, *Control*, Addison-Wesley, Reading, Mass., 1970

PROBLEMS

8-1 Gain asymptotes of a minimum phase system are shown in Fig. P-8-1. Identify the system transfer function.

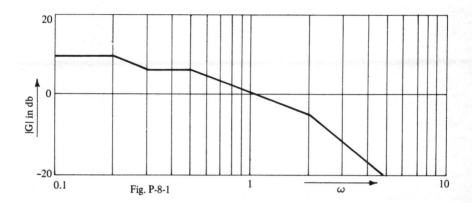

Fig. P-8-1

8-2 From data obtained in a frequency response test, the following values were deduced for the input-output amplitude ratios at the corner frequencies:

ω rad/sec	0.2	2	20	200	2,000
$|G|$ db	+20	0	0	−20	−60

(a) Sketch the Bode amplitude plot (assume that the starting and ending slopes can be extrapolated), (b) estimate the system transfer function, (c) sketch the Bode phase shift plot and (d) sketch the Nyquist plot.

8-3 A transfer function is given as

$$G(s) = \frac{1 + 0.2s + (2s)^2}{1 + 0.2s + s^2}$$

(Prob. 6-11 is a system that has a transfer function of this form). Sketch the gain asymptotes in the Bode diagram. Does the principle shown in Fig. 8-14 apply to obtain gain asymptotes at the resonance peak and notch? If it does not, is it still possible to determine analytically the tangents for the peak and notch?

8-4 Sketch the Bode and Nyquist diagram patterns for

$$G(s) = \frac{1 - Ts}{1 + Ts}$$

Is this a minimum phase system?

8-5 Given that

$$G(s) = \frac{1 - \frac{1}{2}s}{(1 + s)(1 + \frac{1}{2}s)}$$

is the transfer function of a reverse reaction process (see Prob. 7-10), obtain the Bode and Nyquist plots.

8-6 Sketch the Nyquist locus for

$$G(s) = \frac{1 - e^{-s}}{s}$$

(see Prob. 6-13 for its physical meaning). Is there any reason to prefer the Nyquist diagram rather than the Bode diagram for this transfer function?

8-7 An integrating controller, k/s, is applied to a process whose open loop transfer function is

$$G(s) = \frac{1}{(1 + s)(1 + 2s)}$$

Obtain the value of the controller gain k at the stability limit. Also determine the value of k that will satisfy the gain and phase margin criteria of Eq. (8-58).

8-8 A control object is approximated by a delayed integrator and the control law is a P-action, so that the open loop transfer function is

$$G(s) = \frac{ke^{-s}}{s}$$

where the dead time is taken as one (normalized) time unit. Determine the stability limit gain. Sketch the Nyquist diagram of the open loop transfer function.

8-9 Sketch the Nyquist diagram of a typical industrial process whose unit step input response has an S-shaped plot like Fig. 7-14(a), with a final value k_p. Modify the Nyquist theorem for positive feedback and determine the stability limit value of P-control gain k_c applied to this process with positive feedback.

8-10 A model consisting of two time constants plus dead time

$$G(s) = \frac{ke^{-sL}}{(1 + T_1 s)(1 + T_2 s)}$$

is often used to describe a variety of industrial processes and process instruments. The parameter values are $T_1 = 1$, $T_2 = 0.1$ and $L = 1/3$ (min) for a typical SO_2 instrument for pollution monitoring and $k = 1$ if its calibration is correct. A bandwidth is defined in the frequency domain to be the frequency range for which

magnitude ratio $\geqslant -3$ db

What is the bandwidth of the SO_2 instrument?

8-11 A linear plant

$$G(s) = \frac{1}{s(1 + s)(1 + 2s)}$$

is controlled by an on-off type action, of half magnitude M, about a fixed reference point. Using the describing function method, compute the period and amplitude of the limit cycle oscillation.

8-12 A population N(t) in an isolated ecosphere is described by the logistic equation

$$\frac{dN}{dt} = (K + u(t) - \frac{N}{M})N$$

where K and M are positive constants and u(t) is a periodic forcing input (such as daily or seasonal changes), $u(t) = u_0 e^{j\omega t}$, u_0 = magnitude $\leqslant$ K. Obtain the frequency response of the system. (Hint: try $N(t) = C_0 + C_1 e^{j\omega t} + C_2 e^{j2\omega t} + \cdots$)

8-13 A pest population x_1 is described by a Malthusian relation

$$\frac{dx_1}{dt} = rx_1 - bx_2$$

where r and b are positive constants and x_2 is the population of a control agent (predator). The predator population is assumed to decay

$$\frac{dx_2}{dt} = -ax_2$$

where a is a positive constant. A unity amount of the predator (a delta function) is released whenever the pest population reaches a fixed, maximum limit, x_1 = c. State the limiting values of c for which a limit cycle exists.

8-14 Does the describing function method apply to a product-type nonlinearity, such as (output) = (input)^2?

CHAPTER 9
DISCRETE-TIME SYSTEMS AND DIGITAL CONTROL

The widespread use of digital computers, both as computational aids in computing system responses and as actual control components, makes it necessary for us to have a body of theory to deal with these discrete-time devices. Although an *ad hoc* approach can be used very effectively to treat specific problems, such as the problem of obtaining the numerical solution to system equations that we derived in Chapter 4, a theoretical approach can often lead to general results which give much more specific answers to our design questions, albeit for relatively simple, linear systems. For this reason, we discuss the general theory of linear, discrete-time systems in the first part of the chapter, then z-transform theory, a transformation closely related to Laplace transforms, and, finally, some applications to digital computer control.

9.1 DISCRETE-TIME STATE EQUATIONS

The state, or output, of a discrete-time system is a sequence of vectors $\underline{x}(\Delta t)$, $\underline{x}(2\Delta t)$, $\underline{x}(3\Delta t)$, . . .; in general, we use the running index k to represent a particular sampling instant, i.e., $\underline{x}(k) = \underline{x}(k\Delta t)$. Δt is the time interval between data points and is taken as a constant for all the material presented here. The shorthand notation $\underline{x}(k)$ is used for $\underline{x}(k\Delta t)$ throughout. The state equation for linear discrete-time systems is an equation that gives the value of the system at a sampling instant, $t = (k + 1)\Delta t$, as a function of the state at the previous instant, $t = k\Delta t$

288

$$\underline{x}(k+1) = \underline{P}\,\underline{x}(k) + \underline{Q}\,\underline{u}(k) \qquad\qquad (9\text{-}1a)$$

$$\underline{y}(k+1) = \underline{C}\,\underline{x}(k+1) + \underline{D}\,\underline{u}(k+1) \qquad\qquad (9\text{-}1b)$$

where $\underline{u}$ is the input vector and $\underline{y}$ is the output vector. This form of equation is called a *difference* equation. Comparing this to the linear continuous-time state equation

$$\frac{d}{dt}\underline{x}(t) = \underline{A}\,\underline{x}(t) + \underline{B}\,\underline{u}(t) \qquad\qquad (9\text{-}2a)$$

$$\underline{y}(t) = \underline{C}\,\underline{x}(t) + \underline{D}\,\underline{u}(t) \qquad\qquad (9\text{-}2b)$$

we can see that the most important difference is that the running independent variable t is replaced in discrete-time systems with the running variable k, which can only take on integer values. The coefficient matrices $\underline{P}$ and $\underline{Q}$ have the same dimensionality as $\underline{A}$ and $\underline{B}$. Below, we consider stationary systems; i.e., $\underline{P}$, $\underline{Q}$, $\underline{C}$ and $\underline{D}$ are all matrices of constants.

As we have seen in Chapter 4, difference equations are necessary to find digital computer solutions and differential equations are necessary for analog computers. Because of the tremendous importance of both types of computing equipment for the analysis or design of control systems and dynamic systems, we must be able to convert equations from one form to the other. In most cases, either difference or differential equations can be used to describe a system. The mathematical form chosen is related more to the computing equipment or to the analytical tools available than to the nature of the system. The widespread use of digital computers for direct control of systems adds another dimension to discrete-time systems, because we must be able to design a discrete-time control algorithm that may well be used to control a continuous-time process. Although we will make many of the same assumptions in the material that follows that were made in the derivation of the Euler method in Chapter 4, the goals here are quite different. In Chapter 4, we were interested in the development of an efficient numerical computing algorithm. Here we are interested in developing a form of discrete-time state equation which will allow us to apply the powerful tool of mathematical analysis.

To convert the differential state equation, Eq. (9-2), into difference form in the discrete-time domain, we assume that the continuous-time input vector $\underline{u}(t)$ has a *staircase* pattern, as shown in Fig. 9-1(a) for a scalar signal. In general, we assume that

$$\underline{u}(t) = \underline{u}(k) = \text{constant} \qquad \text{for } k\Delta t \leqslant t < (k+1)\Delta t \qquad\qquad (9\text{-}3)$$

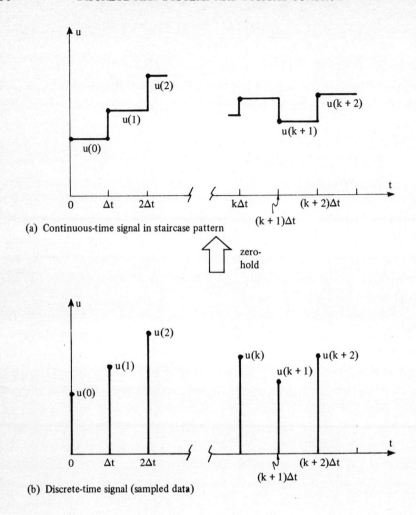

(a) Continuous-time signal in staircase pattern

zero-hold

(b) Discrete-time signal (sampled data)

Fig. 9-1 Zero-Hold Action

This assumption is satisfied if, for instance, a continuous-time input to a plant comes from a stepping motor which, in turn, receives commands from an on-line digital computer. The computer output is a binary coded word once every Δt time units. When the input comes, the stepping motor immediately rotates to its new position, then holds that position and waits for the next signal. Such an action is called a *zero-hold* (or zero-order hold), which refers to a device that holds an instantaneous (sampled) signal (Fig. 9-1(b)) at constant value (zero slope) over a period of Δt (the same figure, part (a)).

The solution of the continuous-time vector state equation, Eq. (9-2a), was given by Eq. (5-31b). We apply this solution over the time interval from $k\Delta t$ to $(k + 1)\Delta t$ to relate the $(k + 1)$-th state $\underline{x}(k + 1)$ to $\underline{x}(k)$. The "initial condition" for this purpose is

$$\underline{x}(t) = \underline{x}(k) \qquad \text{at } t = k\Delta t$$

and the forcing input $\underline{u}(k)$ stays constant (Eq. (9-3)). Therefore $\underline{u}(\tau) = \underline{u}(k)$ may be taken outside of the convolution integral

$$\underline{x}(k + 1) = e^{\underline{A}\Delta t}\underline{x}(k) + [\int_0^{\Delta t} e^{\underline{A}(\Delta t - \tau)}d\tau] \underline{B}\,\underline{u}(k) \tag{9-4}$$

A further simplification of this integral is possible by using a new dummy variable, $\eta = \Delta t - \tau$. Noting that $d\eta = -d\tau$

$$\int_{\tau=0}^{\tau=\Delta t} e^{\underline{A}(\Delta t - \tau)}d\tau = \int_{\eta=\Delta t}^{\eta=0} e^{\underline{A}\eta}(-d\eta) = \int_{\eta=0}^{\eta=\Delta t} e^{\underline{A}\eta}d\eta$$

so that Eq. (9-4) will reduce to Eq. (9-1a) with

$$\underline{P} = e^{\underline{A}\Delta t} \qquad \underline{Q} = [\int_0^{\Delta t} e^{\underline{A}\eta}d\eta] \underline{B} \tag{9-5}$$

Normally a digital computer is needed to determine $\underline{P}$ and $\underline{Q}$ by Eq. (9-5) for a given set of $\underline{A}$, $\underline{B}$ and Δt. However, for simple systems, the Laplace domain solution, Eq. (6-22), can be evaluated manually. If Δt is extremely short, we can use only the first two terms of the series for $e^{\underline{A}\Delta t}$, Eq. (5-28a), to get suitable approximations for $\underline{P}$ and $\underline{Q}$

$$\underline{P} = e^{\underline{A}\Delta t} \approx \underline{I} + \underline{A}\Delta t \qquad \underline{Q} \approx \underline{B}\Delta t \tag{9-6}$$

These equations describe the Euler method of Chapter 4. Substituting Eq. (9-6) back into Eq. (9-1a) and letting $\Delta t \rightarrow dt$ yields, after simple rearrangement, Eq. (9-2a).

The solution $\underline{x}(k)$ of Eq. (9-1) (given in the next section) agrees completely with $\underline{x}(k\Delta t)$ as computed from the continuous-time system if $\underline{P}$ and $\underline{Q}$ are computed by Eq. (9-5) and if the continuous-time input satisfies the zero-hold condition, Eq. (9-3). If the input $\underline{u}(t)$ does not satisfy Eq. (9-3) (which is normally the case for those that are not generated by a digital computer), the accuracy depends on the smoothness of $\underline{u}(t)$. For this case, the accuracy can be improved by reducing the sampling period Δt.

9.2 LINEAR DISCRETE-TIME SYSTEMS

Solving the vector difference equation is much easier than solving the differential equation (Secs. 5.1 and 5.2); it is a repetitive operation exactly like digital computer iteration (Sec. 4.1). First let k = 1 in Eq. (9-1)

$$\underline{x}(1) = \underline{P}\,\underline{x}(0) + \underline{Q}\,\underline{u}(0) \qquad (9\text{-}7)$$

then let k = 2 and substitute Eq. (9-7) into the right side of Eq. (9-1) to get

$$\underline{x}(2) = \underline{P}\,\underline{x}(1) + \underline{Q}\,\underline{u}(1) = \underline{P}(\underline{P}\,\underline{x}(0) + \underline{Q}\,\underline{u}(0)) + \underline{Q}\,\underline{u}(1)$$
$$= \underline{P}^2\,\underline{x}(0) + (\underline{P}\,\underline{Q}\,\underline{u}(0) + \underline{Q}\,\underline{u}(1))$$

and so on. The general form of the solution for $\underline{x}(k)$, k = 1, 2, 3, . . ., is

$$\underline{x}(k) = \underline{P}^k\,\underline{x}(0) + \sum_{j=0}^{k-1} \underline{P}^{k-1-j}\,\underline{Q}\,\underline{u}(j) \qquad (9\text{-}8)$$

The solution is closely parallel to its counterpart for the continuous-time system, Eq. (5-31), i.e.

	continuous-time	discrete-time	
free response:	$e^{\underline{A}t}\,\underline{x}(0)$	$\underline{P}^k\,\underline{x}(0)$	
forced component:	$\int_0^t e^{\underline{A}(t-\tau)}\,\underline{B}\,\underline{u}(\tau)d\tau$	$\sum_{j=0}^{k-1} \underline{P}^{k-1-j}\,\underline{Q}\,\underline{u}(j)$	(9-9)

In actual practice, however, we usually use a digital computer and apply the recursive method presented in Sec. 4.1 rather than the general solution of Eq. (9-8).

Integrals of the form of the forced component of the continuous-time solution in Eq. (9-9) are convolution integrals (see Sec. 5.2); by analogy, we can call the summation for the forced component of the discrete-time solution a convolution summation. These convolution forms occur frequently in linear system theory and can be given a geometric interpretation for the scalar first order case. Consider the input function shown in Fig. 9-2(a), where u has a value for $k = 0$ only and is zero elsewhere. We assume that $x(0) = 0$ and $Q = 1$. A typical output for a first order, stable system is shown on the x vs. k curve just below the u vs. k curve in Fig. 9-2(a). Referring to the discrete-time convolution summation in Eq. (9-9), we see that because $u(j)$ is zero for j greater than zero, there will be only one term in the summation, the term for $j = 0$. For $k = 5$, for example, $k - 1 - j = 4$ and, as shown on the figure, the amplitude of the output at $k = 5$ is $P^4 u_0$. A second simple input to the same system is shown in Fig. 9-2(b). In this case, u has a value only for $k = 3$ and is zero everywhere else. Because we are dealing with a linear, stationary system, the output for this case must have the same shape as the output for the first case but just shifted in time. This is shown in the x vs. k curve of Fig. 9-2(b); for times up to $k = 4$, the output is zero because the initial state is zero and there has been no input. Using the convolution summation, which again will have only one nonzero term, this time for $j = 3$, for k less than 4 we see that the output will be zero. For $k = 8$, for example, $k - 1 - j$ for the nonzero term will be $8 - 1 - 3 = 4$ and the output will be $P^4 u_3$, as shown. For $k = 12$, $k - 1 - j = 12 - 1 - 3 = 8$ and $x(12)$ is $P^8 u_3$.

Fig. 9-2(c) shows a slightly more complex input, this u consisting of two pulses, one at $k = 0$ and one at $k = 3$. Since these are the same two inputs we treated in (a) and (b) of the figure and since this is a linear system, the output will be the sum of the outputs generated for the two simple cases (linear superposition). For k less than 4, the convolution summation will still contain only one nonzero term, the one due to the input at $k = 0$. At $k = 2$, the output is $P^1 u_0$, for example. For k greater than or equal to 4, however, there will be two nonzero terms, one contributed by each of the inputs. At $k = 6$, as we can see from the output curve in Fig. 9-2(c), $x(6) = P^5 u_0 + P^2 u_3$. This case shows the principle of a convolution summation: at a given time k, each term in the summation represents the present influence of one past input. The full summation for the $k = 6$ case shown above is $x(6) = P^5 u_0 + P^4 u_1 + P^3 u_2 + P^2 u_3 + P^1 u_4 + P^0 u_5$. In our case, only u_0 and u_3 are nonzero, so the summation reduces to two terms. Viewing the full summation as a series of weighting factors multiplying past input values, the P^i factors express a system's memory of past inputs. For a linear, stable, first order system, the memory of the past decreases exponentially (note in Fig. 9-2(c) that the input at $k = 0$, u_0, always has relatively less influence on the output than the later input, u_3).

As the sampling interval Δt of the discrete-time system is permitted to get

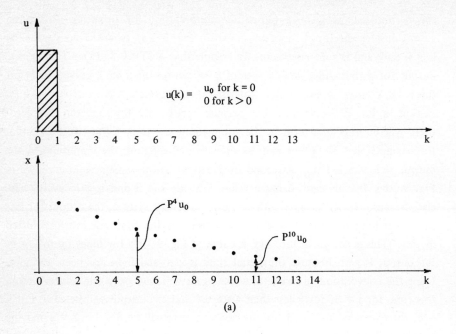

(a)

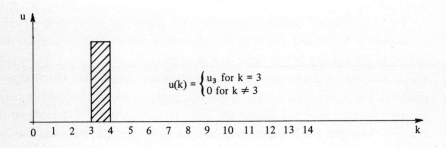

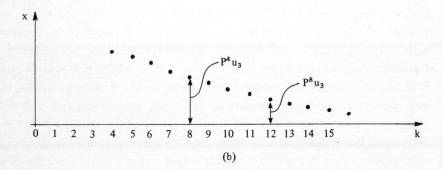

(b)

Fig. 9-2 Convolution Summation for a Discrete-Time System (continued on next page)

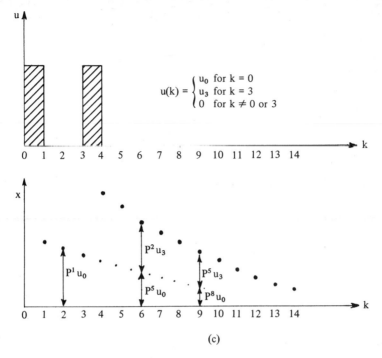

$$u(k) = \begin{cases} u_0 & \text{for } k = 0 \\ u_3 & \text{for } k = 3 \\ 0 & \text{for } k \neq 0 \text{ or } 3 \end{cases}$$

(c)

Fig. 9-2 Convolution Summation for a Discrete-Time System

smaller and smaller, the number of inputs increases; however, each one becomes narrower and contributes less. In the limiting case, as $\Delta t \rightarrow dt$, the summation becomes the integral given in Eq. (9-9) for the forced component of the continuous case. Recalling our earlier discussion of the impulse response of a continuous-time system (Secs. 5.2 and 6.4), we noted that, as input pulses become narrower, the system response ceases to depend on the details of the shape of the pulse and begins to depend only on its area. Each very small pulse can thus be treated as an impulse and the integral describes the combined effect of many very small pulses applied to the system at different times in the past. In cases where the integral cannot be evaluated analytically, the computer solution is expressed by the discrete-time summation.

Population determination is an example of a system in which measurement is almost always done on discrete-time basis, for example, the census every ten years to measure the population of a nation. The population equation $dN(t)/dt = rN(t)$, Eq. (1-2), is linear when r does not depend on N. It is easy to convert the differential equation into the following difference form:

$$N(k+1) = PN(k) \qquad P = e^{r\Delta t} \qquad N(0) = N_0 \tag{9-10}$$

Its solution

$$N(k) = P^k N_0 = e^{r(k\Delta t)} N_0 \tag{9-11}$$

agrees completely with the continuous-time solution, $e^{rt}N_0$ (Eq. (1-3)), at the data points $t = k\Delta t$, $k = 1, 2, \ldots$ Note that the system stability depends on the value of P; that is, the population will explode (instability) when $P > 1$ (i.e., $r > 0$) because the geometric progression $P, P^2, \ldots$ will grow indefinitely, and will tend towards zero (stability) when $P < 1$ (i.e., $r < 0$).

The stability investigation given above for a first order discrete-time system can be generalized to the n-th order case by following a logic that closely parallels the development given in Sec. 5.1. Let us suppose that

$$\underline{x}(k) = \gamma^k \underline{v} \tag{9-12}$$

is a particular solution of the state equation $\underline{x}(k + 1) = \underline{P}\,\underline{x}(k)$, so that by substituting Eq. (9-12) into the state equation the following relation will hold:

$$\gamma \underline{v} = \underline{P}\,\underline{v} \tag{9-13}$$

In order for a nontrivial solution for $\underline{v}$ (i.e., $\underline{v} \neq \underline{0}$) to exist, we must have

$$\left|(\gamma \underline{I} - \underline{P})\right| = 0 \tag{9-14}$$

This is the characteristic equation of the discrete-time system. The roots of Eq. (9-14), γ_i, $i = 1, 2, \ldots, n$, are the eigenvalues of the system. The modes are γ_i^k, $i = 1, 2, \ldots, n$, for distinct eigenvalues. A discrete-time system is asymptotically stable at its equilibrium point (meaning that the time series of its free response will converge to the equilibrium point as k is increased indefinitely) if and only if

$$\left|\gamma_i\right| < 1 \qquad \text{for all i} \tag{9-15}$$

Recalling that the imaginary axis of the complex root plane was the stability boundary for continuous-time linear systems, we see that, for discrete-time systems, the boundary is a *unit circle* centered at the origin of the complex root plane (Fig. 9-3). As in continuous-time systems, we can predict the nature of a discrete-time system's behavior by knowing the locations of its eigenvalues on the complex plane. Jury's method for testing the stability of a discrete-time system using matrix "inners" is presented in Sec. A.3 of the appendix.

The next example demonstrates the characteristic responses for first and second order systems.

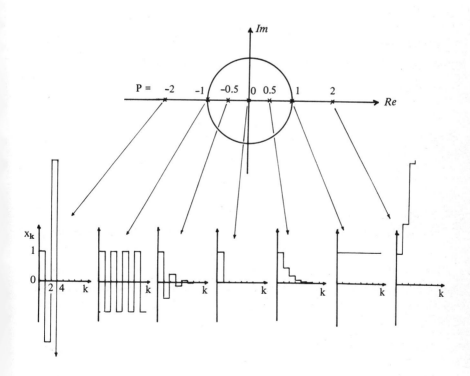

Fig. 9-3 Responses of First Order Discrete-Time Systems

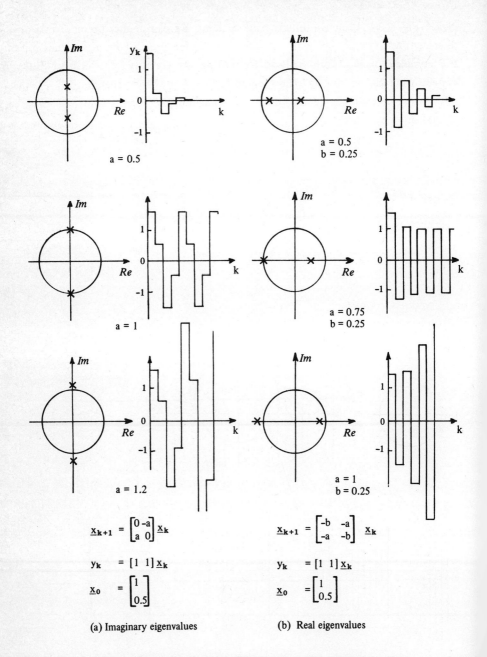

$$\underline{x}_{k+1} = \begin{bmatrix} 0 & -a \\ a & 0 \end{bmatrix} \underline{x}_k$$

$$y_k = [1 \; 1] \underline{x}_k$$

$$\underline{x}_0 = \begin{bmatrix} 1 \\ 0.5 \end{bmatrix}$$

(a) Imaginary eigenvalues

$$\underline{x}_{k+1} = \begin{bmatrix} -b & -a \\ -a & -b \end{bmatrix} \underline{x}_k$$

$$y_k = [1 \; 1] \underline{x}_k$$

$$\underline{x}_0 = \begin{bmatrix} 1 \\ 0.5 \end{bmatrix}$$

(b) Real eigenvalues

Fig. 9-4 Responses of Second Order Discrete-Time Systems

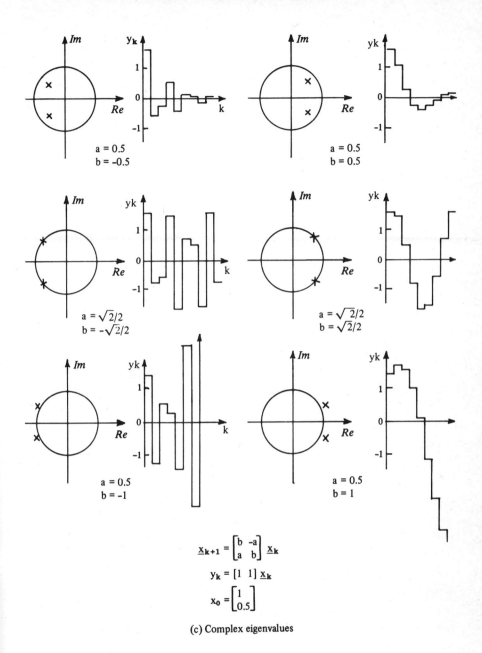

$$\underline{x}_{k+1} = \begin{bmatrix} b & -a \\ a & b \end{bmatrix} \underline{x}_k$$

$$y_k = [1 \quad 1] \, \underline{x}_k$$

$$x_0 = \begin{bmatrix} 1 \\ 0.5 \end{bmatrix}$$

(c) Complex eigenvalues

Fig. 9-4 (continued) Responses of Second Order Discrete-Time Systems

Example 9-1:   Responses of First and Second Order Discrete-Time Systems

Several representative discrete-time systems are shown with their responses in Figs. 9-3 and 9-4. In all cases, the output responses were computed by direct application of Eq. (9-1). In order to display the effects of eigenvalue placement most clearly, only autonomous systems ($Q = \underline{0}$) were considered and $\underline{D}$ was equal to zero for all cases. To make the response curves more distinctive, a zero-order hold was assumed at the output. For a first order system, p is the eigenvalue and, for real valued outputs, the eigenvalue must also be real. Fig. 9-3 shows a set of responses for various placements of the eigenvalue (marked by an "x") along the real axis. Note such properties as stability and oscillations in the response and their relation to eigenvalue position.

Second order systems can have complex valued eigenvalues, but, again, if the system output is to be real valued, any complex eigenvalues must appear in conjugate pairs. This limits the possibilities, but there are still lots of combinations possible. Fig. 9-4 shows responses for some important cases: (a) is for the case of purely imaginary eigenvalues, (b) is for purely real eigenvalues and (c) is for pairs of eigenvalues that are complex conjugates. In all cases, the response is shown to the right of the root location diagram.

The response of a first order system with its root on the negative real axis (Fig. 9-3) is a limiting case from which we can draw an interesting and general conclusion. As we see from the response curves, the output changes sign each sampling interval; this clearly represents the simplest possible oscillatory signal. If we are approximating a continuous-time oscillatory system with a discrete-time system (or are simply sampling a continuous-time oscillatory signal), the largest sampling interval that will fully retain the oscillatory characteristic is that sampling interval which yields a discrete-time model with a negative real eigenvalue. To see what that maximum sampling period is, let's look at the damped sinusoid shown in Fig. 9-5(a) (where T is the period of oscillation). A sampling period equal to half the period of oscillation, as shown, gives the sequence of samples shown by the arrows. They can be represented by a discrete-time system having a negative real eigenvalue with magnitude less than one. If the sampling interval is increased beyond T/2, the situation shown in (b) of the figure where one lobe of the oscillation was completely skipped must arise at some time during the sampling process. As long as the sampling interval is equal to T/2 or less, each lobe of the oscillation will be represented by at least one sample, whereas if the sampling interval is larger than T/2, some lobes will be missed. Since the lobes are fundamental to the oscillatory property of the sig-

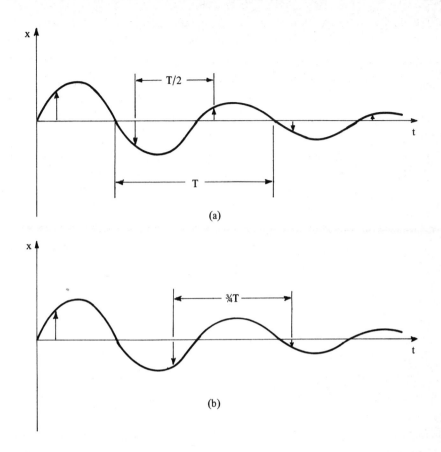

Fig. 9-5   Demonstration of Maximum Sampling Period for Oscillatory Signals

nal, this establishes a rule known as the *sampling theorem* (Ref. [1]):

> For any signal containing one or more oscillatory components, the maximum sampling interval that can be used without loss of fundamental information is equal to one half of the period of the fastest oscillating component

$$\Delta t \leqslant \frac{1}{2} T_{min} \qquad (9\text{-}16)$$

where T_{min} is the period of the fastest oscillation.

It is customary to use sampling intervals that are much shorter than the limit given by Eq. (9-16) to learn more about the shape of the oscillation, but, nontheless, this limit is an important theoretical boundary to be used in the design of sampling systems.

9.3 z-TRANSFORMS

In our discussions of the Laplace transform (Section 6.1), we saw the power of the right transformation to simplify a mathematical model. In the case of ordinary differential equations, Laplace transformation reduces a differential equation to an algebraic equation, allowing us to do much of the mathematical manipulation in this simpler domain. Such a transform, called the *z-transform*, exists for discrete-time systems also (Ref.[1]). In the development below, we establish some of the important z domain relations and point out their usefulness in the analysis of discrete-time systems.

A set of sampled data, f(0), f(1), . . ., consists of pulses (or impulses) Δt time apart. Thus, f(k) is located at time point $k\Delta t$ or it is delayed from the time origin by a length of time $k\Delta t$. Thus, in the Laplace domain, we express the delayed sample by $e^{-sk\Delta t}f(k)$ (see Table 6-1, pair No. 7). Denoting $e^{s\Delta t}$ by z (a time advance operator)

$$z = e^{s\Delta t} \qquad (9\text{-}17)$$

then f(k) in the z domain is $f(k)z^{-k}$. Applying this notation to all the samples of the time series f(0), f(1), f(2), . . ., we obtain the z-transform of the time series

$$F(z) = Z[f(k)] = f(0) + f(1)z^{-1} + \cdots + f(k)z^{-k} + \cdots = \sum_{k=0}^{\infty} f(k)z^{-k}$$
$$(9\text{-}18)$$

This has a very close tie with the Laplace transform of a continuous-time signal f(t), given by Eq. (6-2)

$$\mathcal{L}[f(t)] = F(s) = \int_0^{\infty} f(t)e^{-st}dt$$

versus

$$Z[f(k)] = F(z) = \sum_{k=0}^{\infty} f(k\Delta t)e^{-sk\Delta t} = \sum_{k=0}^{\infty} f(k)z^{-k}$$

Because of this close relation to the Laplace transform via Eq. (9-17), the conditions for the existence of the above summation are the same as the conditions for the existence of the Laplace integral discussed in Sec. 6.1. The z-transform of a unit step (f(k) = 1 for all k) may be obtained from Eq. (9-18) as

$$F(z)_{unit\ step} = 1 + z^{-1} + z^{-2} + \cdots = \frac{1}{1 - z^{-1}} = \frac{z}{z - 1}$$

which is the sum of an infinite geometric series. This is the second pair in row No. 1 of Table 9-1. Other pairs listed in the table may be derived in a similar manner.

The inverse process is simply a division process or an expansion of $F(z)$ into a series in z^{-k}. For instance, for $F(z) = z/(z - c)$, dividing z by $(z - c)$, we obtain

$$\frac{z}{z - c} = 1 + cz^{-1} + c^2 z^{-2} + \cdots$$

where the integer number k as the sole exponent of z indicates the time point where a sample is located. This example is the first pair in row No. 1 of Table 9-1.

An important relation that corresponds to Eq. (6-3) in the Laplace transform is the following: let $Z[f(k)] = F(z)$, then

$$Z[f(k + 1)] = f(1) + z^{-1}f(2) + \cdots = z[f(0) + z^{-1}f(1) + \cdots] - zf(0)$$

where

$$F(z) = [f(0) + z^{-1}f(1) + \cdots]$$

so that

$$Z[f(k+1)] = zF(z) - zf(0) \qquad (9\text{-}19)$$

To see the similarity, Eq. (6-3), which corresponds to Eq. (9-19), is

$$\mathcal{L}[\frac{df(t)}{dt}] = sF(s) - f(0)$$

We can apply this result to the vector state equation for a linear discrete-time system, Eq. (9-1a) repeated below

$$\underline{x}(k + 1) = \underline{P}\,\underline{x}(k) + \underline{Q}\,\underline{u}(k)$$

Letting $Z[\underline{x}(k)] = \underline{X}(z)$, $Z[\underline{u}(z)] = \underline{U}(z)$ and applying Eq. (9-19), we obtain the z domain expression for the vector difference equation

$$z\underline{X}(z) - z\underline{x}(0) = \underline{P}\,\underline{X}(z) + \underline{Q}\,\underline{U}(z)$$

Its algebraic solution in the z domain is

$$\underline{X}(z) = (z\underline{I} - \underline{P})^{-1}z\underline{x}(0) + (z\underline{I} - \underline{P})^{-1}\underline{Q}\,\underline{U}(z) \tag{9-20}$$

which is the z domain version of Eq. (6-18). This formulation again yields the characteristic equation, Eq. (9-14)

$$\left|(z\underline{I} - \underline{P})\right| = 0$$

whose roots are the eigenvalues.

Using the output equation from Eq. (9-1b)

$$\underline{y}(k) = \underline{C}\,\underline{x}(k) + \underline{D}\,\underline{u}(k)$$

or, in the z domain

$$\underline{Y}(z) = \underline{C}\,\underline{X}(z) + \underline{D}\,\underline{U}(z) \tag{9-21}$$

a $\underline{G}(z)$ that closely resembles $\underline{G}(s)$ in Eq. (6-40) can be obtained. It is called the matrix *pulse transfer function*.

A general form for a realizable (scalar) pulse transfer function is

$$G(z) = \frac{Y(z)}{U(z)} = \frac{b_0 + b_1 z^{-1} + b_2 z^{-2} + \cdots + b_m z^{-m}}{1 + a_1 z^{-1} + a_2 z^{-2} + \cdots + a_n z^{-n}}$$

where the real coefficients a_i and b_j can be positive, negative or zero and the order in both denominator and numerator is arbitrary. This is realizable because

$$(1 + a_1 z^{-1} + a_2 z^{-2} + \cdots)Y(z) = (b_0 + b_1 z^{-1} + b_2 z^{-2} + \cdots)U(z)$$

so that present output $y(k)$ depends on present and past inputs and past outputs but not any future values

Table 9-1: z Transform Pairs

	$F(s) = \mathcal{L}[f(t)]$	$f(k\Delta t)$	$F(z) = Z[f(k\Delta t)]$
1	$\dfrac{1}{s+a}$ $a > 0$	c^k $1 > c = e^{-a\Delta t} > 0$	$\dfrac{z}{z-c}$
	$\dfrac{1}{s}$	1 $(c = 1)$	$\dfrac{z}{z-1}$
2	$\dfrac{b-a}{(s+a)(s+b)}$ $b > a > 0$	$c^k - d^k$ $1 > c = e^{-a\Delta t} > d = e^{-b\Delta t} > 0$	$\dfrac{(c-d)z}{(z-c)(z-d)}$
	$\dfrac{b}{s(s+b)}$ $b > 0$	$1 - d^k$ $1 > d = e^{-b\Delta t} > 0$	$\dfrac{(1-d)z}{(z-1)(z-d)}$
3	$\dfrac{1}{(s+a)^2}$ $a > 0$	$(k\Delta t)c^k$ $1 > c = e^{-a\Delta t} > 0$	$\dfrac{(c\Delta t)z}{(z-c)^2}$
	$\dfrac{1}{s^2}$	$k\Delta t$	$\dfrac{(\Delta t)z}{(z-1)^2}$
4	$\dfrac{\beta}{(s+\alpha)^2 + \beta^2}$ $\alpha > 0$	$c^k \sin(k\beta\Delta t)$ $1 > c = e^{-\alpha\Delta t} > 0$	$\dfrac{cz\sin(\beta\Delta t)}{z^2 - 2cz\cos(\beta\Delta t) + c^2}$
	$\dfrac{\beta}{s^2 + \beta^2}$	$\sin(k\beta\Delta t)$	$\dfrac{z\sin(\beta\Delta t)}{z^2 - 2z\cos(\beta\Delta t) + 1}$
5	$\dfrac{s+\alpha}{(s+\alpha)^2 + \beta^2}$ $\alpha > 0$	$c^k \cos(k\beta\Delta t)$ $1 > c = e^{-\alpha\Delta t} > 0$	$\dfrac{z^2 - cz\cos(\beta\Delta t)}{z^2 - 2cz\cos(\beta\Delta t) + c^2}$
		$c^k \cos(k\pi)$ if $\beta\Delta t = \pi$	$\dfrac{z}{z+c}$
	$\dfrac{s}{s^2 + \beta^2}$	$\cos(k\beta\Delta t)$	$\dfrac{z^2 - z\cos(\beta\Delta t)}{z^2 - 2z\cos(\beta\Delta t) + 1}$
		$\cos(k\pi)$ if $\beta\Delta t = \pi$	$\dfrac{z}{z+1}$

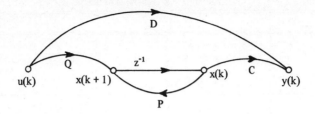

Fig. 9-6 Signal Flow Graph for a First Order Discrete-Time System

$$y(k) = b_0 u(k) + b_1 u(k - 1) + b_2 u(k - 2) + \cdots$$
$$- a_1 y(k - 1) - a_2 y(k - 2) - \cdots$$

A signal flow graph is shown in Fig. 9-6 for the first order system

$$x(k + 1) = Px(k) + Qu(k) \quad y(k) = Cx(k) + Du(k) \tag{9-22}$$

The integrator of Fig. 6-7(c) is replaced by a *delay operator*, z^{-1} in this figure. As shown in Fig. 6-8, a signal flow graph for a continuous-time system (with integrators as its dynamic elements) is almost like an analog computer wiring diagram in which the integrator (Fig. 4-9(d)) is the key element. Time delay, on the other hand, is difficult to implement on an analog computer; it can be realized, for instance, by using a loop of magnetic tape. On the other hand, we have seen that difficulties can arise in performing time integration on a digital computer (Fig. 4-3, for instance). The only dynamic element a digital computer really has is a shift, which simulates a discrete-time time delay. Therefore, the steps shown in a discrete-time signal flow graph like Fig. 9-6 are almost like a digital computer algorithm, in which the old data x(k) and u(k) are used to compute the new state x(k + 1) by

$$X = P*X + Q*U$$

The procedure is repeated as k is incremented. This is what is shown in the middle part of the signal flow graph.

The z-transform method can be used to analyze the zero-hold element introduced in Sec. 9.1 and, in so doing, to establish another procedure for deriving a discrete-time model of a continuous-time process. The unit impulse response of a zero-hold is a pulse (see Fig. 9-7). A unit pulse is composed of two steps, Fig.

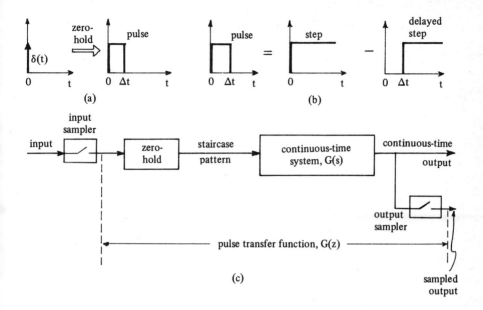

Fig. 9-7 Pulse Transfer Function of a Continuous-Time System with Sampler

9-7(b), so that

$$\mathcal{L}[\text{zero-hold}] = \frac{1}{s} - \frac{e^{-s\Delta t}}{s} = \frac{(1 - z^{-1})}{s} \qquad (9\text{-}23)$$

The pulse transfer function of a continuous-time system, $G(s)$, that has a sampler and a zero-hold at its input side (Fig. 9-7(c)) is, therefore, given by

$$G(z) = (1 - z^{-1}) Z[\mathcal{L}^{-1}(\frac{G(s)}{s})] \qquad (9\text{-}24)$$

Here $G(s)$ is the transfer function of the continuous-time system and $\mathcal{L}^{-1}[G(s)/s]$ is the unit step input response of $G(s)$ in the time domain. The Z indicates the z-transform of output of the step response, using the general z-transform relation, Eq. (9-18), which has been multiplied by $(1 - z^{-1})$ to give the pulse transfer function $G(z)$. The pulse transfer function relates a discrete-time input (which could be the ouput of an on-line digital computer) and the sampled data of the resulting continuous-time output. The output sampler (indicated by a switch) is synchronized with the input sampler and samples the response either conceptually or as the input side of an on-line digital computer. This method for converting a continuous-time system into the discrete-time domain is equivalent to the method that was presented in Section 9.1, where the state differential equation, Eq. (9-2), was changed into a difference equation, Eq. (9-1), by the relation of Eq. (9-5).

9.4 DIGITAL COMPUTER CONTROL

Digital computers have two common uses in real-time control situations: supervisory control, where the original analog controllers are retained and the digital computer is used to provide them with command signals, and direct digital control (DDC), where the digital computer is actually in the control loop. We will direct our attention in this section to DDC because it is a direct application of discrete-time system theory.

Although control laws are implemented by software (i.e., programs) in direct digital control systems and although the hardware restrictions of analog-type controls do not exist, linear control laws in the form of P, PI and PID-actions (see Eqs. (7-24) through (7-27)) are also basic in DDC because they are often satisfactory for normal operations without modification. The continuous-time control law for PID, the most general form, Eq. (7-27), can be converted into the discrete-time domain by first writing it in the time domain

$$u(t) = k_c [e(t) + \frac{1}{T_i} \int_0^t e(t)dt + T_d \frac{d}{dt} e(t)] \qquad (9\text{-}25)$$

where

$$e(t) = r(t) - c(t)$$

is the error signal (controller input), $r(t)$ is the reference input (set point), $c(t)$ is the value of the controlled variable and $u(t)$ is the manipulated variable (controller output). In terms of sampled data for a sampling interval Δt, these are

$$e(k) = e(k\Delta t) \qquad u(k) = u(k\Delta t) \qquad r(k) = r(k\Delta t) \qquad c(k) = c(k\Delta t)$$

where k is an integer, k = 1, 2, 3, . . . Eq. (9-25) in the discrete-time domain is

$$u(k) = k_c [e(k) + \frac{1}{T_i} [\frac{1}{2}(e(0) + e(1)) + \cdots + \frac{1}{2}(e(k-1) + e(k))]$$

$$+ T_d \frac{e(k) - e(k-1)}{\Delta t}] \qquad (9\text{-}26)$$

where the time integration for the I-action was replaced by a trapezoidal summation and the ideal time differentiation for the D-action by a two-point difference form.

The DDC algorithm normally used has the difference

$$\Delta u(k) = u(k) - u(k-1) \qquad (9\text{-}27)$$

as the controller output rather than u(k) itself (this is called the *velocity algorithm*). A primary advantage of the velocity algorithm is that, if the digital computer fails, the control actuators will interpret a zero output from the computer as "don't change" and will hold their last positions. Also, digital-to-analog converters require less precision (fewer bits) with the velocity algorithm because the range of sizes that a change might take in a single step is usually much smaller than the range of total change that could be requested for u.

Eq. (9-26) in the velocity algorithm becomes

$$\Delta u(k) = k_c [(e(k) - e(k-1)) + \frac{1}{T_i} \frac{e(k) + e(k-1)}{2} \Delta t$$

$$+ T_d \frac{e(k) - 2e(k-1) + e(k-2)}{\Delta t}] \qquad (9\text{-}28)$$

Substituting

$$e(k) = r(k) - c(k)$$

in Eq. (9-28) and assuming

$$r(k) = r(k-1) = r(k-2) \qquad (9\text{-}29)$$

we obtain

$$\Delta u(k) = k_c [(c(k-1) - c(k)) + \frac{\Delta t}{T_i} (r(k) - \frac{c(k-1) + c(k)}{2})$$

$$+ \frac{T_d}{\Delta t} (2c(k-1) - c(k-2) - c(k))] \qquad (9\text{-}30)$$

The control parameters (k_c, T_i and T_d) are now replaced by

$$K_P = k_c - \frac{1}{2}K_I \qquad K_I = \frac{k_c}{T_i}\Delta t \qquad K_D = \frac{k_c T_d}{\Delta t} \qquad (9\text{-}31)$$

and we obtain the canonical form

$$\Delta u(k) = K_P[c(k-1) - c(k)] + K_I[r(k) - c(k)]$$
$$+ K_D[2c(k-1) - c(k-2) - c(k)] \qquad (9\text{-}32)$$

The assumption $r(k) = r(k-1) = r(k-2)$ is not strictly correct, but it has the effect of eliminating the undesirable set point and derivative "kick" in the manipulated variable. This simplification cannot be used if I-action is not included in the algorithm.

Example 9-2: Direct Digital Control of a Thermal Process

A schematic diagram of a typical environmental test chamber is shown in

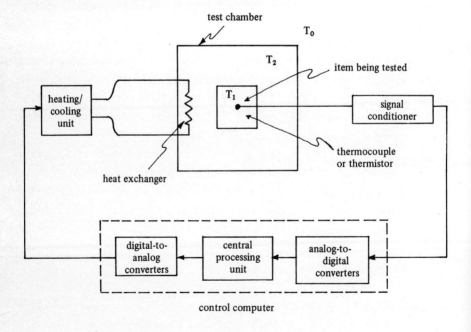

Fig. 9-8 Digital Control of a Thermal Process

Fig. 9-8. The object to be tested is placed inside the chamber and its temperature is measured with a thermocouple or thermistor. The low voltage signal from the temperature transducer is amplified and perhaps filtered to remove any noise components in the signal conditioning unit. This higher powered signal is then fed to the analog-to-digital converter of the digital computer. This unit samples the analog voltage signal on command from the central processor and converts it into a binary word. Using this information, the control algorithm in the computer's memory computes the next control signal for the heating/cooling unit. Before transmission of this signal, though, it must be converted from digital form back into an electrical voltage by the digital-to-analog converter. The heating/cooling unit responds to this signal by providing the appropriate thermal power to the heat exchanger. In most cases, the heating and cooling are supplied by completely different pieces of equipment, for example, electrical resistance heating and liquid nitrogen cooling, and, depending on the sign of u, the correct equipment will be activated. Because we will use a velocity algorithm for the computer control, the first element of the heating/cooling unit must be an integrator. If one does not already exist, an integrator must be supplied.

For this example, rather than using the actual thermal system, we simulated one on an analog computer and controlled the simulated process using a laboratory control computer. For the simulation, the following assumptions were made about the thermal process in order to derive the system equations:

- The test object and the test chamber could each be considered to be single, lumped thermal masses M_1 and M_2, respectively.
- The test object could include an internal heat source (for example, from an internal electric motor, nuclear or chemical reaction, etc.).
- The heat transfer between the test object and the chamber, and between the chamber and the outside environment, could be described by linear heat transfer laws of the form

$$Q_{ij} = U_{ij}(T_i - T_j)$$

where U_{ij} is the overall heat transfer coefficient for heat transfer between object i and object j and T_i and T_j are their temperatures.

Using these assumptions, the system's equations are

$$M_1 C_1 \frac{dT_1}{dt} = U_{12}(T_2 - T_1) + Q_{internal}$$

$$M_2 C_2 \frac{dT_2}{dt} = -U_{12}(T_2 - T_1) - U_{20}(T_2 - T_0) + Q_{control}$$

where C_1 and C_2 are the specific heats of the test object and chamber, T_1 and T_2 are their temperatures, T_0 is the external temperature, $Q_{internal}$ is the heat generated inside the test object and $Q_{control}$ is the heat supplied from the heat exchanger. Note that standard symbols for the heat transfer field are used here rather than control symbols.

Responses of the simulated control system to a step change in set point are shown in Fig. 9-9. The plant parameters chosen were $M_1 C_1 = 0.5, M_2 C_2 = 2, U_{12} = 1$ and $U_{20} = 0.5$. Three sampling intervals were used: 0.25, 0.5 and 1 second, respectively, for (a), (b) and (c) of the figure – all in response to the same change in set point. A PI controller of the form of Eq. (9-32) was used with gains

Δt	K_P	K_I
0.25	2	1.5
0.5	1	0.75
1	0.5	0.375

To prevent excessive overshoot, the gains are decreased as the sampling interval is increased. This gives correspondingly poorer performance for larger sample intervals as can be seen from the output (see Ref.[2] for rules for tuning DDC controllers optimally). The lower curve in each of the sets is the output of the controller.

Applying PID algorithms alone does not seem to give digital control systems much of an advantage over analog systems. There are, however, advantages to using digital control even in those cases where the PID algorithm is retained. Chief among these is the centralization of control activities. A single computer can control many loops (up to 150 or 200 in large systems). This centralization and the greater consistency of control obtainable with digital systems can combine to improve yield by small amounts. In a large petroleum or chemical plant (heavy users of digital control) such small increases in yield are often sufficient to pay for the added expense of computer control because of the tremendous volume processed.

A second important advantage is that the flexibility of stored program digital systems and the ease with which nonlinear operations can be handled

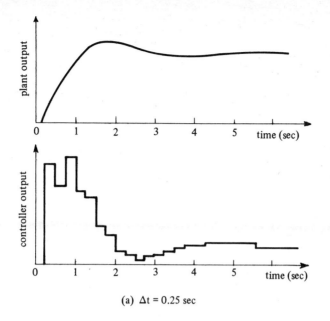

(a) $\Delta t = 0.25$ sec

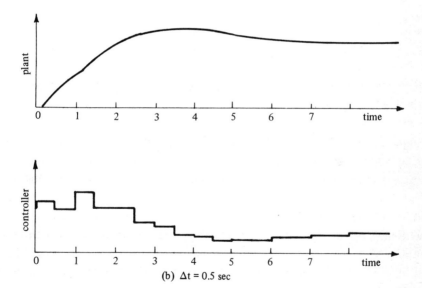

(b) $\Delta t = 0.5$ sec

Fig. 9-9 Responses of Simulated Thermal Process under Direct Digital Control

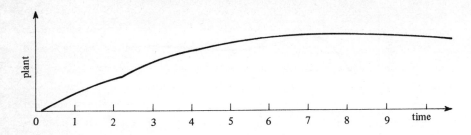

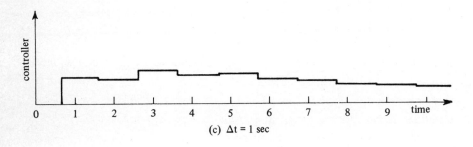

(c) $\Delta t = 1$ sec

Fig. 9-9 (continued)

permit us to use much more sophisticated control algorithms than just PID. These include optimal control, optimal filtering, state estimators, adaptive control and a wide variety of others (see Ref. [3], for example). One such algorithm is the *finite settling time* algorithm. From extensive experience at this point with continuous-time systems described by sets of ordinary differential equations, we have become accustomed to systems having asymptotic behavior; that is, as t→∞, the state approaches its final value. Although this is indeed a trait of systems with PID control, there are algorithms, such as the finite settling time algorithm, which can, in theory, bring a system precisely to some desired state in a finite time. We can see the principle of this algorithm by applying it to a second order discrete-time system with a single input.

Any algorithm that promises better performance generally requires more information for its implementation. We saw that only a general knowledge of the system's dynamics is necessary to achieve satisfactory performance with a PID algorithm; in the case of the finite settling time algorithm, we need an accurate knowledge of the system's state equations, which we assume to be in the form of Eq. (9-1). In addition, we will see that operation of the algorithm requires measurement of the complete state of the system rather than the single output measurement which is typical of PID control. In the case of the second order system under consideration here, that means two measurements. We will assume that the application we are designing for is a digital control system with a zero-hold at the output. The controller output is held constant for a period of Δt time units, then changed to a new value and held for another Δt time units, etc. We can thus apply Eq. (9-8) to find the system output. After two such steps, i.e., $k = 2$, the solution is

$$\underline{x}(2) = \underline{P}^2 \, \underline{x}(0) + \underline{P} \, \underline{Q} \, u(0) + \underline{Q} \, u(1) \qquad (9\text{-}33)$$

If we take $\underline{x}(0)$ to be any arbitrary starting point and $\underline{x}(2)$ to be the desired state $\underline{x}_d$, we can use Eq. (9-33) to solve for the control signals $u(0)$ and $u(1)$ that will drive the system from $\underline{x}(0)$ to $\underline{x}_d$. A matrix manipulation will put this equation in the form we need to accomplish this. The last two terms on the right side of the equation can be written in the form

$$\underline{P} \, \underline{Q} \, u(0) + \underline{Q} \, u(1) = [\underline{P} \, \underline{Q} \quad \underline{Q}] \begin{bmatrix} u(0) \\ u(1) \end{bmatrix} \qquad (9\text{-}34)$$

For this case of a single (scalar) input, though, $\underline{Q}$ is a two element column vector. The matrix $[\underline{P} \, \underline{Q} \quad \underline{Q}]$ is thus a square matrix and can be inverted if it is not singular. When the invertability of a matrix becomes an important factor in carrying out a development of this sort, we should always check to see whether the matrix has a more fundamental significance. As we saw in developing a method for reconstructing a state vector in Chapter 6, the matrix defined by Eq. (6-83) worked out to determine whether or not the system was observable. In this case, the matrix we have to invert determines the controllability of the system; $[\underline{P} \, \underline{Q} \quad \underline{Q}]$ must be nonsingular for the system to be controllable. This makes intuitive sense. In order to guarantee that the state of the system will reach the desired state after exactly two steps, we must assure ourselves that the control input will affect all of the system's modes. This is the definition of a controllable system.

Substituting from Eq. (9-34) into Eq. (9-33), we get

$$\underline{x}_d = \underline{P}^2 \, \underline{x}(0) + [\underline{P} \, \underline{Q} \quad \underline{Q}] \begin{bmatrix} u(0) \\ u(1) \end{bmatrix}$$

Solving for the input vector (which we note is now a vector composed of inputs at two different times rather than two different inputs at the same time)

$$\begin{bmatrix} u(0) \\ u(1) \end{bmatrix} = [\underline{P}\, \underline{Q} \quad \underline{Q}]^{-1}\, [\underline{x}_d - \underline{P}^2 \underline{x}(0)] \tag{9-35}$$

This completes the theoretical solution. If we apply the prescribed inputs, the system will reach the desired state $\underline{x}_d$ in two steps. We might guess that the fact that it takes two steps for a second order system has more general significance, and it does. For n-th order systems with full state vector measurement and scalar input, it generally takes n steps to get from an arbitrary point in the state space to any desired point.

As always, there can be practical difficulties. If we choose a very small sampling interval, for example, the values of u needed to move the system between its initial and desired states in the very short time interval $2\Delta t$ could be very large, larger, perhaps, than the system's actuators can deliver. In this case, it will take more than two steps to achieve the result, but repeated application of the algorithm will ultimately get the system to the desired state. Thus, the minimum time (as opposed to the minimum number of steps) necessary is a function of the maximum allowable magnitude of u. We will examine this and other possible sources of error in the following example.

Example 9-3: Application of Finite Settling Time Control to the Thermal System of Example 9-2

The system equations of the thermal system can be expressed in matrix form as (with numbers already substituted for the parameters)

$$\frac{d}{dt}\begin{bmatrix} T_1 \\ T_2 \end{bmatrix} = \underline{A}\,\underline{T} + \underline{B}\,u = \begin{bmatrix} -2 & 2 \\ 0.5 & -0.75 \end{bmatrix}\begin{bmatrix} T_1 \\ T_2 \end{bmatrix} + \begin{bmatrix} 0 \\ 1 \end{bmatrix} u \tag{9-36}$$

Using a sampling interval of $\Delta t = 1$ second, we can convert this to discrete-time form using Eq. (9-5)

$$\begin{bmatrix} T_1(k+1) \\ T_2(k+1) \end{bmatrix} = \underline{P}\,\underline{T}(k) + \underline{Q}\,u(k) = \begin{bmatrix} 0.253 & 0.631 \\ 0.158 & 0.647 \end{bmatrix}\begin{bmatrix} T_1(k) \\ T_2(k) \end{bmatrix} + \begin{bmatrix} 0.464 \\ 0.780 \end{bmatrix} u(k)$$

$$\tag{9-37}$$

Applying Eq. (9-35) with the desired state set to $T_1 = 1$ and $T_2 = 1$ and the initial state $T_1(0) = T_2(0) = 0$, we get the control inputs $u(0) = 1.52$ and $u(1) = 0.153$. Simulated results using these inputs are shown in Fig. 9-10. Note that

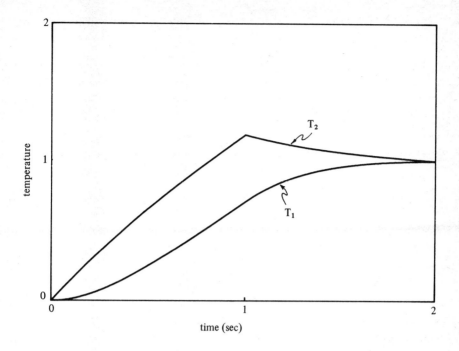

Fig. 9-10 Finite Settling Time Control of a Simulated Thermal Process

with this control both state variables are controlled, whereas in Example 9-2 only T_2 was controlled directly. Thus, the overshoot in T_2, rather than being an undesirable side effect, is necessary if T_1 is to be at the desired value at the end of the second sampling interval. Note also that the last value of u, u(1), is not necessarily the input value that will keep the system at the desired state. A new input value must be calculated at the end of the second time step.

As implemented here, this algorithm is not truly a feedback controller. Any errors in measurement, inaccuracies in the system model, external disturbances, etc. will cause the system to be somewhere other than the desired state after two time steps. To make the system less sensitive to such errors, it can be converted into a true feedback system by measuring the state after every other time step (the full state, T_1 and T_2, must be measured) and computing a new two-step finite settling time control sequence. (A method of using this algorithm in a single-output feedback configuration is shown in Ref. [3], Chapter 11.)

As we mentioned in the discussion above, the minimum time necessary to move the system to its desired state depends on the maximum and minimum power output that is available from the system's actuators (heaters and coolers in this case). Fig. 9-11 shows u(0) and u(1) computed for a variety of sampling intervals. As expected, as Δt decreases, the magnitudes of the u's increase very dramatically for small Δt's. In this case, for example, if the actuation system were limited to heat only, no cooling, any sampling time less than about 0.75 (where the u(1) curve crosses the axis) would be impossible to implement and

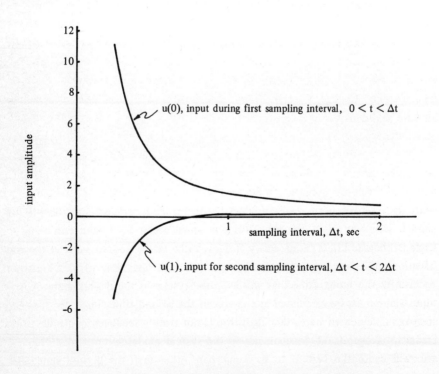

Fig. 9-11 Control Input Magnitudes as a Function of Sampling
Interval for Finite Settling Time Control

would require more than two sampling intervals to reach the desired state. On the other hand, if cooling were available but the heat output was limited to 5, any sampling interval over about 0.5 (where the u(0) curve crosses 5) could be implemented successfully.

SUMMARY

The analytical development of a theory for discrete-time systems is closely parallel to that for continuous-time systems with the exception that the basic dynamic relation for a system is stated in terms of a difference equation instead of a differential equation. In general, when integrals appear in differential equation theory, summations appear in difference equation theory. The stability condition for discrete-time systems is expressed in terms of the unit circle in the complex plane (of the roots of the characteristic equation) rather than in terms of dividing the plane along the imaginary axis.

One important element in discrete-time systems, the zero-order hold, has no counterpart in continuous-time systems. It serves to transform an input function into a series of square pulses so that the input over an entire sampling period can be expressed as a single vector of scalar quantities. The sampling interval, which is assumed constant with time, is the distinguishing feature of discrete-time systems. Changes in state, input and output take place only at sampling instants. Mathematically, the system is not defined for the time between sampling instants.

The z-transform is a convenient way to represent discrete-time transfer functions, especially since the primary dynamic operator in discrete-time theory, the time delay, has no simple notation in common use. In many ways, z domain relations are easier to visualize than s domain relations because the operations implied just refer to values of a variable at future or past time points. Like Laplace transforms, forward and inverse z-transformation can be performed by table look-up.

The digital computer is the primary modern impetus for studying discrete-time theory. Direct digital control systems are discrete-time systems and discrete-time theory is very useful in their design. Discrete-time versions of the P, PI and PID algorithms are in common use in digital control, but the flexibility afforded by using a digital control computer instead of analog control components makes utilization of more sophisticated control algorithms possible in those cases where their use would be advantageous.

REFERENCES

1. E. I. Jury, *Theory and Application of the z-Transform Method*, John Wiley and Sons, Inc., New York, 1964

2. Y. Takahashi et al, "Parametereinstellung bei Linearen DDC-Algorithmen," *Regelungstechnik und Prozess-Datenverarbeitung*, Vol. 19, No. 6, 1971, pp. 237-244

3. Y. Takahashi, M. Rabins and D. Auslander, *Control*, Addison-Wesley, Reading, Mass., 1970

PROBLEMS

9-1 Obtain the solution matrix $\underline{P}^k$ for

$$\underline{P} = \begin{bmatrix} p & 1 \\ 0 & p \end{bmatrix}$$

What are the modes of the system?

9-2 The population of an insect colony is described by the following state equation:

$$\begin{bmatrix} n_{0(k+1)} \\ n_{1(k+1)} \\ n_{2(k+1)} \end{bmatrix} = \begin{bmatrix} 0 & 0 & b \\ s_1 & 0 & 0 \\ 0 & s_2 & 0 \end{bmatrix} \begin{bmatrix} n_{0(k)} \\ n_{1(k)} \\ n_{2(k)} \end{bmatrix}$$

where $n_{i(j)}$ is the number of insects between age i and $[(i+1) - 0(\epsilon)]$ at the j-th sampling instant, where the age is evaluated at the sampling interval and $0(\epsilon)$ is an infinitesimally small positive number. Some of the insects of age group 0 at time instant k, $n_{0(k)}$, will survive during the period from k to $k + 1$ to become part of age group 1 at the next sampling instant $(k + 1)$. Thus

$$n_{1(k+1)} = s_1 n_{1(k)}$$

where s_1 is a positive quantity less than one that represents the part of that age group surviving. It is assumed that only the third (and last) age group will participate in reproduction, so that

$$n_{0(k+1)} = b n_{2(k)}$$

This states that the zeroth age group at time $k + 1$ is proportional to the size of the last age group at time k, where b represents the birth rate and surviving portion of the new born insects until the next sampling period. (a) Determine the eigenvalues and discuss the modes of this system. (b) Is it possible to interpret n_0, n_1 and n_2 as larva, pupa and adult populations of an insect species, respectively?

9-3 A harmonic oscillator is described by

$$\frac{d}{dt} \begin{bmatrix} x_1 \\ x_2 \end{bmatrix} = \begin{bmatrix} 0 & 1 \\ -1 & 0 \end{bmatrix} \begin{bmatrix} x_1 \\ x_2 \end{bmatrix} + \begin{bmatrix} 0 \\ 1 \end{bmatrix} u$$

where x_1 = displacement, x_2 = velocity, u = force input and the relation has been normalized. The output is

$$y = x_1 = [1 \quad 0]\underline{x}$$

The input is applied via a sampler and holder and the output is sampled. Obtain $G(z)$ $= Y(z)/U(z)$ using two approaches: the state-space method (Eq. (9-20)) and the transfer function approach (Eq. (9-24)).

9-4 A continuous-time sinusoidal signal of frequency n Hz is sampled at a rate of N samples/sec. (a) State the sampling theorem in terms of n and N. (b) Show that a periodic fluctuation in the sampled data of a frequency of n^* Hz will appear if the sampling theorem is violated, where $n^* = |(n - mN)|$, $m = 1, 2, \ldots$

9-5 Show that the final value of a time series f_k, $k = 0, 1, \ldots$, if it exists, is given by
$$\lim_{k \to \infty} (f_k) = \lim_{z \to 1} (z - 1)F(z)$$
where $F(z) = Z[f(k)]$.

9-6 Let $Z[r(k)] = R(z)$, $Z[u(k)] = U(z)$ and $Z[c(k)] = C(z)$ in the linear PID-DDC algorithm (Eq. (9-32)). Relate $U(z)$ to $R(z)$ and $C(z)$ in the z domain.

9-7 Consider a continuous-time first order system
$$\frac{dx}{dt} = -x + u + v$$
where u is a controlling input applied to the system through a sampler and zero-hold (i.e., it has a staircase pattern) and v is a continuous-time disturbance signal. (a) Let $v(t) = 0$ and determine the pulse transfer function of the system, $G(z) = X(z)/U(z)$. (b) Let $u(t) = 0$, $v(t) = e^{-at}$ and obtain the input sample to output sample relation, $X(z)/V(z)$. Why does this differ from $G(z)$?

9-8 A first order plant, $G(z) = k/(z - c)$, where $0 < c < 1$, is controlled by a linear DDC-PID algorithm. $V(z)$ in Fig. P-9-8 is a disturbance input approximated by a staircase pattern (see Prob. 9-7). State the conditions under which the closed loop system will have no offset for a reference input as well as for the disturbance input.

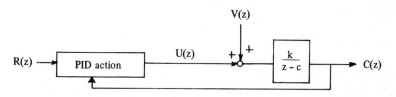

Fig. P-9-8

9-9 A first order control object, $G(z) = k/(z - c)$, $0 < c < 1$, is controlled by a DDC-I-action, $K_I = z/(z - 1)$. Obtain: (a) the open loop pulse transfer function, (b) the closed loop characteristic equation, (c) the root locus for a change of $K = K_I k$ from 0 to infinity, (d) the stability condition and (e) the mode at the stability limit.

9-10 To make the I-control system of the preceding problem finite-time settling, a digital compensator $D(z)$ is introduced into the loop, Fig. P-9-10. Assuming $D(z)$ has a form

$$D(z) = \frac{b_0 z + b_1}{z + a_1}$$

determine b_0, b_1 and a_1 for a finite-time settling control. (Hint: the closed loop characteristic equation reduces to $z^m = 0$, $m =$ an integer.) Compute the error response of the closed loop system for a unit step reference input, $R(z) = z/(z-1)$.

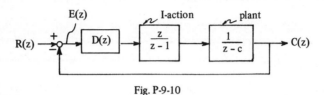

Fig. P-9-10

9-11 Although a direct digital controller's output is normally passed through a zero-order hold, there are various systems where a discrete-time controlling input is applied as an impulse train without using a zero-order hold, such as in releasing a biological control agent (predators) periodically, taking medicine once a day, getting pollutant intake with a meal, etc. Assume that the human body is modeled by a two lump compartmental model (Fig. P-9-11) for chemical intake described by

$$\frac{Y(s)}{U(s)} = G(s) = \frac{K}{(1 + T_1 s)(1 + T_2 s)}$$

where $y(t) = x_2(t)$ is the concentration of interest and $u(t)$ is the chemical intake, which is assumed to take place in discrete-time, each $u(k)$ being an impulse of intensity u_k. Let $K = 10$, $T_1 = 2$, $T_2 = 5$ and determine the pulse transfer function, $G(z) = Y(z)/U(z)$.

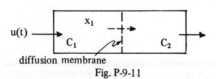

diffusion membrane
Fig. P-9-11

9-12 This is a generalization of the preceding problem. Suppose that in a continuous-time system, described by a state equation

$$\frac{d}{dt} \underline{x}(t) = \underline{A}\,\underline{x}(t) + \underline{B}\,\underline{u}(t) \qquad \underline{x}(0) = \underline{0}$$

the input $\underline{u}(t)$ is an impulse vector train (without zero-hold), such that

$$\underline{U}(z) = \underline{u}(0) + \underline{u}(1)z^{-1} + \underline{u}(2)z^{-2} + \cdots$$

The continuous-time output, $\underline{y}(t) = \underline{C}\,\underline{x}(t)$, is sampled. Assuming the impulses hit the system just before each sampling, determine the matrix pulse transfer function $\underline{G}(z)$

that will relate $\underline{U}(z)$ to $\underline{Y}(z)$ by
$$\underline{Y}(z) = \underline{G}(z)\underline{U}(z)$$

9-13 The open loop pulse transfer function of the I-control system in Prob. 9-9 has the general form
$$G(z) = \frac{Kz}{(z-1)(z-c)}$$
Obtain the stability condition for the closed loop system by means of the Jury test (see Appendix A.3).

9-14 A discrete-time system has the characteristic equation
$$F(z) = 10z^5 + 4z^4 + 8z^3 - 7z^2 + z$$
Test the stability of this system by Jury's method (see Appendix A.3).

9-15 A third order discrete-time system has a real pole c and a pair of conjugate complex poles on the unit circle in the z plane, that is, $\cos(\theta) \pm j\sin(\theta)$, where $0 < \theta < 2\pi$. Therefore, the characteristic polynomial is
$$F(z) = (z-c)(z - \cos\theta - j\sin\theta)(z - \cos\theta + j\sin\theta)$$
$$= z^3 - (c + 2\cos\theta)z^2 + (1 + 2c\cos\theta)z - c$$
Apply the Jury test (see Appendix A.3) to this characteristic polynomial and corroborate the results by your knowledge of these eigenvalues.

CHAPTER 10
NOISE AND
PROBABILISTIC
PROCESSES

Noise, in everyday usage, usually refers to sounds that interfere with something we are trying to do. The source of the interference can range from a highly patterned and deterministic sound to one that seems to have no order and is completely random. Here, we generalize the concept of noise to include spurious signals in any dynamic system. Since we have already discussed many techniques for dealing with deterministic signals, whether they are classified as interference or not, we will restrict our discussions in this chapter to those signals with a strong degree of randomness, that is, those signals arising from probabilistic processes.

Not all signals arising from probabilistic processes constitute noise. Sometimes the primary inputs to a system are probabilistic. Because we often must deal with ensembles of events in our attempts to apply the dynamic system framework to nonengineering systems, we are most likely to encounter probabilistic system forcing functions in this area. We use much of the terminology of the stochastic system field because the great body of work done in connection with solving noise problems in electronic systems is equally applicable to any system which includes probabilistic processes.

The initial part of the chapter is devoted to methods of characterizing probabilistic signals, first according to magnitude characteristics, mean, variance and distribution functions, and then according to time characteristics, using the autocorrelation function. We next consider how to generate random signals for use in computer simulation. Finally, we investigate the separation of a signal from its accompanying noise.

324

10.1 STOCHASTIC PROCESSES

Whether a process is viewed as deterministic, hence predictable, random, hence unpredictable, or something in between often depends more on the relationship of the observer to the process than on the process itself. For example, we are all accustomed to dealing with forces exerted by gases due to their pressure. These can be wind forces as we walk, ride a bicycle or drive a car, forces exerted on the wall of a balloon to keep it inflated, etc. These forces all appear to be highly deterministic and predictable. Gases, however, are composed of molecules, discrete particles whose interactions with their surroundings cause the forces we observe. In an environment where the density of molecules is very low, such as the edge of the earth's atmosphere, we would come to a quite different conclusion. At any given instant, all we could discuss would be the *probability* of a molecule striking a surface within some interval of time. Our viewpoint would become one of waiting for an event to happen rather than seeing the summation of a very large number of events. The probability viewpoint would hold at the earth's surface if the time interval in which we were interested were extremely short. Under such circumstances, the number of molecules striking a surface would be very small. At somewhat higher gas densities or slightly longer time intervals, the number of interactions taking place over a time interval of interest is always fairly large, but that number will vary widely from time interval to time interval. We then view the gas pressure force as a phenomenon that occurs continuously but has randomly varying components. As the gas density gets still higher or the time span longer, the randomly varying components become relatively smaller and smaller until we arrive at pressure forces that appear to be highly deterministic because they result from the summation of an extremely large number of events.

In another sense, processes are characterized as random when, for one reason or another, we do not understand their underlying mechanisms or are unable to compute their responses. The laws of physics can be used to compute the motion of a single molecule of a gas with considerable accuracy, but computing the motions of the air in our atmosphere in this way is wholly beyond our computing means. Likewise, to the person buying a house and to the seller of the house, there is nothing at all random about their transaction. The observer of the real estate market, however, must view this transaction as an unpredictable event because he lacks the information (and techniques) for predicting its outcome.

We call these processes *stochastic*, or *probabilistic*, by which we mean processes made up of individual events which appear unpredictable to the observer but which can be usefully characterized by statistical means. A good example of such a process is birthrate. The number of births registered in San Francisco, by weeks, from the beginning of 1971 to the first week of September, 1972, is shown in Fig. 10-1. A wide variety of people have an interest in extracting the maximum possible information from this data: local diaper service companies, hospital planners, pediatric clinics, school planners and anyone whose business depends on a knowledge of future population or population-age distribution. A limited amount of information with predictive value can be determined just by "eyeballing" the raw data; we will now examine some techniques for being more precise.

10.2 CHARACTERIZATION OF STOCHASTIC INFORMATION

The San Francisco birth information has one property that is very common

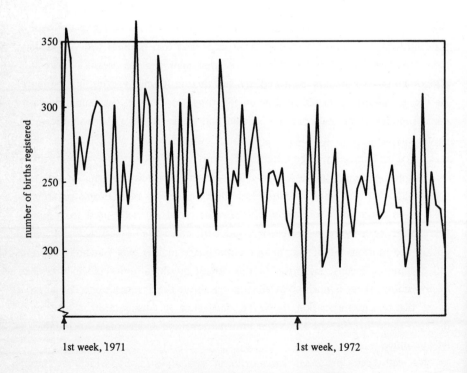

Fig. 10-1 Births Registered in San Francisco, By Weeks

in dealing with stochastic information: it has been discretized in time. That is, although children are born more or less continuously throughout the week, the only information we have is the weekly total. There are two common reasons for this: one, as in this case, is that it is either too difficult or too expensive to collect the data on a continuous basis. The second reason is that many of the methods of characterizing stochastic information are best suited for digital computer implementation and, even if we were to have the data in continuous form, the input must be discretized. Note that there is a significant difference between this time-discretized data and the time-discretized sampled data we discussed in Chapter 9. The birth registration data, although it is available only at sampling intervals of one week, is an average value for the week, whereas the sampling process of Chapter 9 supplied the instantaneous value of the signal at the sampling instant. Both types of discretized data must be dealt with in analyzing systems with noise.

The San Francisco birth data have another property common to almost all stochastic processes: the measurement process itself is probabilistic and subject to noise. For example, some hospitals are more efficient than others in getting reports in, births at home tend to be reported very late, hospital clerical staffs don't usually work on holidays, etc. In the case of this data, we have tabulated the number of births registered, not the actual number of births in a given week. If measurement errors seriously reduced reliability, we would have to treat the process as a combination of two stochastic processes — the birth process itself and the measurement process.

Mean and Variance

Assuming for the moment that we can neglect the measurement error, we can apply the simplest measure to the data: the mean value (also called the expected value). This is the usual arithmetic average obtained by summing over all the samples and dividing by the number of samples. The average number of births registered per week in San Francisco over the period of our interest was 254.5. This is probably a sufficiently detailed description for those who do not care about week to week variations in the number of children born. Before moving on to more complex measures, though, we should test the data for *stationarity*. A stationary stochastic signal has statistical properties that do not change with time. Is the mean, as computed for a two year period, equally valid for any part of that time, and what was it for the previous period? The answer to this question is of vital interest even to those concerned only with the mean value because it gives an indication of how far into the future the mean value can be used. For others, if the mean is changing, it is interesting to see what other variations the change in birthrate correlates with (such as change in total population, change in the age structure of the population, new taxing methods, etc.) and to speculate on the possible causal links. The moving mean is one of the easiest methods for making this determination. Instead of using all of the available samples to compute the mean, only a small block is used, say ten weeks of birth registration data. The first value is obtained with the first ten weeks of data, the second with the data of weeks 2 through 11, the third with 3 through 12, etc. If we associate each number computed with the time period at the middle of the block, we get curves like the ones shown in Fig. 10.2, which shows the moving mean using ten week and twenty week blocks. The curves show a steadily declining birthrate in San Francisco. Because of the small number of samples used for each of the means in the moving mean, a fairly high degree of variability is expected in the result. Since we are looking for a systematic variation, we could compare the moving mean with, say, a sequence of means computed with groups of randomly chosen samples to see how much variability is attributable to the small sample size and how much to actual variation.

The next quantity we can compute, the *variance*, gives a measure of how much variation there is in the data from sample to sample. The variance is computed by taking the mean of the square of the data from which the mean has been subtracted. The formal definition of the variance for continuous-time signals is

$$\text{variance} = \lim_{T \to \infty} \frac{1}{2T} \int_{-T}^{T} [x(t) - x_{av}]^2 dt$$

and for discrete-time signals

$$\text{variance} = \lim_{N \to \infty} \frac{1}{N} \sum_{i=1}^{N} [x(i) - x_{av}]^2$$

where the mean value x_{av} is

$$x_{av} = \lim_{T \to \infty} \frac{1}{2T} \int_{-T}^{T} x(t) dt$$

or

$$x_{av} = \lim_{N \to \infty} \frac{1}{N} \sum_{i=1}^{N} x(i)$$

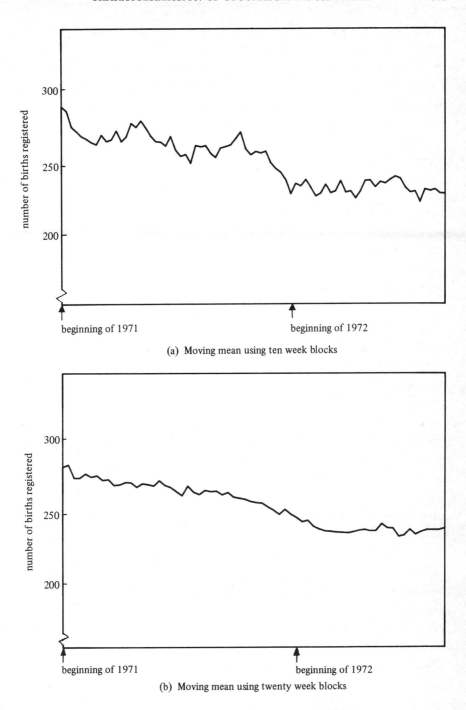

(a) Moving mean using ten week blocks

(b) Moving mean using twenty week blocks

Fig. 10-2 Moving Mean Averages for San Francisco Birth Data

Since the mean value of a set of data is almost always computed, many of the methods we will talk about for processing stochastic information operate on zero-mean data, that is, data from which the mean has been subtracted. In that case, $x_{av} = 0$ and we get

$$\text{variance} = \lim_{T \to \infty} \frac{1}{2T} \int_{-T}^{T} x(t)^2 dt \qquad (10\text{-}1a)$$

for continuous-time signals and

$$\text{variance} = \lim_{N \to \infty} \frac{1}{N} \sum_{i=1}^{N} x(i)^2 \qquad (10\text{-}1b)$$

for sampled signals, where x is a zero-mean stochastic signal and N is the number of samples. Note that because of the square in the definition, variations on either side of zero count equally and do not cancel. In any real case, we can only get an approximation to the variance since we can never actually carry out the limiting process. The positive square root of the variance (and thus the RMS, root mean square, of the original zero-mean data) is called the *standard deviation*.

The variance is not only easy to compute (the square is easy to implement in digital or analog computers and automatically reverses the signs of negative data), but it is also important to statistical theory and to physical systems where it is often related to power. The variance for the San Francisco data is 1,796 and the standard deviation is 42.4. This indicates that one should expect considerable variation in the weekly data and gives a measure of just how much variation there is on the average. For this computation, the data was assumed to have a stationary mean value of 254.5, even though some time variation was noted in the moving mean test.

Probability Density Function

The mean and variance provide a great deal of information about a stochastic signal but they are only two numbers describing a signal that may be a complex distribution of values. For example, the mean and variance of men's waist sizes can give a clothing store manager a good idea of the range of pants sizes to stock, say 30 to 50, but how much of each size should be stocked? That is, what is the probability that a random customer will request a particular size? To answer this, we must look to some form of *probability density function* $p(x_1)$. For continuous functions x(t), this function is given as a limit

$$p(x_1) = \lim_{\Delta x \to 0} \frac{1}{\Delta x} \text{Prob}[(x_1 - \frac{1}{2}\Delta x) < x \leq (x_1 + \frac{1}{2}\Delta x)] \qquad (10\text{-}2)$$

In words, $p(x_1)$ represents the probability of x having a value in the region of width Δx surrounding x_1. As usual with these computations, in practice we cannot go all the way to the limit. Thus we must be satisfied with stopping at some finite value of Δx. For systems in which x is quantized in some way, the quantization increment represents the smallest possible Δx that can be used in Eq. (10-2). For example, since men's pants usually come in only integer sizes, the clothing industry is only concerned with probability distribution functions with $\Delta x = 1$; in that case, p(34) would be the probability of having a waist size between 33½ and 34½. For the birth data we have been examining, the minimum Δx is again one, but it is more convenient and illustrative to use a larger· grouping because of the relatively small number of samples.

Example 10-1: Probability Density Function for San Francisco Birth Data

A simple computer program for calculating the probability density function from a set of sampled, zero-mean data is shown below. The object of the program is to find out what fraction of the samples falls into each region, $(x_1 - \Delta x/2) < x \leq (x_1 + \Delta x/2)$, where x_1 is the center of the region. It works by taking advantage of Fortran integer arithmetic to compute a *class number*, IP in the program, for each sample. The classes are defined by dividing the interval being studied into subregions. For example, if we have data with values from −5 to +5 and are using $\Delta x = 1$, there will be ten subregions, the first covers −5 to −4, the second −4 to −3, etc. IP is the number of the region a particular data point falls in. For each sample falling into the IP-th class, PX(IP) is incremented by $1/(\Delta x * N)$, where dividing by Δx takes care of the Δx in the denominator of Eq. (10-2) and dividing by N converts the sum to a fraction. XHIGH and XLOW are the upper and lower limits of the data, suitably adjusted so that XHIGH − XLOW is an even multiple of Δx (DX in the program), and NCLASS = (XHIGH − XLOW)/DX will be an integer number. XNORM is the sample value scaled to fall into the range 0 to 1 (commonly called a *normalized value*); multiplying XNORM by (NCLASS − 1) and adding 1 to the product gives the class number IP. The extra 0.5 in the addition is to get around the standard Fortran convention of truncating real numbers when they are converted to integers. The 0.5 makes sure they are rounded off properly. For instance, 1.4 and 1.6 would both be truncated to 1 in the statement K = A, which is undesirable. If we use K = A + 0.5, for A = 1.4, A + 0.5 is 1.9 which is truncated to 1 while, with A = 1.6, A + 0.5 is 2.1. This is then truncated to 2.

```
        read in (X(I),I=1,N),DX,
            XLOW,XHIGH
        NCLASS = (XHIGH–XLOW)/DX
        DO 10 J = 1,NCLASS
  10    PX(J) = 0.0
        DO 200 I = 1,N
        XNORM = (X(I)–XLOW)/
            (XHIGH–XLOW)
        IP = XNORM*(NCLASS–1)+1.5
 200    PX(IP) = PX(IP)+1.0/(DX*N)
        print or plot probability density
            distribution
```

– X( ) is the set of N zero-mean observations and PX( ) the probability density distribution.

– Each PX( ) is set to zero initially in this DO loop.

The resulting probability density function for the San Francisco birth registration data with $\Delta x = 20$ is shown in Fig. 10-3; since the data used here has already had its mean value subtracted from it, p(0) is the probability density at the mean value. As we might expect, the results show that values near the mean are most probable; the farther from the mean we go, the more the probability decreases.

The probability density function p(x) can be estimated for a zero-mean, stationary continuous-time signal by measuring for what fraction of a suitably long time span T the value is between $(x_1 - \Delta x/2)$ and $(x_1 + \Delta x/2)$: $p(x_1)$ is that fraction, T_{x_1}/T, divided by Δx. A simple but effective analog computer circuit for performing this operation on a voltage signal is shown in the next example. Unlike the analog computer problems solved in Chapter 4, the analog computer is used here as part of a measurement and instrumentation circuit rather than in the solution of a set of system equations.

Example 10-2: Analog Determination of Probability Density Function

An electronic noise generator is a device whose output is a voltage signal that is "pure" noise. Although it may seem absurd to purchase a device whose only function is to produce noise, it can be extremely useful in testing components that may be subject to noisy inputs, for example, or in simulating systems which include probabilistic processes. In this problem, we are interested in measuring the probability density function of one of these devices.

A photograph of some typical output of the laboratory noise generator is shown in Fig. 10-4. To find the probability density function at some voltage V_1

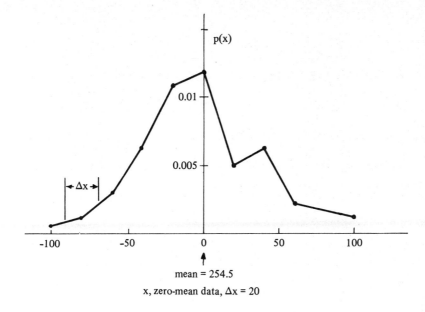

Fig. 10-3 Probability Density Function for San Francisco Birth Registration Data

using an increment of size ΔV, we must know what fraction of the time, on the average, the output of the noise generator is between $(V_1 - \Delta V/2)$ and $(V_1 + \Delta V/2)$. An analog device that has input-output characteristics as shown in Fig. 10-5(a) will have an output only when the input signal is in the desired region; otherwise its output will be zero. If we attach the noise generator output to the input of such a device and connect the output to an integrator as shown in Fig. 10-5(b), the output of the integrator gives us a measure of the amount of time the noise signal spends between the prescribed limits. The easiest way to find out what fraction of the total time this is is to run a second integrator with constant input at the same time. If both integrators are started with zero initial conditions, any time the computer is switched to "hold" the ratio of the two voltages will give the desired fraction.

The diode limiter shown in Fig. 10-5(c) is what makes this circuit possible. Use of diodes in this way is one of the most common nonlinear analog com-

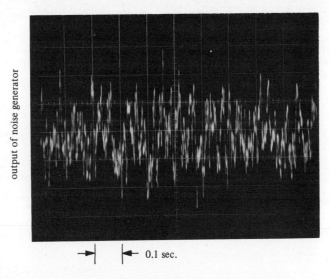

output of noise generator

|← 0.1 sec.

Fig. 10-4 Output of Laboratory Noise Generator

puter applications. The particular form of diode limiter shown here has the input-output relation that appears next to it in the figure. It works because the diodes will act almost like open circuits when the voltage is negative (the positive to negative direction is defined by the arrow on the diode) and almost like short circuits when the voltage is positive. In the circuit shown, if the input voltage is greater than the bias, the output voltage will start to swing negative (because of the sign inversion in the amplifier). When the voltage becomes negative, however, diode D2 will start acting like a short circuit, or zero resistance. With a zero feedback resistance, the circuit will have zero overall gain and the output will be zero. This accounts for the region of zero output to the right of V_{bias} on the input-output curve. On the other hand, if the input is less than V_{bias}, the output voltage will start to swing positive. The voltage at the output of the pot, V_p, is a weighted average of the source, V_s, which is a negative voltage, and the amplifier output (the value of the weight depends on the position of the arm of the pot). At first, the output of the amplifier is very small, so V_p is negative. As long as V_p stays negative, diode D1 acts as an open circuit (infinite resistance). With both diodes in their open circuit mode, the feedback resistance around the amplifier is nearly infinity, so the gain is very high. Therefore, the output voltage of the amplifier continues to increase. When it gets high enough so that V_p begins to become positive, diode D1 starts to change to its

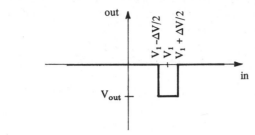

(a) Input-output relation

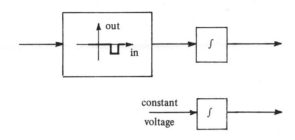

(b) Complete computing diagram

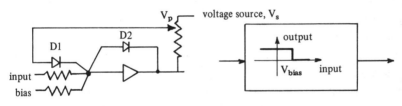

(c) Diode limiter

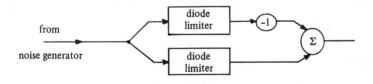

(d) General computing diagram for nonlinear part

Fig. 10-5 Probability Density Function Measurement Circuit

zero resistance mode, again inserting a zero resistance in the feedback. The
output voltage thus can no longer increase and will remain at a value such that
V_p is just slightly positive. This accounts for the portion of the input-output
curve to the left of the V_{bias} point.

By combining two diode limiters as shown in Fig. 10-5(d) and properly
adjusting the biases, weights and V_s's, we can obtain the characteristics we are
after, that of Fig. 10-5(a).

The probability density function, shown in Fig. 10-6, is computed by
adjusting the biases of the two diode limiters for the region desired and making
several runs. The results shown are the average of three runs each. Note the
similarity in general shape between this probability density function and the one
for the San Francisco birth data; in both cases, the most likely outputs are
those near the mean with decreasing probability as the distance from the mean
increases.

The analog noise generator of Example 10-2 is designed in such a way that

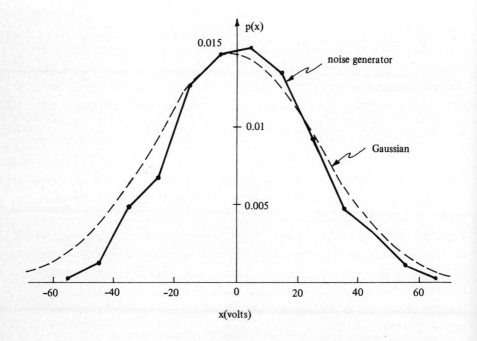

Fig. 10-6 Probability Density Function for Noise Generator

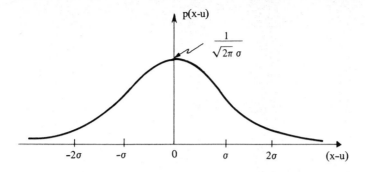

Fig. 10-7 Gaussian Distribution

the noise signal will have a specific probability density function — the *Gaussian* (or *Normal*) *distribution*, the familiar bell-shaped curve of Fig. 10-7. A Gaussian distribution is superimposed (as the dashed line) on the distribution we have measured for the noise generator in Fig. 10-6, so we can see how close the manufacturer came.

A Gaussian distribution can often be applied to processes which tend to be symmetric about their mean values. The two examples solved earlier in this chapter have distributions that are distinctly Gaussian in appearance. Gaussian distributions are described by the following probability density function:

$$p(x) = \frac{1}{\sqrt{2\pi}\ \sigma} e^{-(x-\mu)^2/2\sigma^2} \tag{10-3}$$

where μ is the mean value and σ is the standard deviation, as defined earlier. An important property of Gaussian distributions is that, if the input to a linear system is a Gaussian process, the output will also be Gaussian. An even more important property, and one that serves as a partial explanation for why Gaussian distributions are observed so commonly in nature, is that the output of a linear system tends to have a distribution that looks more like a Gaussian distribution than the input (see Example 10-5). This means that in complex but linear systems, even if the inputs to the system are not Gaussian, the outputs may very closely approximate Gaussian distributions.

For zero-mean data, the Gaussian distribution, Eq. (10-3), depends on only one parameter, the standard deviation σ. Since we have already computed the

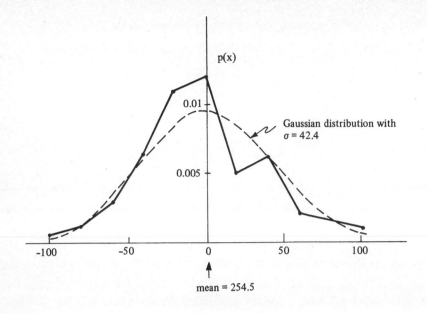

Fig. 10-8 Probability Distribution Function for San Francisco Birth Data
with Gaussian Distribution Overlaid

standard deviation for the San Francisco birth data, we can overlay a Gaussian distribution on the distribution computed directly from the data. This is shown in Fig. 10-8; the original distribution is the same as the one shown in Fig. 10-3. The fit is hardly exact but it may be good enough to make using the Gaussian distribution worthwhile in some situations. Also, the relatively low number of data points (88) used in constructing the original distribution means that its exact shape is not fixed and may change with the addition of more data.

In systems which contain inherent asymmetries because, for example, areas, populations, volumes, etc. cannot be negative, the *Poisson distribution* (Ref. [1]) is very often a good fit. A good example of this is given in Ref. [2] for predicting the number of caterpillars (larvae) likely to be on a given area of leaves. If we define "a" as the area of leaves and f as the mean density of larvae distribution, then p(n,a) is the probability of finding a specified number n of larvae in a specified area a. Because n can take on only integer values, p is dis-

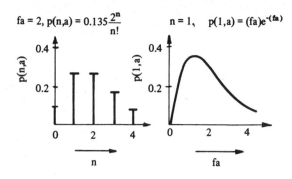

$fa = 2, \; p(n,a) = 0.135\dfrac{2^n}{n!}$ $n = 1, \quad p(1,a) = (fa)e^{-(fa)}$

Fig. 10-9 Poisson Distribution for Larvae Distribution

crete in n and continuous in a. The equation for the Poisson distribution is

$$p(n,a) = \frac{(fa)^n}{n!} e^{-fa} \tag{10-4}$$

An example of a Poisson distribution is shown in Fig. 10-9

In addition to the probability density function, the *probability distribution function* (also called the cumulative probability distribution function) is used. It is the probability that $x(t)$ will be less than some particular value, x_1. $P(x_1)$ is then just the integral of $p(x)$ with respect to x

$$P(x_1) = \text{Prob}(x(t) \leqslant x_1) = \int_{-\infty}^{x_1} p(x)dx \tag{10-5}$$

Since $P(x)$ and $p(x)$ are so similar in both name and meaning, it is always wise to make sure which one is meant when they are referred to in books and papers. If, for a given process, all of the data falls below some limiting value x_m, the value of $P(x_1)$ reaches one at x_m and remains at 1 for any $x_1 > x_m$. In terms of the probability density function $p(x_1)$

$$\int_{-\infty}^{x_1} p(x)dx = 1 \quad x_1 \geqslant x_m$$

This is more often stated as: the area under the whole $p(x)$ curve (which could be from $-\infty$ to $+\infty$) is one.

10.3 CORRELATIONS IN TIME

If we flip a coin and it comes up heads seven times in a row, what is the probability of getting tails on the next flip? This is a classic illustration of a question about time correlation, that is, the effect of preceding states or events on current or future outputs. In the case of the coin, the probability of getting tails is the same as it has always been, 0.5, because the coin has no way of "knowing" what the previous outcomes were. In this case, there is no time correlation; each event is independent. In analyzing the stability of an auto-mobile in gusty cross-wind conditions, however, even though the wind gusts have random components, the analyst can count on the wind force and directions at any instant being somewhat dependent on the past history of these variables. But how much dependent? A function whose purpose is to give quantitative answers to these questions is the *autocorrelation function*. The autocorrelation function also gives information about how rapidly the signal is changing and whether there is deterministic information (particularly periodic signals) mixed in with the stochastic information.

To find out if there is any correlation between two sets of data, we examine the products of pairs of data points a fixed distance (or time) apart in the series of data points. For zero-mean data, if there is no correlation, the average of the products of many such pairs will be zero since any product is just as likely to be negative as it is to be positive. On the other hand, if there is some correlation, the sign of the product will tend to favor either positive or negative and the average of all the products will be nonzero. Consider as an illustrative example the road surface profile shown in Fig. 10-10, where the vertical measure $y(z)$ has been magnified while the horizontal distance scale z has been compressed. Let us look at the product $y(z) \cdot y(z + l)$ of a pair of vertical measures separated by some interval l. If the value $y(z + l)$ is completely independent of the neighboring value $y(z)$, that is, if there is no correlation between the two, the average of the product over a large span in z should converge to zero. This

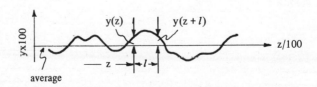

Fig. 10-10 Irregular Road Surface

is not true for a paved road surface where even a bump or a dip will have a continuous profile (unless the concrete itself is broken). At the other extreme, if y(z) is, for example, a sinusoidal pattern, then y(z) and y(z + *l*) will always have the same sign (and thus have a positive product) when *l* is an integer multiple of the wavelength. The average of the product will then be nonzero no matter how long *l* is, providing it remains a multiple of the wavelength of the sine wave. To return to the road surface example, since we expect some continuity in bumps and the like, if *l* is fairly short we would expect the correlation to be high and the average of the products to be high. As *l* is increased, the correlation should decrease.

The formal definition of the autocorrelation function for this example is

$$\phi(l) = \lim_{L \to \infty} \frac{1}{2L} \int_{-L}^{L} y(z)y(z + l)dz \qquad (10\text{-}6)$$

The road surface irregularity will be converted into a time signal (or noise) and probably a stationary noise for an automobile suspension system as long as the car speed is constant and the road quality remains the same. For this more usual case of writing the autocorrelation function with time as the independent variable, we have

$$\phi(\tau) = \lim_{T \to \infty} \frac{1}{2T} \int_{-T}^{T} x(t)x(t + \tau)dt \qquad (10\text{-}7)$$

It is a function of the time interval τ; for $\tau = 0$, note that it is equal to the variance (mean square value) of a zero-mean noise. An example of the autocorrelation function, Eq. (10-6), taken on an actual road (Ref. [3]) is shown in Fig. 10-11. Using a recorder rolling on a straight guide rail which was laid on the surface of a test road section, the vertical distance from a reference level (fixed by the rail) to the road surface was measured over a section of 56 meters. The two parallel lines, AA and BB in the figure, along which the measurement was made showed a difference in their autocorrelations (see Fig. 10-11) probably due to circumstances in the construction work and differences in wear by traffic. In interpreting these autocorrelations, we first note that the high peak at $l = 0$ (about 18 mm^2 for B and 31 mm^2 for A) indicates the presence of a strong random component. The value of $\phi(0)$ is the variance of the signal. Both then show what appears to be sinusoidal behavior. This indicates the presence of sinusoidal components in addition to the random part. The first minimum of the curve gives an estimate of the wavelength and amplitude; the wavelength is double the abcissa value (e.g., for A, the minimum is at 7 m so the

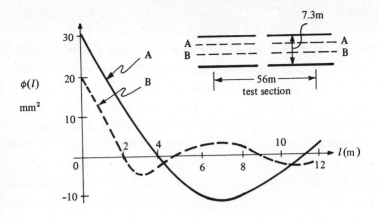

Fig. 10-11 Autocorrelation Function of a Road Surface (Ref. 2)

wavelength is 14 m) and the amplitude is the square root of the absolute value of the ordinate (= $\sqrt{|11|}$ = 3.3 mm for A). For a 60 km/hr (37 mph) vehicle speed, it will generate a (60·1,000/3,600)/14 = 1.2 Hz forcing input. If an auto-correlation function were computed for an unpaved road, the *washboard pattern* caused by natural vibrations of the unsprung mass of passing vehicles (Fig. 2-2(b)) would show up as a conspicuous periodic form in $\phi(l)$.

For sampled data, the integrals defining the autocorrelation function be-come summations and we are never able to carry out the operation to the speci-fied limit but must always be satisfied with an approximation. In fact, most autocorrelations of continuous-time signals are done by first sampling the data and then using a program of the sort given in the next example.

Example 10-3: Autocorrelation Function for Sampled Data

The program below differs from the basic autocorrelation definition only in that it replaces the integration with a summation and, for convenience, the sum-mation is carried out over a time period defined as 0 to T instead of −T to T. The TT in the denominator of the statement following 500 is the same as the 2T in the defining equation, Eq. (10-7). X( ) is a set of N data points sampled at uniform time intervals DT. INCR is equivalent to the τ in Eq. (10-7), only here it is in units of number of samples. IMAX represents the highest value of τ that will be used. It is limited by the number of data points available. Since each summation requires $(N - IMAX)$ points, IMAX must be small enough so that this does not become a small number.

```
100   read in: (X(I),I=1,N),DT,IMAX          — INCR will vary from zero
      INCR = 0                                  to IMAX.
110   SUM = 0.0
      NLIMIT = N–INCR
      TT = NLIMIT*DT
      DO 500 I = 1,NLIMIT
500   SUM = SUM+X(I)*X(I+INCR)
      AC(INCR) = SUM/TT                        — AC( ) is the autocorrela-
      INCR = INCR+1                              tion function.
      IF(INCR .LT. IMAX)GO TO 100
      print (or plot) AC( )
```

Fig. 10-12 shows the results of applying this program to the San Francisco birth data. Note that except for $\phi(0)$, which is the variance (the data was entered into the autocorrelation program in zero-mean form, so $\phi(0)$ is the variance), the values of the autocorrelation function are all small, indicating low correlation. Two factors in this autocorrelation function attract our attention: the nonzero average value caused by the mild nonstationarity of the data we observed in the moving mean tests, Fig. 10-2, and the apparent 3 to 4 week periodicity. We have no explanation for this (perhaps the phase of the moon?!). Note that only the autocorrelation test has been able to reveal this periodic component of the data.

Fig. 10-13 shows a set of three analog noise generator signals and their autocorrelation functions as obtained by sampling and use of a digital computer program such as the one above. Note the correspondence between your visual observations of how fast the signals are changing and the shapes of the autocorrelation functions.

10.4 WHITE NOISE

With the autocorrelation function available to us as a tool now, we can ask

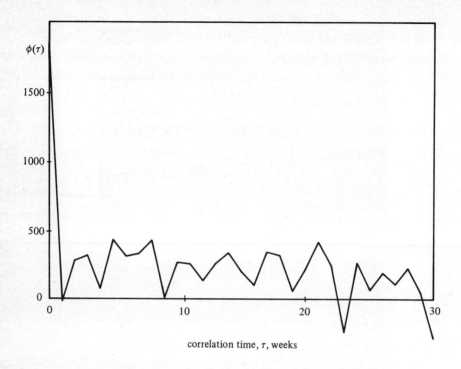

Fig. 10-12 Autocorrelation Function for San Francisco Births Data (zero mean)

an interesting question: what is "pure" noise or "pure" randomness? It seems clear that any signal whose autocorrelation function is zero everywhere except at the origin can qualify as pure noise because knowing the past behavior of the process doesn't help us predict its behavior in the immediate future (the coin toss, for example). We would like to know the effect of purely random signals on dynamic systems. We can deduce some of the characteristics of purely random noise by using a noise signal generated by a laboratory digital computer and converted to an analog signal by a digital-to-analog (D/A) converter and zero-order hold. The signal will take on values between plus and minus some desired output voltage with equal probability and will hold that value for a sampling interval Δt. Successive output values are independent of each other. This gives a characteristic output pattern as shown in Fig. 10-14(a), the probability density function shown in Fig. 10-14(b) and the autocorrelation function of Fig. 10-14(c). The magnitude of p(u) is $1/(2V_{max})$, as shown, because we

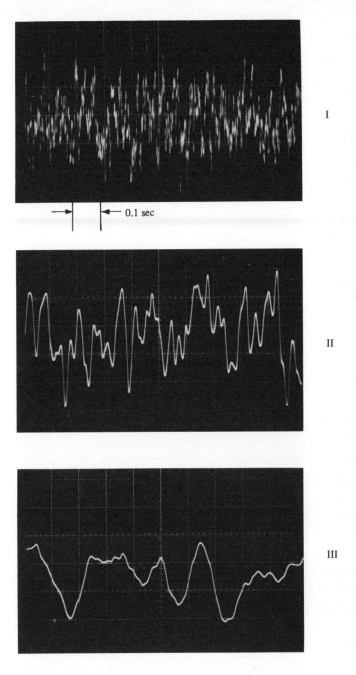

Fig. 10-13 (a) Three Signals from an Analog Noise Generator
(all voltage and time scales are the same)

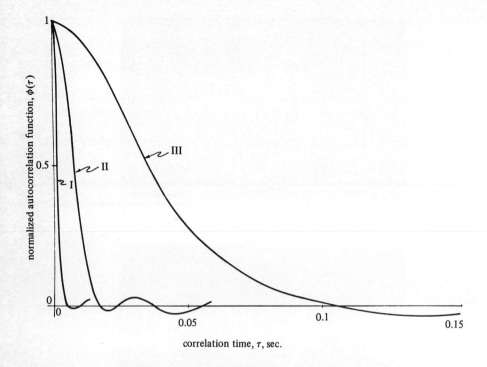

Fig. 10-13(b) Autocorrelations for Noise Generator Signals

know that the area under the p(u) curve must be unity; its width is $2V_{max}$ so its height must be $1/(2V_{max})$.

We can use an intuitive argument to see why the autocorrelation is the shape it is (see Ref. [4] for a more complete derivation). First of all, for times greater than Δt, the autocorrelation should be zero because successive samples are independent. The autocorrelation is a measure of how useful, on the average, past information is in predicting present and future values. If we know the value of the output at some time τ ago, where τ is less than Δt, the probability is $(1 - \tau/\Delta t)$ that the signal has not changed because it stays constant for a time Δt. Thus, we observe a linear decrease in the autocorrelation as τ goes from zero to Δt. The peak value $\phi_{uu}(0)$ can be derived from the following: $\phi_{uu}(0)$ is

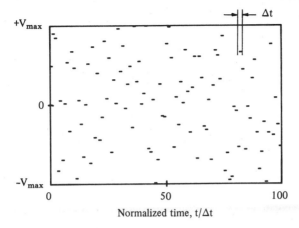

Normalized time, t/Δt

(a) Digitally generated random signal

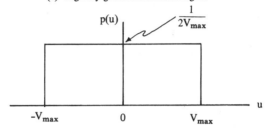

(b) Probability density function

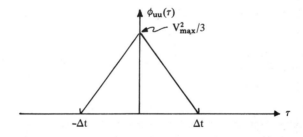

(c) Autocorrelation function

Fig. 10-14 Noise Signal Generated by Laboratory Digital Computer

the variance, defined as

$$\phi_{uu}(0) = \lim_{T \to \infty} \frac{1}{2T} \int_{-T}^{T} u^2 dt$$

for a continuous signal. Because this noise signal is so simple, we can compute this directly by replacing u with a function that varies linearly with time. This will have the same variance as u because values of u are evenly distributed over $-V_{max}$ to $+V_{max}$. Thus, using $V_{max}(\tau/\Delta t)$ as the function gives $\phi_{uu}(0) = V_{max}^2/3$.

This system is very interesting to experiment with because we can vary the autocorrelation at will by varying V_{max} and the sampling interval Δt. By observing a system's behavior as Δt is decreased and the autocorrelation grows ever more narrow, we can attempt to deduce what might happen when the signal reaches the limit of pure randomness (note that in the laboratory there is a lower limit on Δt). For the sake of simplicity, we will use this signal as an input to a first order system

$$\frac{dx}{dt} = -x + u$$

where u is our digitally generated random signal. The D/A converter produces the signal as a voltage and we can use the analog computer to simulate the first order system.

In the first series of experiments, we make u more and more random by continually decreasing Δt while maintaining V_{max} constant. Since u is a zero-mean input, we can use the variance of x to characterize the output. The variance is plotted against Δt and shown as case I for this experiment in Fig. 10-15. Though we have to stop the experiment at the lower limit of Δt, it seems clear that the variance is approaching zero as Δt gets smaller. Repeating this experiment with other, perhaps more complex systems, would lead to a similar conclusion for most common, stable systems. Thus, the limiting case for this experiment is a purely random signal, one that is not of very much interest or importance because it has no effect on the system output.

In a second experiment, we again let Δt continually decrease, but, this time, we increase V_{max} at the same time we decrease Δt in such a way that the area under the autocorrelation function remains unchanged. These results are shown as case II in Fig. 10-15. Here we see that there is some change in the variance for the larger Δt's, but below some limit the variance of the output stops changing. This leads us to another, more interesting result: if we continue to decrease Δt

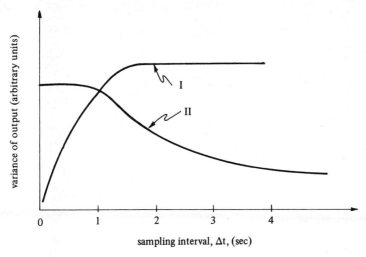

Fig. 10-15 Variance of Output of First Order System with Time Constant = 1 sec.

so that $\Delta t \rightarrow dt$ (while still keeping the area constant by increasing V_{max}), the results of this experiment indicate that the system output will not change. This is indeed the case and we call the purely random signal obtained at the limit *white noise*. Recalling the derivation of the impulse function in Secs. 5.2 and 6.4, we see that the autocorrelation function of white noise is an impulse. Furthermore, there is a strong similarity between the two derivations because in both cases we saw the characteristic switch from dependence on shape and size to dependence only on the area under the curve, either as the pulse got narrower or as the autocorrelation function got narrower. This similarity is more than coincidence, for white noise plays a role in the theory of stochastic systems that is similar to the role of the impulse function for deterministic systems.

Because white noise has considerable theoretical importance, many laboratory devices have been developed to generate approximate white noise. It is impossible to produce true white noise, however, since this requires infinite power. Viewed from the frequency domain, white noise is a signal with constant spectral content all the way to infinite frequency. In fact, the name white noise refers by analogy to the visible light spectrum where white light contains components of all the frequencies in the visible spectrum.

10.5 COMPUTER SIMULATION OF PROBABILISTIC PROCESSES

Computer simulation can be an important supplement to the large body of theory pertaining to stochastic systems (see Ref. [4], for example) because it permits us to visualize a system's behavior better and because it can be applied to nonlinear and non-Gaussian systems whereas the theory is primarily applicable to linear, Gaussian systems. Probability distribution programs and autocorrelation programs of the sort discussed earlier in this chapter can be used to evaluate the results of the simulations. Because these programs demand large amounts of data to produce reliable results use of digital computer simulation for probabilistic processes can be expensive.

The major problem in computer simulation of probabilistic processes is generating the appropriate random input. Since computers are designed specifically to be highly deterministic machines which give completely reproducible results, high accuracy, etc., they do not take willingly to simulating nondeterministic problems. On analog computers, the problem is solved by adding an external piece of electronic equipment: a noise generator; we have already seen some output from one of these devices earlier in this chapter. Most noise generators produce a signal that is "approximately" white and Gaussian. That is, they have the flat frequency spectrum characteristic of white noise but only over a finite range of frequency. Many processes of interest act as low-pass filters so the very high frequency part of the input spectrum has very little effect on the output. Noise generators are built by reversing the usual design procedure. In normal electronic design, a great deal of effort is spent on suppression of noise. In designing a noise generator, an element which normally has problems with noise is selected, the "worst" possible components (i.e., noisest) are used and components which tend to increase the noise level are added For instance, the primary noise source of the noise generator used in the example in this chapter is a gas discharge tube placed in a magnetic field.

The pseudo-random number generator is the noise generator for digital computer simulation. It consists of a program which produces numbers between zero and one with equal probability; that is, the probability density function is one between zero and one and zero everywhere else (thus, this is not a Gaussian source). It works by repeated multiplication of carefully selected numbers. At each stage of the multiplication, usually only one digit in the middle of the product is used in constructing the random number. It is called pseudo-random because the sequence of numbers produced is not truly random but will repeat if run long enough. The length of the sequence before it starts repeating depends on the precision of the computer being used but is generally high enough to be infinite for practical purposes. Another quirk in most digital random number generators is that the program generates the same sequence of random numbers each time unless provision is made for a different sequence. This can be very helpful in the debugging stages of program development but quite annoying in production runs where the variability due to the unknown nature of a random process is desired.

The following examples illustrate the use of the digital random number generator.

Example 10-4: Population Growth with Births and Deaths Viewed as Discrete Events with Random Timing

In all of our previous models of population change, we have represented birth and death rates as coefficients or nonlinear functions in differential equations. An alternative, however, is to focus our attention on the time interval between births or deaths and build a model by developing an algorithm for computing that time interval and deciding whether the event is a birth or death. We would expect that this approach would be a much more valid representation of the dynamics of a small population than the differential equation approach.

Let us assume that the time interval until the next event can be characterized in terms of a random number R_1 as

$$\Delta t = \frac{CR_1}{N}$$

where C is a constant and N is the current population. Further, let the nature of the event (birth or death) be decided by comparing a second random number R_2 to a constant K

and $\quad$ birth if $R_2 \geqslant K$
$\qquad$ death if $R_2 < K$

If we use a digital computer to simulate this system and use the standard digital random number generating algorithm, R_1 and R_2 will be uniformly distributed between zero and one. Thus, K = 0.5 will yield a stable population, K > 0.5 yields a shrinking population and K < 0.5 yields a growing population. Note, however, that only the long term averages of population change can be characterized by the value of K. Regardless of the value of K, the population always has a finite probability of increasing, decreasing or remaining the same over a short period. In fact, for small populations, there is always a probability that

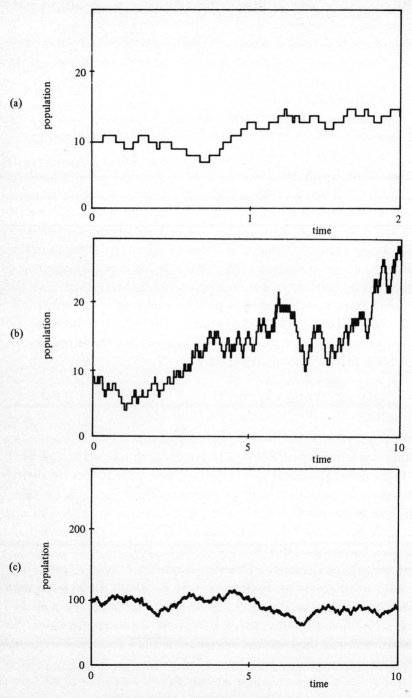

Fig. 10-16 A Random Birth/Death Process

the population will reach zero at some time and thus become extinct, even if K is less than 0.5.

The algorithm for digital simulation of a system described by these equations is

```
      REAL N,NZERO,K,IN
      read in: NZERO,C,K,TFINAL
      T = 0
      N = NZERO
100   DT = C*RANF(0)/N


      IN = 1


      IF(RANF(0) .LT. K)IN = -1
      N = N+IN
      T = T+DT
      print or plot T and N
      IF(T .LE. TFINAL)GO TO 100
      STOP
```

— RANF is the random number generator; its argument is usually not used but must be there in order for Fortran to recognize it as a function.

— IN is the population increment.

— The second call to RANF generates the second random number, R_2.

Some results are shown in Fig. 10-16. All three cases are for K = 0.5 and C = 1. In the first case, (a) of the figure, the initial population is 10 and the simulation is continued to t = 2. The random nature of the process is clearly visible, both in the population changes and in the intervals between events. The second case, (b) of the figure, is for exactly the same system parameters and initial state, but the simulation is continued to t = 10. Over this time span, the random nature of the intervals is somewhat suppressed although it is still visible on close examination, but the randomness in the population change is magnified because there is more time for a change to take place. Thus, the population reaches a high of about thirty and a low of about four within the time of the simulation. With such large changes relative to the initial population, the probability of extinction is quite high, even though with K = 0.5 the population should be constant over a long time interval. The third case, (c) of the figure, has the same parameters and final time as the second, but the initial population is 100 rather than 10. Here the randomness in the time interval between events is completely suppressed in the output and the signal has the characteristic constant average value we expect from K = 0.5. This output looks very much like the signals we have seen in previous examples and, for this case where the number of events occurring over the simulation interval is very large, a differential equation model with random forcing or random parameter change would probably give equivalent results and be computationally more efficient. Note, however, that a differential equation model would not be suitable for the first two cases.

Example 10-5: Non-Gaussian Signal Processed by a Linear System

The usual digitally generated random numbers have a probability density function of the form of Fig. 10-14(b), which is not at all like the Gaussian distribution, Fig. 10-7. We stated above, however, that one reason for the importance of the Gaussian distribution is that when a non-Gaussian signal is used as an input to a linear system the output tends to be more Gaussian than the input. In this case, we have used the digitally generated random signal as the input to the linear system

$$\frac{d}{dt}\underline{x} = \begin{bmatrix} -1 & 0.25 \\ 1 & -0.5 \end{bmatrix} \underline{x} + \begin{bmatrix} 1 \\ 0 \end{bmatrix} u$$

$$y = \begin{bmatrix} 0 & 1 \end{bmatrix} \underline{x}$$

The probability density function for a typical run, using 1,000 input samples, is shown in Fig. 10-17. The solid line is the probability density function for the system output and the dashed line is a Gaussian distribution fit so that the two match at y = 0. The probability density function of the system output is not Gaussian by any means, but it is more like a Gaussian than the square density function of the input.

10.6   NOISE FILTERING

Filtering means separation, usually separation of a desirable component from an undesirable one. We often encounter probabilistic processes in their role as "contaminants," that is, noise signals which, despite our best efforts, add on to the information we are interested in to produce a signal which is partly noise and partly valuable information. These situations arise in virtually every field

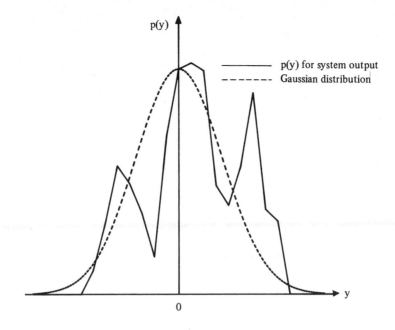

Fig. 10-17 Probability Density Function for System with Non-Gaussian Input

that uses numerical measurements of any kind: polls of all kinds, sampling everyting from political opinion to consumer preferences, suffer from noise due to poll-taker errors, people not at home, poorly worded questions, people not giving truthful answers, etc.; economic data, used in governmental decision-making, suffers from noise due to incorrect reporting, late reporting, etc.; and, of course, any measurement in an engineering system has some systemic noise contamination. Control systems are particularly susceptible to noise because their closed loop structure can allow the noise to "come around the loop," causing deviations from the desired operating point.

Measurements are not the only source of noise, nor are all noise signals probabilistic, although the probabilistic variety is our concern in this chapter. All electronic systems, for example, are subject to 60 Hz sinusoidal noise coming from the normal electric power lines. This disturbance can enter through the power supply (see Example 4-3), through the load or, via inductive coupling, directly into the middle of the circuit. A large power plant has many noise sources, some inside — due to turbulent flow, incomplete mixing, etc. —

and some from outside — like load disturbances. A power plant's load change over some short time interval can be regarded as probabilistic. Although each component of load change is deterministic (like turning off a light, starting a motor, etc.), the total number of individual load changes is so large that the ensemble is probabilistic. In the case of a power plant, however, the boiler firing rate will follow a trend (or some average curve) of longer term change without flickering, due to a higher frequency noise component of output load.

To separate the desirable components of a signal from the undesirable ones, we must know the properties of both parts of the signal and be able to manipulate them to take advantage of their differences. Even very small differences in properties can be used if necessary. For example, Uranium-235 is separated from Uranium-238 by using their very slight difference in density. In general, the closer the two signals are in properties the more expensive and difficult separation is. Our interest focuses primarily on the frequency spectrum as a property on which to base filtering. In the power plant example, we are interested only in the long term, i.e., low frequency, component of the load changes, since it is not only costly but also unnecessary for the plant to follow the short term changes. Power plants have a series of natural low-pass filter elements, mostly of the energy storage type in the heat exchange components, which assure that the state of the plant will change at moderate speed even if there are some very high frequency components in the load change. A low-pass filter is any component whose frequency response is such that below some frequency there is little or no distortion and above that frequency signals are attenuated more as the frequency is increased (see Chapter 8). In these discussions of filtering, frequency spectra are a convenient way to characterize signals and frequency response a convenient and useful way to characterize systems and filters.

Some systems, such as the power plant, contain low-pass filters by virtue of their inherent structure; others do not, so we must provide them with filters if the input signals are strongly contaminated by noise. The next example compares two common data acquisition instruments: one, the XY recorder, already contains some low-pass filtering due to the mass of the moving parts, limited speed of the servomotors in responding to changes in the input, etc. and the other, a laboratory digital computer with analog-to-digital conversion (A/D), has no such filtering because the sampler in the A/D converter looks at the signal for only a very short period of time while doing the conversion. We will also examine the effect of using the simplest form of low-pass filter, the first order lag, with both devices.

Example 10-6: Data Acquisition for Signals with Noise

Any time we wish to record information, either for further processing or for future reference, we must examine the properties of the data acquisition device we are using so that the maximum fidelity consistent with reasonable cost can be achieved. Here we will study the behavior of two data acquisition devices, an XY plotter and a digital computer with analog-to-digital conversion, when the input signal to them is contaminated with noise. An oscilloscope will also be used to display the input signals and the computer output. Since the oscilloscope has a frequency response that goes well beyond the highest frequency present in the noise signal, we will use it to show the "true" nature of the input signals.

To get a good feeling for how these systems work, we will use the triangular shaped oscillating signal, Fig. 10-18(a), as the information carrying part of the input signal. To that we add noise from an analog noise generator to get the signal shown in Fig. 10-18(b), which is an oscilloscope photo.

When this signal is fed into an XY pen recorder, the output shown in Fig. 10-19(a) results. There has been considerable attenuation in the noise part of the signal because the servomechanism that drives the pens acts as a low-pass filter and removes the higher frequency components from the noise. The output of the digital computer, shown in Fig. 10-19(b) and (c), however, shows no such attenuation. In fact, the amplitude of the noise part of the output signal appears to be about the same as the amplitude of the noise part of the input (the triangular part of the input is shown as the solid line). Also, comparing (b) and (c) of the figure, we see that this behavior is independent of the sampling rate. This phenomenon of preserving the amplitude of a signal even though its frequency characteristics are changed because of different sampling rates is known as *aliasing*. It occurs because, in converting from an analog to a digital signal, the A/D converter only "looks" at the analog signal for a very short period of time and, in effect, gets an instantaneous value of the input signal. As long as the sampling window of the A/D converter is so short that the input signal does not change significantly while the sample is being taken, the probability density function of the computer output will be the same as the probability density function of the input. Thus, the input and output noise amplitudes will be the same. The autocorrelation will change as a function of the time interval between samples because of the zero-hold on the output side of the computer.

To reduce the effect of the noise in the input signal, we can introduce a filter between the input signal and the data acquisition device. As we have seen from Fig. 10-19, this is essential if we are going to use a digital computer for

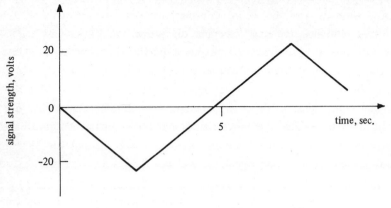

(a) Information carrying part of the input signal

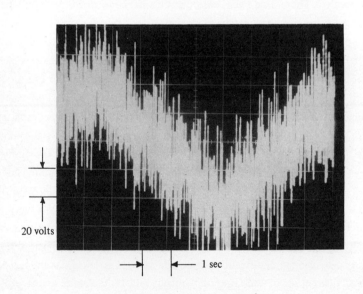

(b) Input signal with noise added

Fig. 10-18 Input Signal for Test of Data Acquisition Devices

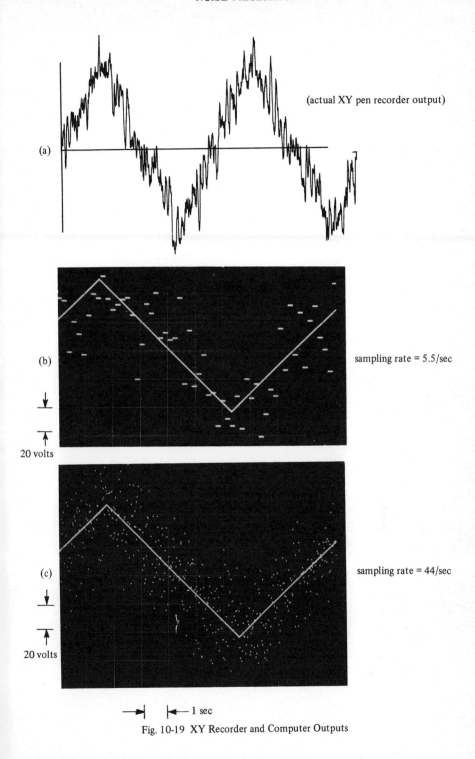

Fig. 10-19 XY Recorder and Computer Outputs

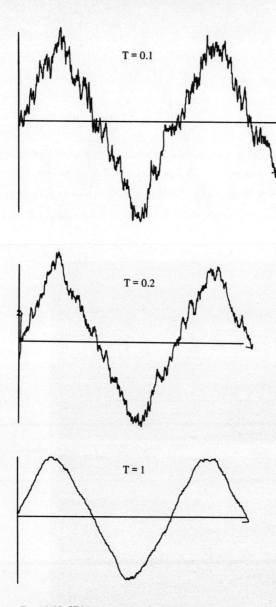

T = 0.1

T = 0.2

T = 1

Fig. 10-20 XY Recorder Output with Filter at Input

data acquisition. The simplest low-pass filter is the first order "lag," a first order system with the following differential equation

$$T\frac{dy}{dt} = -y + u$$

where T is the time constant. This can be easily implemented with an analog computer. The input to the filter, u, is the noisy signal of Fig. 10-18(b) and the output y is passed on to the XY recorder or to the computer. The filtering effectiveness is a function of T. For very small T's, the breakpoint frequency is very high and very little of the noise is filtered. If T is very large, there will be excessive loss of information. Fig. 10-20 shows the output of the XY recorder for three different filter time constants. For the shortest, T = 0.1, only a modest amount of filtering is achieved and the output is only marginally "cleaner" than the unfiltered output. At the longest time constant, T = 1,

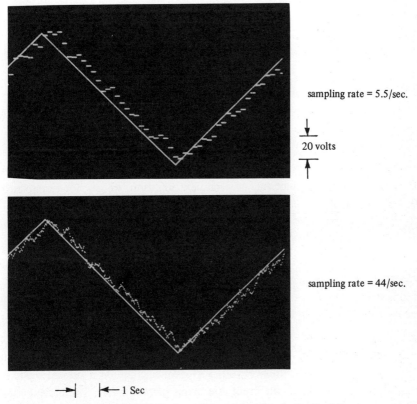

sampling rate = 5.5/sec.

20 volts

sampling rate = 44/sec.

|←— 1 Sec

Fig. 10-21 Digital Computer Output with Filter having T = 0.2 sec.

hardly any of the noise gets through, but the corners of the triangular wave are so rounded off that it is almost impossible to tell if it is triangular or sinusoidal. Because the filter reduces the high frequency components that cause aliasing in the digital data acquisition, there is a remarkable improvement in the output using a filter with T = 0.2, Fig. 10-21, as compared to the unfiltered output.

In some cases, it is impractical or undesirable to use analog filters in digital computer data acquisition systems. As long as the sampling rate of the digital system is fast enough, it is possible to do the filtering with a program in the digital computer. One possible filtering algorithm is the digital equivalent of the first order filter used in the above example. The digital filtering algorithm can be derived from the continuous-time low-pass filtering equation

$$T\frac{dy}{dt} + y = u$$

where u is the filter input (signal with noise) and y is the filtered output, by using Eq. (9-5), as

$$y(k + 1) = e^{-\Delta t/T}y(k) + (1 - e^{-\Delta t/T})u(k) \qquad (10\text{-}8)$$

where T is the filter time constant and Δt is the sampling period.

Looking at Eq. (10-8) simply as an algorithm rather than as the digital approximation to a first order continuous-time filter, we see that it is really a special averaging algorithm that gives exponentially decreasing weight to past values of the input. Repeatedly using the output (the left side) of Eq. (10-8) for the value of y on the right side of each next iteration, we get, for example, for $y(k + 3)$

$$y(k+3) = e^{-3\Delta t/T}y(k) + \\ (1 - e^{-\Delta t/T})[e^{-2\Delta t/T}u(k) + e^{-\Delta t/T}u(k+1) + u(k+2)] \quad (10\text{-}9)$$

In this relation, the oldest value of the input, $u(k)$, counts least while the newest value, $u(k + 2)$, counts most in the averaging. This suggests two approaches to the design of digital filtering algorithms: one is the adaptation of analog algorithms and the other is the investigation of various averaging schemes. Averaging algorithms of this sort, which compute a present value on the basis of past values of the input, are forms of *time series*. The moving mean we discussed earlier puts equal weight on a constant number of past values whereas the algorithm derived from the first order filter puts decreasing weight on past values but includes all of them. The two approaches are sometimes equivalent, as in this case, where a time series with decreasing exponential weighting turns out to be equivalent to the first order analog filter.

The dilemma of filter design is that we pay a price for inserting a filter into a system. For a first order filter of the sort we discussed above, for example, the time constant T of the filter must be large enough for effective noise suppression but it must be as small as possible to avoid losing information in the original signal being measured. As we saw in Example 10-6, if the time constant gets too large, we do a very good job of filtering the noise but the sharp corners of the original triangular wave disappear also! When the separation between signal and noise is very great, there is no problem designing a filter. We don't need very much information about either the process producing the original signal or the noise, only the approximate frequency range of each. Then, a simple first order filter will be very effective and the value of the filter time constant need not be determined precisely for best filter performance. As the frequency spectra of the signal and noise get closer, we must know those spectra in much more detail. Moreover, the structure of the filter has to be more complex to achieve satisfactory performance. As the spectra converge still further and begin to overlap, we must use accurate models of the plant producing the signal of interest and models of the noise process in order to apply the optimal filtering theory of Weiner and Kalman (Ref. [4]), which are related to the model reference adaptive systems mentioned at the end of Sec. 6.8.

SUMMARY

Our primary challenge in dealing with random signals, or signals with random components, is characterizing them quantitatively in a meaningful way. The need to characterize a random signal on the basis of probability rather than deterministic certainty (although our model may be deterministic and "certain" in the mathematical sense, a degree of uncertainty always creeps in when we attempt to apply it to the real world) has lead to a two-part formulation. The amplitude characteristics are described by the probability density function. Numbers like the mean and the variance are reduced descriptions of the probability density function.

The probable characteristics of changes with time are described by the autocorrelation function. Although the mean and the variance of a signal can be determined from its autocorrelation function, further details of the probability density function (such as whether or not a signal is Gaussian) cannot be deduced from the autocorrelation function.

Several important special cases have been noted, including two particular probability density functions, the Gaussian and the Poisson distributions, which are good approximations to a wide variety of significant processes and have simple enough forms to be manipulated analytically. White noise is a particularly useful special case of a "pure" random signal. It has an autocorrelation function which is an impulse and can have any probability density function (for example, a white noise could be Gaussian, Poisson, binary or etc.). Its importance also lies in its simple analytic description and its ability to approximate many interesting processes accurately.

In some instances, the random process is the focus of our interest, such as in some population problems. In others, it is a "noise" that masks the information in the signal. In the latter cases, various filtering techniques are available to aid in separating the information from the noise, as long as they have distinct enough characteristics to make separation theoretically possible. The most commonly used filter in engineering systems is the low-pass filter which can separate a signal with predominantly low frequency characteristics from one with predominantly high frequency characteristics. It is simple to implement and effective on a wide range of problems.

Computer simulation, analog or digital, is an effective tool for analysis of systems with random processes although special techniques must be used to introduce randomness into these highly deterministic machines. Simulation can be an expensive technique for systems with randomness because of the large number of trials that may be necessary to achieve consistent results.

REFERENCES

1. G. C. Newton et al, *Analytical Design of Linear Feedback Controls*, John Wiley and Sons, Inc., New York, 1957

2. E. C. Pielou, *An Introduction to Mathematical Ecology*, Wiley Interscience, New York, 1969

3. Y. Takahashi, "Spectral Density Distribution of Road Surface and Car Vibrations," *Proceedings of 3rd Japan National Congress for Applied Mechanics*, Science Council of

Japan, May, 1954

4. Y. Takahashi, M. Rabins and D. Auslander, *Control*, Addison-Wesley, Reading, Mass., 1970, Chap. 13

PROBLEMS

10-1 Referring to Eq. (10-4) and Fig. 10-9, plot a Poisson distribution for (a) fa = 3 and $0 \leqslant n \leqslant 5$ and (b) n = 2 and $0 \leqslant fa \leqslant 5$.

10-2 A series of random numbers u(k) can be generated by U(k) = RANF(0) on many digital computers. The probability density function of the random number has the form of Fig. 10-14(b), where the range is between 0 and 1 (that is, V_{min} = 0 and V_{max} = 1). Using a digital computer, find (a) the mean and (b) the probability density function of u(k) using 100, 200 and 300 samples. Discuss the effect of the sample size (i.e., the number of samples used for calculation).

10-3 The random numbers u(k) in the preceding problem are an input to a first order discrete-time system

$$x(k+1) = px(k) + u(k)$$

where p = 0.4. Using 200 samples and a digital computer, find the autocorrelation function of the output, which is

$$\phi_{xx}(i) = \frac{1}{N-i} \sum_{j=1}^{N-i} x(j)x(j+i) \qquad N = 200 \quad i = 0, 1, \ldots, 10$$

10-4 The random number u(k) generated by a digital computer (see Prob. 10-2) can be normalized to a zero-mean number

$$v(k) = 2[u(k) - 0.5]$$

with range from −1 to +1. This random series is an input to a first order discrete-time system

$$x(k+1) = px(k) + qv(k)$$

where $|p| \leqslant 1$. Analytically determine the autocorrelation function $\phi_{xx}(i)$. (Hint: Note that

$$x(k+1)^2 = p^2x(k)^2 + 2pqx(k)v(k) + q^2v(k)^2$$
$$x(k)x(k+1) = px(k)^2 + qx(k)v(k) \quad \text{etc.}$$

and compute average values of each term on the left. Since v(k) is an input independent of the system state x(k), the mean value of v(k)x(k) is zero.)

10-5 Pressure variations in a pipeline connected to a reciprocating pump sometimes appear to be purely sinusoidal. Approximating such noise by a sine function, $a\sin(\omega t)$, compute the variance and the standard deviation.

10-6 A noise generator for an analog computer normally has a zero mean Gaussian distribution whereas random numbers generated by a digital computer have a flat probability density function (see Fig. 10-14(b)). For computer experimentation of stochastic problems, it is sometimes desirable to change the distribution of the random number u(k) so that it is approximately Gaussian. For this purpose, one first normalizes u(k), as in Problem 10-4, into a zero-mean, ±1 range random number v(k) by the relation

$$v(k) = 2[u(k) - 0.5]$$

The latter is then changed into another random variable, w(k), by the relation

$$w(k) = [Fv(k) + (2 - F)(v(k))^2]\sigma \quad \text{where } F = \sqrt{\frac{\pi}{2}}$$

Show that w(k) has the probability distribution function shown by the short dashed curve in Fig. P-10-6, which is close to that of the Gaussian distribution except that the range of w(k) is limited to within ±2/σ, where σ is the standard deviation. Using this variable change and taking σ = 0.5, run a computer test to find the probability density function of w(k) for 300 samples.

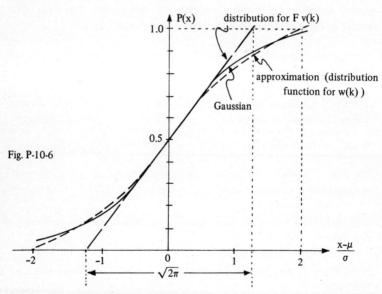

Fig. P-10-6

10-7 Using w(k) of the preceding problem as an input to a first order discrete-time system, repeat Prob. 10-3. Discuss whether or not the pattern of the output autocorrelation function will depend upon the magnitude distribution of the input noise.

10-8 Suppose that the output of the first order discrete-time system in the preceding

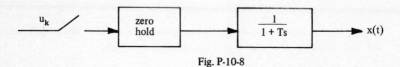

Fig. P-10-8

problem is converted into a continuous-time signal by a zero-hold. Sketch the pattern of the autocorrelation function of the continuous-time output. Would the pattern of the output autocorrelation function change if the output of the zero-hold is the input to a first order continuous-time system, as shown in Fig. P-10-8?

10-9 A signal $y(t)$, for instance, an outdoor temperature, is measured and fed into a digital computer at discrete time intervals — every minute, for example. Every sample $y(k)$, $k = 1, 2, \ldots$, is subject to noise perturbation, so that it is desired to smooth it out by computing an average. Suppose we take three samples, $y(k)$, $y(k-1)$ and $y(k-2)$, and compute some form of an average $c(k)$ at the k-th instant in such a way as to minimize a squared error criteria

$$J = w_1 [y(k) - c(k)]^2 + w_2 [y(k-1) - c(k)]^2 + w_3 [y(k-2) - c(k)]^2$$

where w_1, w_2 and w_3 are weighting factors, such as $w_1 = 0.5$, $w_2 = 0.3$ and $w_3 = 0.2$. Obtain $c(k)$ for which J is minimal and derive a recursive algorithm that computes it.

10-10 Assume that the weighting factors $w_1, w_2, \ldots$ in the preceding problem are given by a geometric series

$$w_1 = 1 \qquad w_2 = w \qquad w_3 = w^2 \quad \ldots$$

where w is a positive constant less than one, like $w = 0.5$. Show that the following relation will satisfy the minimum squared error criterion of the preceding problem:

$$c(k+1) = c(k) + \frac{y(k+1) - c(k)}{h(k+1)}$$

where

$$h(k) = 1 + w + w^2 + \cdots + w^k$$

Obtain a recursive algorithm that will start at $k = 0$ and compute the average.

APPENDIX

A.1 THE ROUTH TEST

This is a useful method for testing the stability of a linear system without solving the system characteristic equation for its roots (i.e., eigenvalues). The characteristic equation presented in the text, either Eq. (5-20) for systems described by a state equation or Eqs. (6-66) and (7-40) for systems described by a transfer function, will reduce to the following polynomial form:

$$a_0 s^n + a_1 s^{n-1} + \cdots + a_{n-1} s + a_n = 0 \qquad \text{(A-1)}$$

where $a_0 \neq 0$ for an n-th order system.

In order for a linear system to be asymptotically stable, the coefficients must be nonzero and either all plus or all minus. If plus, then

$$a_i > 0 \qquad i = 0, 1, 2, \ldots, n \qquad \text{(A-2)}$$

This is the first condition of the Routh stability criterion, which provides a necessary condition for asymptotic stability. If, for instance, the system has a free integration, $a_n = 0$ so that Eq. (A-2) is thus violated.

The second (and final) step of the stability test provides a sufficiency condition. The following array of numbers must be constructed for this step:

369

$$\begin{array}{llllll} (1) & a_0 & a_2 & a_4 & \cdots & a_n & 0 \\ & \downarrow \nearrow \downarrow \nearrow \downarrow & & & & \nearrow \\ (2) & a_1 & a_3 & \cdots & \cdots & 0 \\ (3) & b_1 & b_2 & \cdots & 0 \\ (4) & c_1 & \cdots & 0 \\ & \vdots & \vdots \\ (n+1) & z_1 \end{array}$$

The first two rows of the array show a zig-zag arrangement of the coefficients of the original characteristic polynomial. The last term, a_n, will appear in the right end of the first row, as shown, if the order of the system is even; a_n terminates in the second row if n is odd. Elements on the righthand side of the last element in these rows are considered to be zero.

We next compute the b's in the third row by the following rule:

$$b_1 = \frac{-1}{a_1}\begin{vmatrix} a_0 & a_2 \\ a_1 & a_3 \end{vmatrix} \quad b_2 = \frac{-1}{a_1}\begin{vmatrix} a_0 & a_4 \\ a_1 & a_5 \end{vmatrix} \cdots$$

The first column of each determinant is always the first column of rows (1) and (2). The second column of each determinant, however, is the $(i+1)$-th column of rows (1) and (2) for b_i, $i = 1, 2, \ldots$. Each determinant is divided by a_1 to obtain the b's. The computation of the third row ends when zeros on the right end of the first two rows make the determinant zero.

The rule for computing the fourth and following rows is the same as the rule presented for the b's but shifted down a row at a time. For instance

$$c_1 = \frac{-1}{b_1}\begin{vmatrix} a_1 & a_3 \\ b_1 & b_2 \end{vmatrix} \quad c_2 = \frac{-1}{b_1}\begin{vmatrix} a_1 & a_5 \\ b_1 & b_3 \end{vmatrix} \cdots$$

The determinants are computed using the two rows that precede the row to be computed. The computation ends when n+1 rows have been computed. Therefore, the entire array will show a triangular form. For example, if n = 5

$$\begin{array}{lll} a_0 & a_2 & a_4 \\ a_1 & a_3 & a_5 \\ b_1 & b_2 \\ c_1 & c_2 \\ d_1 \\ e_1 \end{array}$$

The sufficient condition for stability is: a system is asymptotically stable if and only if there is no sign change in the first column of the array. For instance, a_0, a_1, b_1, c_1, d_1 and e_1 must all be positive for a fifth order system. For a more detailed treatment that includes such cases as a zero or indeterminate form appearing in the first column of the array, see Ref.[1].

A.2 THE NYQUIST TEST

The asymptotic stability of a controllable and observable feedback control system can be tested by using the following rule:

$$P_c = N + P_o \tag{A-3}$$

where

N = the number of clockwise revolutions around the −1 point of the plot of G(s) in its Nyquist plane as s sweeps the entire imaginary axis and the infinite semi-circle in the s plane as shown in Fig. A-1(a),

P_o = the number of open loop poles with positive real parts

and

P_c = the number of closed loop poles with positive real parts. P_c must be zero for the system to be stable.

In the Nyquist test, which is represented by Eq. (A-3), P_o is known (as determined by the Routh criterion perhaps), P_c is the required unknown and N is obtained by inspection of the Nyquist diagram.

Consider, for example, a third order, open loop transfer function

$$G(s) = \frac{K}{(s - \lambda_1)(s - \lambda_2)(s - \lambda_3)} \tag{A-4}$$

where

$$Re\,\lambda_i < 0 \quad \text{for } i = 1, 2, 3$$

The open loop system is asymptotically stable. Thus $P_0 = 0$ in Eq. (A-3). Suppose that A-B-C-D in Fig. A-1(b) is the vector locus of this transfer function, such that the intersection of the locus and the real axis, point C, is on the right-hand side of the −1 point. A normal vector locus is for $\omega = 0 \to \infty$ in $G(j\omega)$,

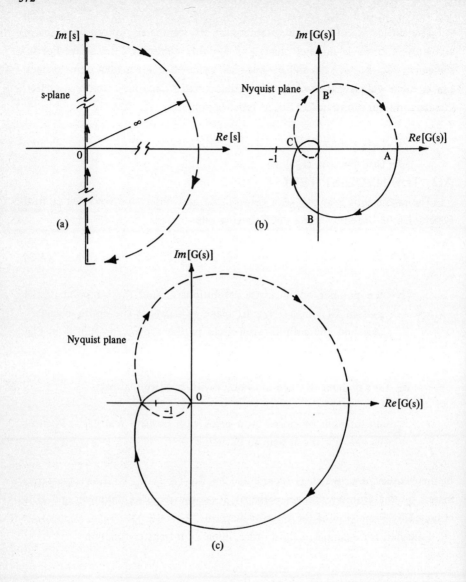

Fig. A-1 A Semi-Circular Contour in the s-plane, (a), and a Conformal Mapping
of the Contour onto the G(s)-plane, (b) and (c).

consequently, for a sweep of $s = j\omega$ along the entire positive half of the imaginary axis in the s plane. A sweep of s along the entire negative half of the imaginary axis, that is, $\omega = -\infty \rightarrow 0$, will produce a mirror image of the vector locus in the G(s) plane, as shown by the dashed curve in Fig. A-1(b). This is because of the following conjugate relationship:

$$Re\ G(j\omega) = Re\ G(-j\omega)$$
$$Im\ G(j\omega) = -Im\ G(-j\omega)$$

The semi-circle of infinite radius in the s plane (Fig. A-1(a)) will reduce to the origin in the G(s) plane (point D in Fig. A-1(b)) in our example because

$$\left|G(s)\right| = \frac{K}{\left|(s - \lambda_1)(s - \lambda_2)(s - \lambda_3)\right|} \rightarrow 0 \quad \text{for } |s| \rightarrow \infty$$

Since the -1 point is on the outside of the closed contour A-B-D-B'-A in Fig. A-1(b), we see that

$$N = 0$$

Therefore, by Eq. (A-3)

$$P_c = P_o$$

where $P_o = 0$, hence $P_c = 0$. The closed loop system is stable when its open loop transfer function has a vector locus as shown in Fig. A-1(b). If, however, the gain K in Eq. (A-4) is increased and, as a consequence, the closed contour encloses the -1 point, as shown in Fig. A-1(c), we have $N = 2$ for this example. Since $P_o = 0$ for our system, Eq. (A-3) yields

$$P_c = 2$$

The closed loop system with an increased open loop gain will thus have two poles with positive real parts. Hence it is unstable. A G(s) vector locus will pass through the -1 point in the Nyquist diagram if the closed loop system is at its stability limit.

To see why Eq. (A-3) is true, consider a closed loop system that has G(s) = B(s)/A(s), which is Eq. (6-65), as its open loop transfer function. The closed loop system characteristic equation was given by Eq. (7-39)

$$1 + G(s) = 0$$

Substituting $G(s) = B(s)/A(s)$ and factoring out

$$1 + G(s) = 1 + \frac{B(s)}{A(s)} = \frac{A(s) + B(s)}{A(s)} = \frac{\sum\limits_{j=1}^{n}(s - \rho_j)}{\sum\limits_{i=1}^{n}(s - \lambda_i)} \qquad (A\text{-}5)$$

Here we see that λ_i, $i = 1, 2, \ldots, n$, are the roots of $A(s) = 0$, hence the open loop poles, and ρ_j, $j = 1, 2, \ldots, n$, are the roots of $A(s) + B(s) = 0$, hence the closed loop poles.

In general, a factor $(s - p)$, as shown in Fig. A-2(a), is a phasor in the s plane. The angle of this phasor will change by θ, as shown in Fig. A-2(b), if s is changed from a to b. The phasor will make a complete clockwise rotation if p is located inside a closed contour and s is moved along the contour in the clockwise direction, as, for example, from a through b-c-d and back to a in Fig. A-2(c). The angle of rotation of the phasor for this case is 2π (radians), where we define the angle to be positive in the clockwise direction. If, however, p is

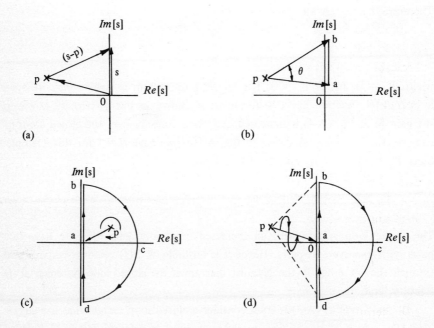

Fig. A-2 Phasor in the s-Plane and its Angle of Rotation

outside the closed contour, as shown in Fig. A-2(d), the angle of rotation of the phasor is zero when s is moved completely around the contour.

Returning to Eq. (A-5), we note the following phase relation:

$$\underline{/1 + G(s)} = \sum_{j=1}^{n} \underline{/(s - \rho_j)} - \sum_{i=1}^{n} \underline{/(s - \lambda_i)} \tag{A-6}$$

Here the $(s - \rho_j)$'s and the $(s - \lambda_i)$'s are phasors for closed loop poles and open loop poles, respectively. If s in Eq. (A-6) makes a complete cycle along the semi-infinite closed contour which is shown in Fig. A-1(a), from what we saw in Fig. A-2(c) and (d) the total angle of rotation of each component in Eq. (A-6) must have the following relation:

$$2\pi N = 2\pi P_c - 2\pi P_o$$

and this leads to Eq. (A-3). Since the semi-infinite closed contour encompasses the entire right half of the s plane where the real parts of poles are positive, P_c and P_o are the number of closed and open loop poles with positive real parts, respectively. The number of rotations of vector $[1 + G(s)]$ about its origin, $1 + G(s) = 0$, is N. Therefore, the number of revolutions of $G(s)$ about the -1 point in the $G(s)$ plane must also be N.

Caution is required if an open loop system has one or more poles on the imaginary axis in the s plane. For instance, an open loop system involving an I-control action has a pole at $s = 0$, and an undamped oscillator as an open loop system will have a pair of conjugate imaginary poles. Those cases are treated in Ref. [1].

A.3 THE JURY TEST

The characteristic equation of a discrete-time system described by a linear state equation is, according to Eq. (9-14)

$$\left| (z\underline{I} - \underline{P}) \right| = 0$$

For a closed loop system having an open loop pulse transfer function $G(z)$, the characteristic equation is

$$1 + G(z) = 0$$

Both of these can be reduced into the following polynomial form:

$$F(z) = a_0 z^n + a_1 z^{n-1} + \cdots + a_{n-1}z + a_n = 0 \tag{A-7}$$

where a_0 is taken as positive. A discrete-time system is asymptotically stable if and only if all the roots (i.e., eigenvalues) of Eq. (A-7) lie within the unit circle centered at the origin of the complex z plane.

Like the Routh method, the Jury test (Refs. [2] and [3]) consists of two parts: a simple first test for necessity and a second test for sufficiency. The first condition for stability is

$$F(1) > 0 \quad (-1)^n F(-1) > 0 \tag{A-8}$$

This test is performed by substituting $z = 1$ and $z = -1$ into the characteristic polynomial, $F(z)$. The test ensures that some real eigenvalues are within the ± 1 range.

Two triangularized matrices, $\underline{X}$ and $\underline{Y}$, are required for the second test. These matrices are constructed using the coefficients of the characteristic polynomial as elements in the following general form:

$$\underline{X} = \begin{bmatrix} a_0 & a_1 & \cdots & & a_{n-2} \\ 0 & a_0 & \cdots & & a_{n-3} \\ 0 & 0 & a_0 & \cdots & a_{n-4} \\ \vdots & & & & \vdots \\ 0 & 0 & \cdots & & a_0 \end{bmatrix} \quad \underline{Y} = \begin{bmatrix} a_2 & a_3 & \cdots & a_{n-1} & a_n \\ a_3 & a_4 & \cdots & a_n & 0 \\ a_4 & & \cdots & a_n & 0 & 0 \\ \vdots & & & & \vdots \\ a_n & & \cdots & 0 & 0 & 0 \end{bmatrix}$$

$\underline{X}$ and $\underline{Y}$ are $(n-1) \times (n-1)$ for an n-th order system.

The two matrices are next combined into a sum and a difference

$$\underline{H}_1 = \underline{X} + \underline{Y} \quad \underline{H}_2 = \underline{X} - \underline{Y} \tag{A-9}$$

where $\underline{H}_1$ and $\underline{H}_2$ must be "positive innerwise" in order for a system to be asymptotically stable. A square matrix $\underline{H}$ is said to be "positive innerwise" when all the determinants, starting with the center element(s) and proceeding outwards up to the entire matrix, are positive. Consider, for instance, a sixth order system, for which $\underline{H}_1$ and $\underline{H}_2$ are both 5x5. Thus the following general form will apply:

$$\underline{H} = \begin{bmatrix} b_1 & b_2 & b_3 & b_4 & b_5 \\ c_1 & c_2 & c_3 & c_4 & c_5 \\ d_1 & d_2 & d_3 & d_4 & d_5 \\ e_1 & e_2 & e_3 & e_4 & e_5 \\ f_1 & f_2 & f_3 & f_4 & f_5 \end{bmatrix}$$

As indicated by dashed lines, the determinants for this case are

$$d_3, \quad \begin{vmatrix} c_2 & c_3 & c_4 \\ d_2 & d_3 & d_4 \\ e_2 & e_3 & e_4 \end{vmatrix}, \quad \begin{vmatrix} b_1 & \cdots & b_5 \\ \vdots & & \vdots \\ f_1 & \cdots & f_5 \end{vmatrix}$$

The determinants for $\underline{H}_1$ and $\underline{H}_2$ (three each, six in all) must all be positive in order for the sixth order system to be asymptotically stable. The first determinant is a scalar (like d_3 in this example) if n is even and it is a 2x2 determinant if n is odd, as we shall see in the next example.

Example: Test for the Stability of a Fifth Order System
  Consider

$$F(z) = a_0 z^5 + a_1 z^4 + a_2 z^3 + a_3 z^2 + a_4 z + a_5$$

where a_0 is positive.
  The first test is

$$F(1) = a_0 + a_1 + a_2 + a_3 + a_4 + a_5 > 0$$

$$(-1)^5 F(-1) = a_0 - a_1 + a_2 - a_3 + a_4 - a_5 > 0$$

(A-10)

For the second test, we construct

$$\underline{X} = \begin{bmatrix} a_0 & a_1 & a_2 & a_3 \\ 0 & a_0 & a_1 & a_2 \\ 0 & 0 & a_0 & a_1 \\ 0 & 0 & 0 & a_0 \end{bmatrix} \qquad \underline{Y} = \begin{bmatrix} a_2 & a_3 & a_4 & a_5 \\ a_3 & a_4 & a_5 & 0 \\ a_4 & a_5 & 0 & 0 \\ a_5 & 0 & 0 & 0 \end{bmatrix}$$

and

$$\underline{H}_1 = \begin{bmatrix} a_0+a_2 & a_1+a_3 & a_2+a_4 & a_3+a_5 \\ a_3 & a_0+a_4 & a_1+a_5 & a_2 \\ a_4 & a_5 & a_0 & a_1 \\ a_5 & 0 & 0 & a_0 \end{bmatrix}$$

$$\underline{H}_2 = \begin{bmatrix} a_0-a_2 & a_1-a_3 & a_2-a_4 & a_3-a_5 \\ -a_3 & a_0-a_4 & a_1-a_5 & a_2 \\ -a_4 & -a_5 & a_0 & a_1 \\ -a_5 & 0 & 0 & a_0 \end{bmatrix}$$

$\underline{H}_1$ and $\underline{H}_2$ are both "positive innerwise" when

$$\begin{vmatrix} a_0+a_4 & a_1+a_5 \\ a_5 & a_0 \end{vmatrix} > 0 \quad |\underline{H}_1| > 0 \quad \begin{vmatrix} a_0-a_4 & a_1-a_5 \\ -a_5 & a_0 \end{vmatrix} > 0 \quad |\underline{H}_2| > 0$$

$$(A\text{-}11)$$

Eqs. (A-10) and (A-11) constitute a complete set of stability conditions for a fifth order discrete-time system.

REFERENCES

1. Y. Takahashi, M. Rabins and D. Auslander, *Control*, Addison-Wesley, Reading, Mass., 1970, pp. 137-142

2. E. I. Jury, " 'INNERS' Approach to Some Problems of System Theory," *IEEE Transactions on Automatic Control*, June, 1971, pp. 233-240

3. E. I. Jury and S. M. Ahn, "Interchangeability of 'Inners' and 'Minors'," *ASME Transactions Journal of Dynamic Systems, Measurement, and Control*, Vol. 93, Ser. G, No. 4, Dec., 1971, pp. 257-260

PROBLEM SOLUTION GUIDE

CHAPTER 1

1-1 stable. **1-2** $t_d = 0.7/0.02 = 35$ years. **1-3** temperature $= 20 + 70e^{at}$, $a = -0.117$ (min^{-1}). **1-4** dynamic. **1-5** it blinks. **1-6** the state will decay to zero (stable) but may involve regenerative feedback driving the system to a negative state if the latter is allowed. **1-7** it will grow (unstable). **1-8** theoretically possible; an orifice in the bottom where the area is zero is physically unrealizable. **1-9** stable, exponential. **1-10** stepwise oscillation, constant amplitude at a unity lever ratio.

CHAPTER 2

2-1 two. **2-2** only x_1 and x_2. **2-3** displacement and velocity in three directions and angular displacement and angular velocity about three axes. **2-4** normally oscillates; the analogy will hold. **2-5** potential energy of water and thermal energy. **2-6** thermal energy storage; analogy holds. **2-7** temperature – concentration; heat balance – material balance; $w = 1/R_1$. **2-8** θ_2 and θ_3 are state variables, θ_1 and θ_4 are input variables. **2-9** temperature and humidity are the most important. **2-10** temperature, humidity and CO_2 concentration in the green house are state variables. Controlling inputs are lights, belt speed and supply of air (flowrate and conditions). **2-11** water temperature, populations, concentration of important components (dissolved oxygen, nutrients, toxic substance) and water level if it changes.

CHAPTER 3

3-1 state variables are: amount of the product on the market, consumer demand, retail price, production level, and inventory. **3-2** x_1 = fuel storage, x_2 = heat storage, x_3 = reservoir level; fuel delivery and power demand are inputs from outside. **3-3** important inputs are: waste heat flowing into the pond, intensity of spray, and ambient conditions (air temperature, humidity, sunshine and wind). **3-4** $C_1Dx_1 = w(u - x_1)$, $C_2Dx_2 = w(x_1 - x_2)$; if the reservoirs are assumed to be adiabatic, analogy holds. **3-5** $a_{11} = -1/(C_1R_1) - 1/(C_1R_2)$, $a_{12} = 1/(C_1R_1)$, $a_{21} = 1/(C_2R_1)$, $a_{22} = -1/(C_2R_1) - 1/(C_2R_3)$, $b_{11} = 1/C_1$, $b_{12} = 1/(C_1R_2)$, $b_{21} = 0$, $b_{22} = 1/(C_2R_3)$. **3-6** equilibrium states at $\theta = 0$ (stable) and $\theta = 180°$ (unstable). **3-7** $Dx_1 = x_2$, $Dx_2 = -(k/I)x_1$; will oscillate in the absence of a damping force. **3-8** equilibrium states at $N = 0$ (unstable) and $N = N_1$ (stable); an S-shaped response curve. **3-9** $Dn = -k_1n$; the population will decay back to N_1 with time constant $(1/k_1)$ as long as n is small. **3-10** the equilibrium state is unstable (called a *saddle point*).

CHAPTER 4

4-1 since this is a first order system, the Euler and Euler variant methods are identical. Eq. (4-6) can be applied directly for $n = 1$; f is the instantaneous difference between the flow in and the flow out. **4-2** be careful in choosing the step size. The critical conditions are when the tank is nearly full or nearly empty and the cross-sectional area is minimum. **4-7** no. **4-10** a harmonic oscillation; the oscillation may grow or decay, like in Fig. 4-3(a), if the computer is not accurate. **4-11** resistance in the input side, for instance an internal resistance in the capacitor, makes the system causal but with a nonideal derivative stage; since $KD/(1 + TD) = K/T - (K/T)/(1 + TD)$, an approximate derivative stage can be built using an integrating stage and a summation; the latter is less sensitive to noise. **4-12** a saturation element.

CHAPTER 5

5-3 it does vanish. **5-4** slow mode is e^{-t}, fast mode is e^{-2t}; asymptotically stable. **5-5** $\underline{T}_a\underline{x} = \underline{x}^*$. **5-6** $\underline{w}_i\underline{A} = \lambda_i\underline{w}_i$; right multiply $\underline{v}_j$ to get $\underline{w}_i\underline{A}\underline{v}_j = \lambda_i\underline{w}_i\underline{v}_j$ where $\underline{A}\underline{v}_j = \lambda_j\underline{v}_j$ so that $\underline{w}_i\lambda_j\underline{v}_j = \lambda_i\underline{w}_i\underline{v}_j$ or $(\lambda_i - \lambda_j)\underline{w}_i\underline{v}_j = 0$; since $\lambda_i - \lambda_j \neq 0$ for $i \neq j$, $\underline{w}_i\underline{v}_j = 0$ (the two vectors are orthogonal). **5-7** apply Eq. (5-28) and compute the first few terms. **5-9** $(e^{pt} - e^{at})/(p - a)$ if $p \neq a$, te^{at} if $p = a$. **5-10** elements of $\underline{S}(t)$ are: $S_{11} = e^{pt}$, $S_{12} = te^{pt}$, $S_{13} = (t^2/2!)e^{pt}$, $S_{21} = 0$, $S_{22} = S_{11}$, $S_{23} = S_{12}$, $S_{31} = S_{32} = 0$, $S_{33} = S_{11}$. **5-11** $x_1 = 1 - e^{-t/T_1}$, $x_2 = 1 + [T_2/(T_1 - T_2)]e^{-t/T_2} - [T_1/(T_1 - T_2)]e^{-t/T_1}$ if $T_1 \neq T_2$, $x_2 = 1 - e^{-t/T_1} - (t/T_1)e^{-t/T_1}$ if $T_1 = T_2$. **5-12** see Ref. [1], p. 69.

CHAPTER 6

6-1 $-\underline{A}^{-1}\underline{B}h$ where $\underline{A}^{-1}$ exists if all eigenvalues are in the lefthand side of the s plane (i.e., negative real or conjugate complex with negative real part). **6-2** (a) elements of $\underline{S}(t)$ are: $S_{11} = e^{-2t}$, $S_{12} = 0$, $S_{21} = 5e^{-2t} - 5e^{-3t}$, $S_{22} = e^{-3t}$; (b) $2e^{-2t}$, $10e^{-2t} - 13e^{-3t}$; (c) $x_1 = (1/2)(1 - e^{-2t})$, $x_2 = (5/2)(1 - e^{-2t}) - (7/3)(1 - e^{-3t})$ **6-3** (a) Same as **6-2** (c) (b) $1/2$, $1/6$. **6-4** (a) diagonal with elements e^{-3t} and e^{-5t}; (c) $2e^{-3t}$, $-3e^{-5t}$; (d) 0, $(1 - e^{-5t})/5$; (e) $0,3/s + 5$). **6-5** (a) $a_{11} = -5$, $a_{12} = 2$, $a_{21} = 0$, $a_{22} = -3$, $b_1 = 1$, $b_2 = 0$, $C_{11} = 0$, $C_{12} = 4$, $C_{21} = 3$, $C_{22} = -3$; (c) $x_1(0) = -2$, $x_2(0) = 1$, $x_1(t) = e^{-3t} - 3e^{-5t}$, $x_2(t) = e^{-3t}$; (d) $0,3/(s + 5)$). **6-7** note that $\underline{Y} = X_2 + 2X_1$, $U = z + 3X_3 + 4X_2 + 6X_1$ or $z = U - 3X_3 - 4X_2 - 6X_1$. **6-8** $\theta_0 = -\omega_0\sqrt{l/g}$, unstable. **6-9** $G(s) = \underline{C}(s\underline{I} - \underline{A})^{-1}\underline{B} = 0$; observable mode x_1 is uncontrollable, controllable mode x_2 is unobservable, but the feedforward control is most effective. **6-10** $0.75/(15s + 1)$, $1.5/(15s + 1)$. **6-11** $(m_2 s^2 + bs + k)/[m_1 m_2 s^2 + (m_1 + m_2)(bs + k)]$. **6-12** $G(s)$ takes the form: $k(1 - T_3 s)/[(1 + T_1 s)(1 + T_2 s)]$, a black box approach. **6-13** $(1 - e^{-sT})/s$. **6-14** $x(0)/s$. See Ref. [3], pp. 551-552 and Fig. 12-24(a).

CHAPTER 7

7-2 (a) $a_n/(a_n + k_c b_m)$; (b) $-b_m/(a_n + k_c b_m)$; (c) no difference. **7-3** $k'_c = k_{ci}k_{cd}(1 + T_d/T_i)$, $T'_i = T_i + T_d$, $T'_d = (T_i T_d)/(T_i + T_d)$, where k_{ci} and k_{cd} are the gain of the original PI and PD control laws, respectively. **7-4** feedforward compensation, effective for inlet temperature change, no offset if k_c is exactly tuned for the compensation. **7-5** positive and negative real axis. **7-6** $m/(T_d T_i)$. **7-7** stable. **7-8** oscillate unless there is sufficient damping, the rate signal does not help unless P or PI control is used instead of I action. **7-9** $u = -kx_4$. **7-10** (a) $k = 3$; (b) $k = 0.0718$, 14; (c) part of real axis and a circle. **7-11** (a) more stable; (b) serious offset, take $1/s$ outside the inner loop. **7-13** $K_4 = 1/k_1$, a reverse reaction response when $k_2 > 1/k_1$ and $4Tk_3 > 1$. **7-14** hunting for maximum sustainable yield is normally too close to the critical hunting pressure; leaving a margin of safety is advisable. **7-15** impossible.

CHAPTER 8

8-1 $(1/3)(1 + s/0.3)/[(1 + s/0.2)(1 + s/0.5)(1 + s/2)]$. **8-2** $2(1 + s/2)/[(s)(1 + s/20)(1 + s/200)]$. **8-3** only approximate, gain for the tangents $kj\omega$ must be modified to $k = 14.93$ and 0.27 for exact fit. **8-4** Nyquist diagram is a semi-circle, nonminimum phase. **8-5** gain asymptotes are determined by $1/(1 + s)$, but phase changes from $0°$ to $-270°$. **8-6** Nyquist diagram is clearer. **8-7** 1.5 for stability limit, 0.38 for 8 db gain margin. **8-8** 1.5708. **8-9** $k_c < 1/k_p$. **8-10** $\omega < 0.995$ (radians/min). **8-11** period $= 8.8$ time units, amplitude of the controlled variable $= 0.85M$. **8-12** $C_0 = KM$, $C_1 = KMu_0/(j\omega + K)$, etc. **8-13** $c < b/r$. **8-14** No (see Fig. 8-5).

382

CHAPTER 9

9-1 elements of $\underline{P}^k$ are: p^k, kp^{k-1}, 0, p^k where p^k and kp^{k-1} are the modes. **9-2** $z_1 = c$, $z_{2,3} = c\cos(\theta) \pm jc\sin(\theta)$, where $c = (s_1 s_2 b)^{1/3}$, $\theta = 120°$; an exponential mode and an oscillatory mode – increasing amplitude if $c > 1$, stationary if $c = 1$, decay if $c < 1$; not possible unless larva period = pupa period = adult period. **9-3** $(1 + z)[1 - \cos(\Delta t)]/(z^2 - 2z\cos(\Delta t) + 1)$. **9-5** compute $Z[f_k]$, $Z[f_{k+1}]$ and $Z[f_k] = Z[f_{k+1} - f_k]$. **9-6** $U(z) = [K_I/(1 - z^{-1})]R(z) - [K_P + K_I/(1 - z^{-1}) + (1 - z^{-1})K_D]C(z)$. **9-7** (a) $(1 - c)/(z - c)$, $c = e^{-\Delta t}$; (b) $[1/(1 - a)][z/(z - d) - z/(z - c)]$, $d = e^{-a\Delta t}$, X/V depends on $v(t)$. **9-8** both $R(z)$ and $V(z)$ have a final value of zero. **9-9** (a) $Kz/[(z - c)(z - 1)]$; (b) $Kz + (z - c)(z - 1) = 0$; (c) a circle, positive real axis from c to 1, and negative real axis; (d) $0 < K < 2(1 + c)$; (e) an oscillation characterized by an eigenvalue at -1. **9-10** $a_1 = 0$, $b_1 = c$, $b_0 = 1 + c$, $E(z) = 1 - cz^{-1}$. **9-11** $3.33z(c - d)/[(z - c)(z - d)]$, $c = e^{-0.2\Delta t}$, $d = e^{-0.5\Delta t}$. **9-12** $\underline{G}(z) = z\underline{C}(z\underline{I} - \underline{P})^{-1}\underline{B}$, where $\underline{P} = e^{\underline{A}\Delta t}$. **9-13** $1 > c > -1$ and $2(1 + c) > K > 0$. **9-14** unstable because $|\underline{H}_2| < 0$. **9-15** $1 > |c|$, $1 > \cos(\theta) > -1$, $|\underline{H}_1| > 0$ but $|\underline{H}_2| = 0$.

CHAPTER 10

10-1 0.224. **10-4** $E[x(k)^2] = q^2/[3(1 - p^2)]$, $E[x(k)x(k+i)] = p^i q^2/[3(1 - p^2)]$, $i = 1, 2, 3,$ . . . **10-5** $a^2/2$, $a/\sqrt{2}$. **10-6** V = 2.0*RANF(0)–1.0, SIGMA = 0.5, F = SQRT (3.1416/2.0), W = SIGMA*(F*V+(2.0–F)*(V**3)). **10-7** it does not. **10-8** the pattern will change, giving a lower variance. **10-9** $c(k) = [w_1 x(k) + w_2 x(k-1) + w_3 x(k-2)]/(w_1 + w_2 + w_3)$. **10-10** specify W, K = 0, C = 0.0, H = 1.0, then DO loop; K = K+1, read in y(k), k = 1, 2, . . ., H = 1.0+W*H, C = C+(Y–C)/H.

iNDEX

operator (Cont.)
   time-advance 302
oscillation 47, 55, 57, 199, 215, 220, 301
oscillator 48, 121, 149, 167, 216, 245, 271
output 2, 43, 242, 289
output equation 43, 153, 289, 305

P-action 212, 308
partial fraction expansion 150
Paynter, H. M. 21
PD-action 213
performance of control 8, 314
periodic solution 246
pest control 230
pest population 230
phase angle 250, 252, 256, 267
phase crossover 275
phase margin 275
phase shift 251
phasor 374
PI-action 212, 308
PI controller 235
PID-action 212, 308
pneumatic controller 195
Poisson distribution 339
poles 152, 167, 218
pole-zero cancellation 178
population 4, 43, 287, 295, 320, 328, 351
   competing species 51, 131, 241
   pest 230, 287
   predator-prey 56, 121, 135
   whale 226
population dynamics, linear 62
population explosion 5, 296
population movement 31
port
   one- 29
   two- 29
position control system (see servomechanism)
positive definiteness 28
positive innerwise 376
pot (see potentiometer)
potential energy storage 22, 29, 48
potentiometer 89
power dissipation 28
power plant 18, 38, 47, 65, 355
predator-prey system 56, 121, 135
pressure controller 196
probabalistic process (see stochastic process)
probability 325
probability density function 330
probability distribution function 339
process control 200, 201, 268

proportional action (see P-action)
proportional plus integral action (see PI-action)
proportional plus integral plus derivative action (see PID-action)
pseudo-random number 350
pulse 162, 306
pulse input 157
pulse transfer function 304, 307

quality of control (see performance of control)

random signal (see noise)
random timing 351
rate variable 21
ratio control 196
realizability condition 168, 213, 304
reference input (see set point)
regenerative instability 224
regenerative reaction 198
reliability of component 9
reservoir 19
resistance 51, 170
resistive element 26, 49
resistor 21
resonance 244, 263
response
   impulse 128, 161, 306
   step 12, 126, 171
response pattern 171
reverse reaction 107, 173, 239, 264
root locus 219
Routh array 370
Routh test 369

s-domain (see Laplace domain)
S-shaped process response 268
sampled data system (see discrete-time system)
sampling interval 288, 293, 301, 319
sampling period (see sampling interval)
sampling theorem 301, 321
saturation 248
scaling of analog computer 89, 93, 100
secant approximation 101
self-operated controller 195
self regulation 198, 216
servomechanism 195, 201, 273
set point 195, 199, 308

unit circle as stability boundary 296
unit impulse 156
unit step 126, 161, 303
unnatural causality 25, 44
unobservability 176
unstable equilibrium state 54
unstable limit cycle 283
urban dynamics 200

variance 328
vector equations (see output equation,
    matrix state equation)
vector locus 258, 371
vector state equation (see matrix state
    equation)
velocity 24, 46
velocity algorithm 309
velocity input 47
Verhulst equation 67

vibration, mechanical 47, 243, 263
viscous friction 27
Volterra-Lotka equation 67

water clock 192, 202
Watt governor (see flyball governor)
whaling 225
white noise 349
Wiener, N. 194, 200

XY plotter 95, 357

z domain 302
z-transformation 302
z-transformation pairs 305
zero-hold 291, 306, 319
zeros 167, 172, 174
Ziegler-Nichols rule 222